Pets Come Too!
2008

visit**Britain**™

Contents

Greenwich Park,
London

VisitBritain

VisitBritain is the organisation created to
market Britain to the rest of the world, and
England to the British.

Formed by the merger of the British Tourist
Authority and the English Tourism Council,
its mission is to build the value of tourism
by creating world-class destination brands
and marketing campaigns.

It will also build partnerships with – and
provide insights to – other organisations
which have a stake in British and English
tourism.

The guide that gives you more

This official VisitBritain guide is packed with information from where to stay, to how to get there and what to see and do. In fact, everything you need to know to enjoy England.

Quality accommodation

Choose from a wide range of quality-assessed accommodation to suit all budgets and tastes. This guide contains a comprehensive listing of all hotels, bed and breakfast accommodation and self-catering properties where pets are made welcome. Every establishment participates in VisitBritain's Enjoy England Quality Rose assessment scheme – the official marque of Enjoy England quality-assessed accommodation.

Regional information

Every region has its own unique attractions – in each section we highlight a selection of interesting ideas for memorable days out. Regional maps show their location as well as National Trails and sections of the National Cycle Network.

You'll also find a selection of great events and regional tourism contact details. For even more ideas go online at enjoyengland.com.

Tourist information centres

For local information phone or call in to a Tourist Information Centre. Location and contact details can be found at the beginning of each regional section. Alternatively, you can text **INFO** to 62233 to find your nearest Official Partner Tourist Information Centre.

MANOR COTTAGE

Aldbury,
Hertfordshire

5

Corfe, Dorset

How to use this guide

In this invaluable Welcome Pets! guide, you'll find a great choice of hotels, bed and breakfast accommodation and self-catering properties.

Each property has been visited annually by Enjoy England assessors to nationally agreed standards so that you can book with confidence knowing your accommodation has been checked and rated for quality.

Detailed accommodation entries include descriptions, prices and facilities. You'll also find special offers and themed breaks to suit your tastes, interests and budget.

Finding accommodation is easy

Regional entries
The guide is divided into nine regional sections and accommodation is listed alphabetically by place name within each region.

Colour maps
Use the colour maps, starting on page 28, to pinpoint the location of all accommodation featured in the regional sections. Then refer to the place index at the back of the guide to find the page number. The index also includes tourism areas such as the New Forest and the Cotswolds.

Indexes
The place index at the back makes it easy to find accommodation in a particular location – and if you know the name of the establishment, use the property index.

Welcome Pets!

There's no need to feel guilty as you say goodbye to your cherished companion at the kennels or cattery. Why not take your pet with you on your holiday?

Whether you're off on a weekend break or for a fortnight away, proprietors of all establishments in this guide will happily welcome you and your pet.

 VisitBritain has recently launched a new Welcome Pets! scheme – look out for the special sign used in this guide and outside participating accommodation. The sign indicates that proprietors go out of their way to meets the needs of guests bringing dogs, cats and/or small birds. See page 22 for further information.

Of course, even the pet-friendliest of proprietors would appreciate advance warning of your animal's arrival – particularly if your two- or four-legged friend is unusual or extra large. Horse owners will be pleasantly surprised at the growing number of establishments offering stabling and grazing.

When contacting the owners it's wise to check out exactly what facilities are available:

• Do they provide dog/cat baskets, pet rugs, food and water bowls?

• Can favourite food be purchased locally?

• Are pets allowed in the bedrooms and are there any restrictions on where else they may go?

• Are there lots of good country walks on the doorstep?

Some animal-loving proprietors may even provide an animal welcome pack for your pampered pet.

Top tips

During your stay it would be courteous to adhere to the following guidelines:

- Allow sufficient time for your pet to get used to their new environment and try to stick to their normal daily routine as far as possible.

- Try to ensure that your pet is well-behaved and quiet at all times so they do not become a nuisance to other guests.

- Do not shut your pet up in your bedroom for lengthy periods as they could become distressed.

- Do not allow your pet on the furniture, unless agreed in advance with the proprietor.

- If your pet is used to sleeping on your bed, cover it with your own rug or bedspread.

- Dog owners should take an old towel for drying off their pet after wet and muddy walks.

- If your dog should foul the garden, clean up immediately.

Take one of the hundreds of footpaths along the eastern end of Hope Valley in the Peak District and you'll find yourself at Stanage Edge, a bold outcrop of gritstone worshipped throughout the climbing world.

The wind whips the flap of your rucksack, the material snapping like a spinnaker in a force 9, as you pedal up the last few yards of muddy track to where the rock emerges from the stunted bracken. It's only a five-minute walk from the road side car park and an easy drive to find this spot. But make this small effort and you're rewarded with one of the most astounding views in the country.

Out here you feel the full primitive energy of nature. And whether you've packed the crampons and ropes, a pair of hiking boots and a flask or you've brought the Rover and simply come to stretch your legs, it's one of those precious places where you can escape the crowds, taste true freedom and find inner peace.

England boasts an astonishing diversity of natural wonders, from the flat waterscapes of the Norfolk Broads to the jutting peaks of the Lake District, from the ancient woodlands of the New Forest to Dorset's fossil-jewelled Jurassic Coast.

This is our natural heritage, shaped by primeval forces and just waiting to be explored. Do so and you'll return with weary legs, a ravenous appetite and that wonderful tingling sensation you get on your face after a day in the fresh air.

For lots more great ideas visit
enjoyEngland.com/ideas

Whinstone Lee Tor,
Peak District, Derbyshire

The edge of the world – just a short stroll away

Kids and weather. They change mood from one moment to the next. Fortunately, that's also one of the most striking things about England's great outdoors and attractions: you just step across the threshold and its landscapes and entertainment venues offer all the varied play potential you need to fill holidays, sunny afternoons or rainy weekends.

So, there you are on the beach building sandcastles, paddling, eating ice cream and basking in the warm memory that you'll take home. You watch the teenagers hanging out with their surfboards, part of the family outing but doing their own thing. There's something for all ages and that's priceless in every sense of the word. Next time, maybe picnicking in woods, leaping through treetops on an aerial adventure, or getting your hands on heritage - whatever makes everyone happy.

Then it rains and you want to stay indoors. London's Science Museum is free, like a good number of England's top attractions, and that pleases Money Bags. Everyone immediately vanishes into one of the galleries: in Who Am I? you're morphing your face older and younger, in another you're discovering how to forecast weather and learning about climate change, which could be useful for planning your next trip!

Anticipate the family's next mood. Animal magic at Chester Zoo, following Harry Potter to Alnwick Castle, or screaming your heads off at Drayton Manor Theme Park in Staffordshire? There's always another boredom-buster just around the corner.

For lots more great ideas visit enjoyEngland.com/ideas

Seaside fun,
Brighton & Hove

Make fun of England, it runs in the family

It's the kids who first spot them, those surfers with kites. You pull over and stare open-mouthed from the safety of the promenade. For hours on end they skip over waves like a shoal of exotic flying fish, the wind's power made visible by the taught cables yanking them through the air.

Just 24 hours of pestering later, and you and the kids are lining up at the peeling door of the Kite Surf Shack for your first lesson. They (in sleek new wetsuits) take to it like ducks to water; you (in baggy Hawaiian shorts) don't. The rest of that day is a tumble of memories - pounding waves, stinging eyes, blistered palms and a feeling of sheer, utter exhilaration. And the best bit is this: that glorious afternoon is something you'll always share.

Kite surfing is one of the new breed of adrenalin sports to hit these shores, coming (rather fast) to a coastline near you. It's not something most of us have seen before. But give it a go and you'll be hooked.

Of course, you could simply dust off the old bat and ball, take the kids to the beach and show them just why you were captain of the school cricket team. But discover the world of emerging sports in England, leave your comfort zone where it belongs (at home) and we guarantee you'll experience the great outdoors like you've never experienced it before. And you don't even have to own a dayglo wetsuit.

For lots more ideas visit
enjoyEngland.com/ideas

Watergate Bay,
Cornwall

Flying kites – what could be more relaxing?

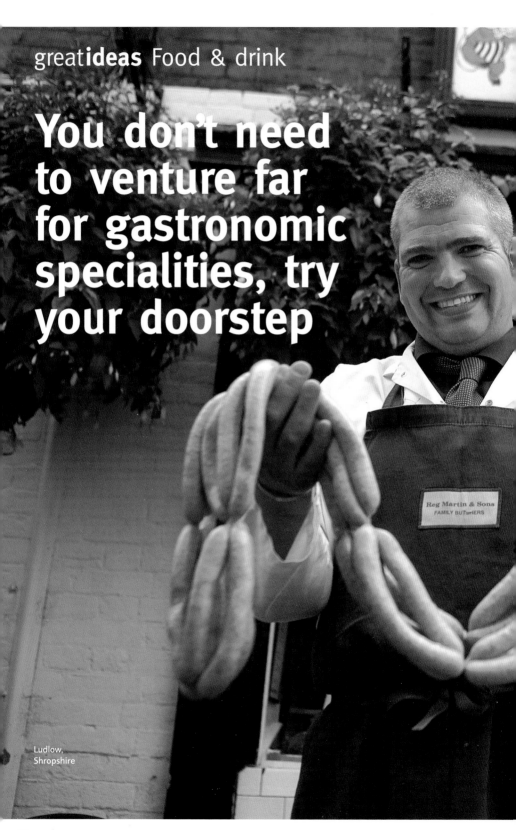

You don't need to venture far for gastronomic specialities, try your doorstep

Ludlow,
Shropshire

Reg Martin & Sons
FAMILY BUTCHERS

A quiet revolution has been simmering away in Britain. Fresh, locally-sourced and organic ingredients have become the order of the day. From bustling farmers' markets to family kitchens turning out hand-made puddings, jams and breads, Dining in or out, you'll more than likely be presented with fresh wholesome food cooked with passion.

Start with the famous Ludlow Food Festival and follow the little-known Sausage Trail, an event in which the town's five independent butchers create new sausage varieties and vie for the crown of People's Choice. You'll find everything from organic rare breeds sausages to the Shropshire Sizzler - a rich blend of local pork, peaches and blue cheese. Take some back to base and spark up the barbie for a fantastic feast.

Fancy lunch while out exploring? Three cheers for the gastropub where high quality cooked-from-scratch bistro meals are served at bar room prices. As you tuck into a crisp salad and garlic mayo (made with free range eggs, of course) you begin to wonder if Chicken in a Basket wasn't just a bad dream.

At the charming Waffle House in St Alban's you can't help but admire the blend of inventiveness, quality produce and sheer dedication that goes into the cooking. Here you'll find waffles of every conceivable shape and size, served with freshly made toppings such as chick pea curry and mango chutney as well as an endless choice of sweet varieties.

The good news is, you'll find places like this all over Britain: it's a foodies' heaven.

For lots more ideas visit
enjoyEngland.com/ideas

Ratings and awards at a glance

Reliable, rigorous, easy to use – look out for the following ratings and awards to help you choose with confidence:

Ratings made easy

★ Simple, practical, no frills

★★ Well presented and well run

★★★ Good level of quality and comfort

★★★★ Excellent standard throughout

★★★★★ Exceptional with a degree of luxury

For full details of the Enjoy England Quality Rose assessment schemes, go online at
enjoyengland.com/quality

Star ratings

Establishments are awarded a rating of one to five stars based on a combination of quality of facilities and services provided. Put simply, **the more stars, the higher the quality and the greater the range of facilities and level of service.**

The process to arrive at a star rating is very thorough. Enjoy England professional assessors visit establishments annually and work to strict criteria to check the available facilities and service. A quality score is awarded for every aspect of the experience. For hotels and bed and breakfast accommodation this includes the comfort of the bed, the quality of the breakfast and dinner and, most importantly, the cleanliness. For self-catering properties the assessors also take into consideration the layout and design of the accommodation, the ease of use of all the appliances, the range and quality of the kitchen equipment, and the variety and presentation of the visitor information provided. They also score the warmth of welcome and the level of care that each establishment offers its guests.

From January 2006, all the national assessing bodies (VisitBritain, VisitScotland, Visit Wales and the AA) have operated to a common set of standards, giving a clear guide on exactly what to expect at each level (see page 244).

Gold and Silver Awards

If you want a superior level of quality guaranteed seek out accommodation with a Gold or Silver Award. They are only given to properties offering the highest levels of quality within their star rating (see page 24).

Enjoy England Awards for Excellence

The prestigious and coveted Enjoy England Awards for Excellence showcase the very best in English tourism. Run by VisitBritain in association with England's regions, the awards include categories for Large and Small Hotel of the Year, Bed & Breakfast of the Year and Self-Catering Holiday of the Year. For more information, and to see the current winners, visit enjoyengland.com.

National Accessible Scheme

Establishments with a National Accessible Scheme rating have been thoroughly assessed to set criteria and provide access to facilities and services for guests with visual, hearing or mobility impairment (see page 26).

Welcome schemes

Enjoy England runs four special Welcome schemes: Cyclists Welcome, Walkers Welcome, Welcome Pets! and Families Welcome. Participants actively encourage these types of visitors and make special provision to ensure a welcoming, comfortable stay (see page 22).

Classifications explained

The following classifications will help you decide which type of establishment is right for you, whether you are seeking a non-stop, city-buzz holiday, a quiet weekend away or a home-from-home break for all the family.

Hotels

Hotel	A minimum of six bedrooms, but more likely to have over 20.
Small Hotel	A maximum of 20 bedrooms and likely to be more personally run.
Country House Hotel	Set in ample grounds or gardens, in a rural or semi-rural location, with the emphasis on peace and quiet.
Town House Hotel	In a city or town-centre location, high quality with a distinctive and individual style. Maximum of 50 bedrooms, with a high ratio of staff to guests. Possibly no dinner served, but room service available. Might not have a dining room, so breakfast may be served in the bedrooms.
Metro Hotel	A city or town-centre hotel offering full hotel services, but no dinner. Located within easy walking distance of a range of places to eat. Can be of any size.
Budget Hotel	Part of a large branded hotel group, offering limited services. A Budget Hotel is not awarded a star rating.

Bed and Breakfast

Guest Accommodation   Encompassing a wide range of establishments from one-room bed and breakfasts to larger properties, which may offer dinner and hold an alcohol licence.

Bed and Breakfast   Accommodating no more than six people, the owners of these establishments welcome you into their home as a special guest.

Guest House   Generally comprising more than three rooms. Dinner is unlikely to be available (if it is, it will need to be booked in advance). May possibly be licensed.

Farmhouse   Bed and breakfast, and sometimes dinner, but always on a farm.

Restaurant with Rooms   A licensed restaurant is the main business but there will be a small number of bedrooms, with all the facilities you would expect, and breakfast the following morning.

Inn   Pubs with rooms, and many with restaurants as well.

Self Catering

Self Catering   Choose from cosy country cottages, smart town-centre apartments, seaside villas, grand country houses for large family gatherings, and even quirky conversions of windmills, railway carriages and lighthouses. Most take bookings by the week, generally from a Friday or Saturday, but short breaks are increasingly offered, particularly outside the main season.

Serviced Apartments   City-centre serviced apartments are an excellent alternative to hotel accommodation, offering hotel services such as daily cleaning, room service, concierge and business centre services, but with a kitchen and lounge area that allow you to eat in and relax when you choose. A telephone and Internet access tend to be standard. Prices are generally based on the property, so they often represent excellent value for money for families and larger groups. Serviced apartments tend to accept bookings for any length of period, and many are operated by agencies whose in-depth knowledge and choice of properties makes searching easier at busy times.

Approved Caravan Holiday Homes   Approved caravan holiday homes are let as individual self-catering units and can be located on farms or holiday parks. All the facilities, including a bathroom and toilet, are contained within the caravan and all main services are provided. There are no star ratings, but all caravans are assessed annually to minimum standards.

A special welcome

To help make your selection of accommodation easier there are four special Welcome schemes which accommodation can be assessed to. Owners participating in these schemes go the extra mile to welcome walkers, cyclists, families or pet owners and provide additional facilities and services to make your stay even more comfortable.

Families Welcome

If you are searching for a great family break look out for the Families Welcome sign. The sign indicates that the proprietor offers additional facilities and services catering for a range of ages and family units. For families with young children, the accommodation will have special facilities such as cots and highchairs, storage for push-chairs and somewhere to heat baby food or milk. Where meals are provided, children's choices will be clearly indicated, with healthy options available. They'll also have information on local walks, attractions, activities or events suitable for children, as well as local child-friendly pubs and restaurants. Not all accommodation is able to cater for all ages or combinations of family units, so do check when you book.

Welcome Pets!

Want to travel with your faithful companion? Look out for accommodation displaying the Welcome Pets! sign. Participants in this scheme go out of their way to meet the needs of guests bringing dogs, cats and/or small birds. In addition to providing water and food bowls, torches or nightlights, spare leads and pet washing facilities, they'll buy in food on request, and offer toys, treats and bedding. They'll also have information on pet-friendly attractions, pubs, restaurants and recreation. Of course, not everyone is able to offer suitable facilities for every pet, so do check if there are any restrictions on the type, size and number of animals when you book.

Walkers Welcome

If walking is your passion seek out accommodation participating in the Walkers Welcome scheme. Facilities include a place for drying clothes and boots, maps and books for reference and a first-aid kit. Packed breakfasts and lunch are available on request in hotels and guesthouses, and you have the option to pre-order basic groceries in self-catering accommodation. A wide range of information is provided including public transport, weather, local restaurants and attractions, details of the nearest bank and all night chemists.

Cyclists Welcome

If you like to explore by bike seek out accommodation displaying the Cyclists Welcome symbol. Facilities include a lockable undercover area and a place to dry outdoor clothing and footwear, an evening meal if there are no eating facilities available within one mile, and a packed breakfast or lunch on request. Information is also provided on cycle hire and cycle repair shops, maps and books for reference, weather and details of the nearest bank and all night chemists and more.

For further information go online at enjoyengland.com/quality

Accommodation entries explained

Each accommodation entry contains detailed information to help you decide if it is right for you. This has been provided by proprietors and our aim is to ensure that it is as objective and factual as possible.

ALDEBURGH, Suffolk Map ref 3C2 — HOTEL

★ ★ ★
**COUNTRY HOUSE HOTEL
GOLD AWARD**

Hanover Lodge Hotel

High Place, Bury Road, Aldeburgh IP53 5BG **t** (01724) 555329 **f** (01724) 555331
e info@hanoverlodge.co.uk **w** hanoverlodge.co.uk

B&B per room per night
s £80.00-£120.00
d £150.00-£250.00
HB per person per night
£110.00-£160.00

open All year
bedrooms 35 double, 20 twin, 14 single, 2 family
bathrooms All en suite
payment Credit/debit card, euros

In 63 acres of beautiful parkland, the Hanover offers a choice of luxury bedrooms, some featuring jacuzzi bath, four-poster bed and extensive views. Open fires and comfortable sofas abound in spacious lounges. Our award-winning restaurant is open for breakfast, lunch and dinner for residents and non-residents.

⊕ *A12 south of Saxmundham, A1094 to Aldeburgh. Right at first roundabout, past the church to crossroads. Right onto Bury Road, first left to High Place.*

♥ *Special weekend and mid-week breaks available throughout the year.*

Room ... General ☎5 ... Leisure ...

Sample enhanced entry

1 Listing under town or village with map reference

2 Enjoy England star rating plus Gold or Silver Award where applicable

3 Classification

4 Prices
   Hotels – per room for bed and breakfast (B&B) and per person for half board (HB)

Bed and breakfast – per room for bed and breakfast (B&B) and per person for evening meal
Self catering – per unit per week for low and high season

5 Establishment name and booking details

6 Indicates when the establishment is open

7 Accommodation details and payment accepted

8 Accessible rating where applicable

9 Walkers, cyclists, pets and families welcome where applicable

10 Travel directions

11 Special promotions and themed breaks

12 At-a-glance facility symbols

**A key to symbols can be found on the back-cover flap.
Keep it open for easy reference.**

Gold and Silver Awards

Enjoy England's unique Gold and Silver Awards are given in recognition of exceptional quality in hotel and bed and breakfast accommodation.

Enjoy England professional assessors make recommendations for Gold and Silver Awards during assessments. They will look at the quality provided in all areas, in particular housekeeping, service and hospitality, bedrooms, bathrooms and food, to see if it meets the highest quality for the star level achieved.

While star ratings are based on a combination of quality, range of facilities and level of service offered, Gold and Silver Awards are based solely on quality. You may therefore find that a two-star Gold Award hotel offering superior levels of quality may be more suited to your needs if, for example, enhanced services such as a concierge or 24-hour room service are not essential for your stay.

Here we list hotels and bed and breakfast accommodation featured in this guide with a Gold or Silver Award.

Exceptional properties excelling in outstanding quality

Gold Award

Old Rectory Hopton
Diss, *Norfolk*

Rye Lodge Hotel
Rye, *East Sussex*

Silver Award

Ascot House
York, *North Yorkshire*

Barnsdale Lodge Hotel
Oakham, *Rutland*

Bower Farm House
Canterbury, *Kent*

Brudenell Hotel
Aldeburgh, *Suffolk*

Budock Vean Hotel on the River
Falmouth, *Cornwall*

Castle of Comfort Country House
Nether Stowey, *Somerset*

Corse Lawn House Hotel
Corse Lawn, *Gloucestershire*

Crofton Lodge
Marlborough, *Wiltshire*

The Devonshire Fell Hotel and Restaurant
Burnsall, *North Yorkshire*

Gables Farm
Wingfield, *Suffolk*

Garrack Hotel
St Ives, *Cornwall*

The Grasmere Hotel
Grasmere, *Cumbria*

Harefield Cottage
Bude, *Cornwall*

Headlam Hall Hotel, Spa and Golf Course
Darlington, *Tees Valley*

The King William IV Country Inn & Restaurant
Hunstanton, *Norfolk*

Lawford Hill Farm
Rugby, *Warwickshire*

The Manor House Hotel
Studland, *Dorset*

The Old Manse
Pickering, *North Yorkshire*

The Pheasant
Bassenthwaite, *Cumbria*

Rose Bank Guest House
Porlock, *Somerset*

Royal Castle Hotel
Dartmouth, *Devon*

Sentry Mead Hotel
Totland Bay, *Isle of Wight*

Spread Eagle Hotel & Health Spa
Midhurst, *West Sussex*

Thornham Hall and Restaurant
Thornham Magna, *Suffolk*

Waren House Hotel
Bamburgh, *Northumberland*

Woodlands Country House
Padstow, *Cornwall*

Yorke Lodge
Canterbury, *Kent*

National Accessible Scheme

Finding suitable accommodation is not always easy, especially if you have to seek out rooms with level entry or large print menus. Use the National Accessible Scheme to help you make your choice.

The criteria VisitBritain and national/regional tourism organisations have adopted do not necessarily conform to British Standards or to Building Regulations. They reflect what the organisations understand to be acceptable to meet the practical needs of guests with mobility or sensory impairments and encourage the industry to increase access to all.

Proprietors of accommodation taking part in the National Accessible Scheme have gone out of their way to ensure a comfortable stay for guests with special hearing, visual or mobility needs. These exceptional places are full of extra touches to make everyone's visit trouble-free, from handrails, ramps and step-free entrances (ideal for buggies too) to level-access showers and colour contrast in the bathrooms. Members of the staff or owners may have attended a disability awareness course and will know what assistance will really be appreciated.

Appropriate National Accessible Scheme symbols are included in the guide entries (shown opposite). If you have additional needs or special requirements we strongly recommend that you make sure these can be met by your chosen establishment before you confirm your reservation.

For a wider selection of accessible accommodation, order a copy of the Easy Access Britain guide featuring almost 500 places to stay. Available from Tourism for All for £9.99 (plus P&P).

The National Accessible Scheme forms part of the Tourism for All Campaign that is being promoted by VisitBritain and national/regional tourism organisations. Additional help and guidance on finding suitable holiday accommodation can be obtained from:

Tourism for All
c/o Vitalise, Shap Road Industrial Estate, Kendal LA9 6NZ

information helpline 0845 124 9971
reservations 0845 124 9973
(lines open 9-5 Mon-Fri)

f (01539) 735567

e info@tourismforall.org.uk

w tourismforall.org.uk

Mobility Impairment Symbols

 Typically suitable for a person with sufficient mobility to climb a flight of steps but who would benefit from fixtures and fittings to aid balance.

 Typically suitable for a person with restricted walking ability and for those who may need to use a wheelchair some of the time and can negotiate a maximum of three steps.

 Typically suitable for a person who depends on the use of a wheelchair and transfers unaided to and from the wheelchair in a seated position. This person may be an independent traveller.

 Typically suitable for a person who depends on the use of a wheelchair in a seated position. This person also requires personal/mechanical assistance to aid transfer (eg carer, hoist).

 Access Exceptional is awarded to establishments that meet the requirements of independent wheelchair users or assisted wheelchair users shown above and also fulfil more demanding requirements with reference to the British Standards BS8300:2001.

Visual Impairment Symbols

 Typically provides key additional services and facilities to meet the needs of visually impaired guests.

 Typically provides a higher level of additional services and facilities to meet the needs of visually impaired guests.

Hearing Impairment Symbols

 Typically provides key additional services and facilities to meet the needs of guests with hearing impairment.

 Typically provides a higher level of additional services and facilities to meet the needs of guests with hearing impairment.

Map 1

A   B

Location Maps

Every place name featured in the regional accommodation sections of this Enjoy England guide has a map reference to help you locate it on the maps which follow. For example, to find Poole, which has 'Map ref 2B3', turn to Map 2 and refer to grid square B3.

All place names appearing in the regional sections are shown in black type on the maps. This enables you to find other places in your chosen area which may have suitable accommodation – the place index (at the back of this guide) gives page numbers.

1

2

3

MAP 5
Newcastle upon Tyne
Carlisle
MAP 4   York
Manchester
Lincoln
Birmingham   Ipswich
MAP 2   Oxford   MAPS 6&7
Bristol   London
MAP 1   Southampton   Dover
Exeter   MAP 3

Camelford
Padstow   Chapel Amble
St Mawgan   A389
Newquay Cornwall
International
Newquay
Crantock   Lostwithiel
CORNWALL
A3058
Fowey
Ruan High
Truro   Lanes
St Ives   Veryan
Penzance
Land's End   Ashton   Falmouth
(St Just)   Penzance   Helston   Constantine
Praa
Sands
Mullion

Tresco *Isles of Scilly*
St Mary's

Map 1

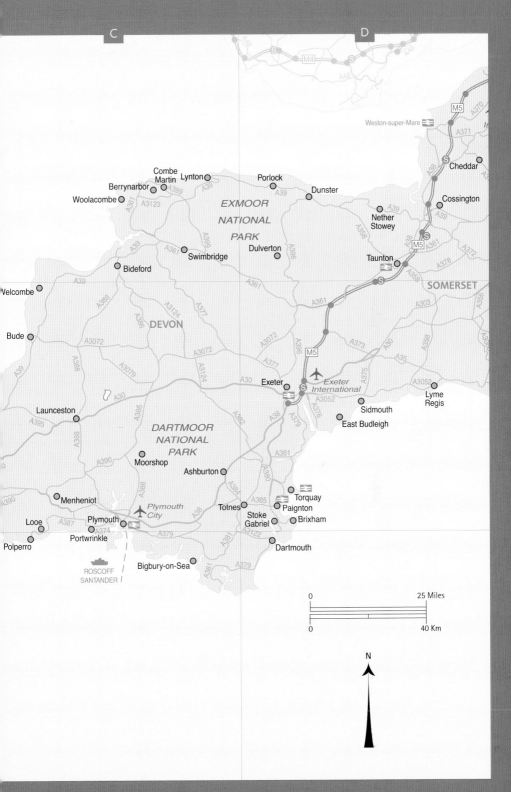

C · D

Weston-super-Mare

M5

A371

Cheddar

Combe
Martin · Lynton · Porlock · Dunster

Berrynarbor · Cossington

Woolacombe

EXMOOR
NATIONAL
PARK

Nether
Stowey

Taunton

SOMERSET

Swimbridge · Dulverton

Bideford

Velcombe

DEVON

Bude

Exeter
Exeter
International

Launceston

Lyme
Regis

Sidmouth

East Budleigh

DARTMOOR
NATIONAL
PARK

Moorshop

Ashburton

Menheniot

Plymouth
City

Torquay
Paignton

Looe

Plymouth

Totnes
Stoke
Gabriel · Brixham

Portwrinkle

Polperro

Dartmouth

ROSCOFF
SANTANDER

Bigbury-on-Sea

0 · 25 Miles

0 · 40 Km

N

Map 2

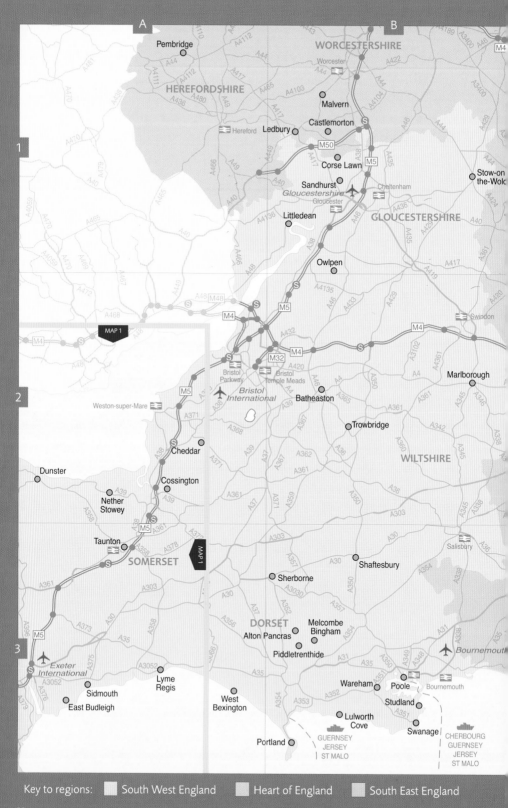

Key to regions: ■ South West England ■ Heart of England ■ South East England

Map 2

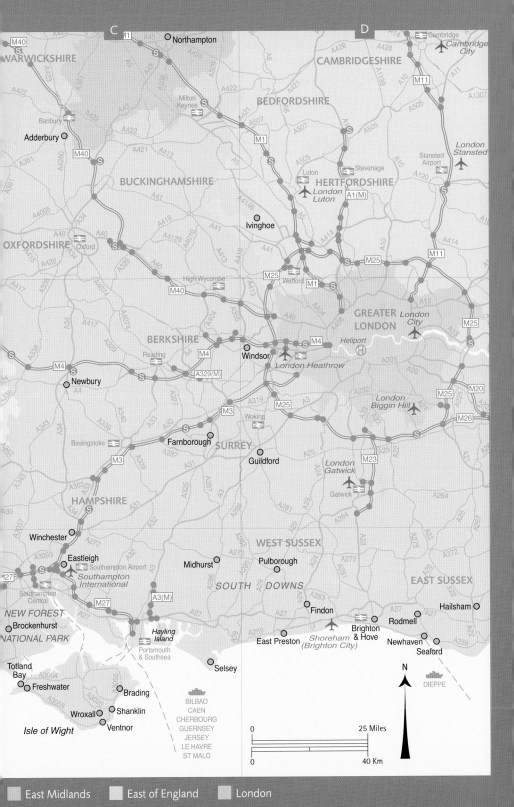

East Midlands   East of England   London

All place names in black offer accommodation in this guide

Map 3

Key to regions: ■ East Midlands ■ South East England ■ East of England ■ London

Map 3

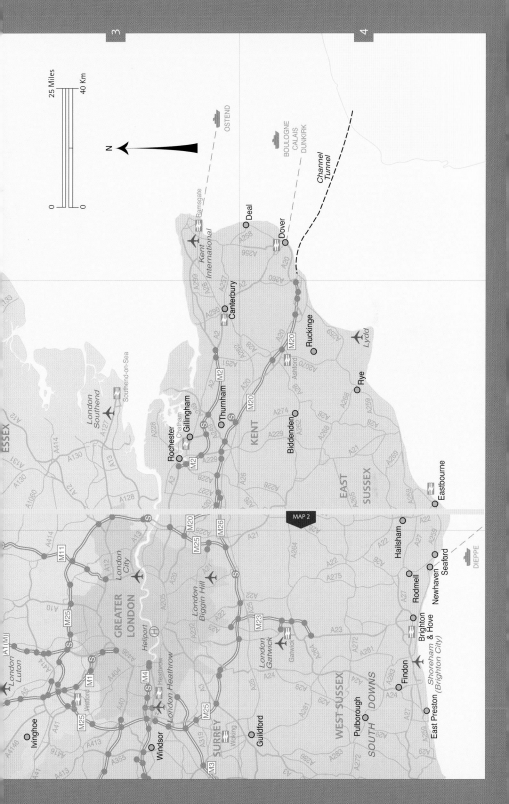

Map 4

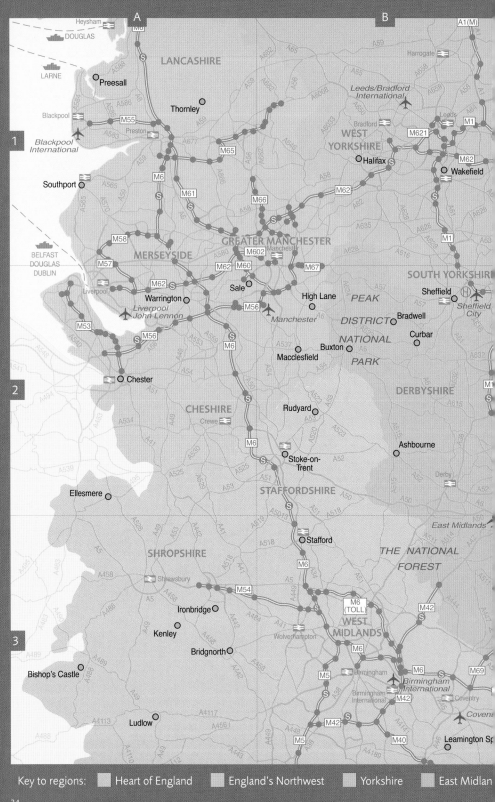

Key to regions: ▮ Heart of England ▮ England's Northwest ▮ Yorkshire ▮ East Midland

Map 4

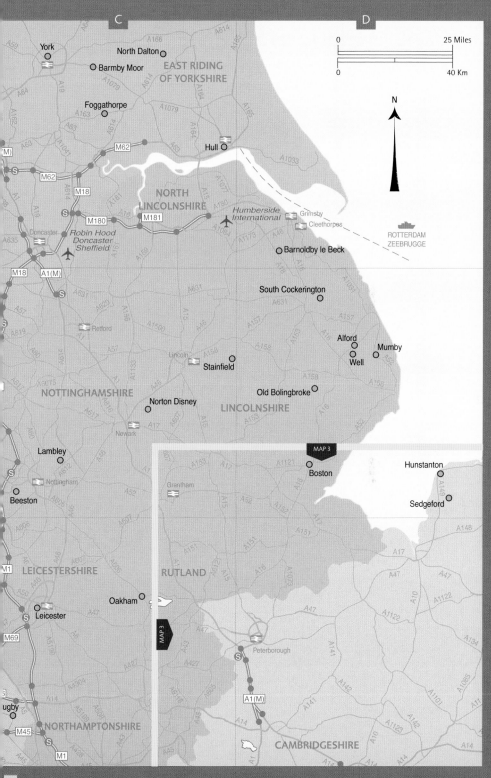

East of England

All place names in black offer accommodation in this guide

Map 5

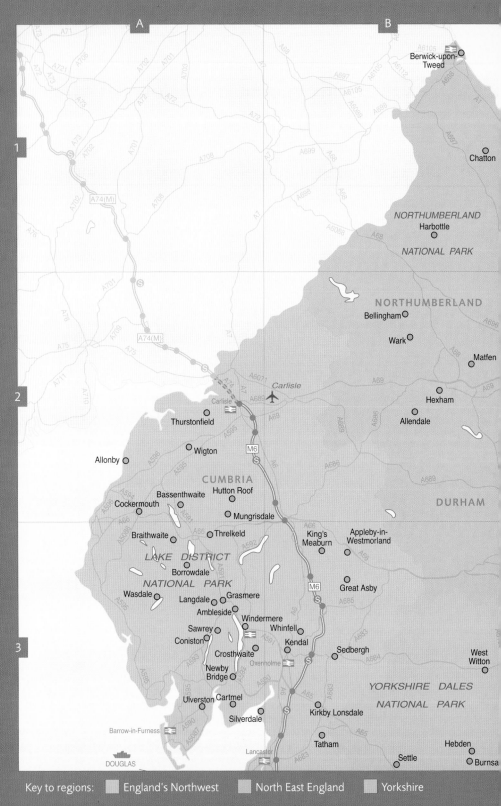

Key to regions: ▢ England's Northwest ▢ North East England ▢ Yorkshire

Map 5

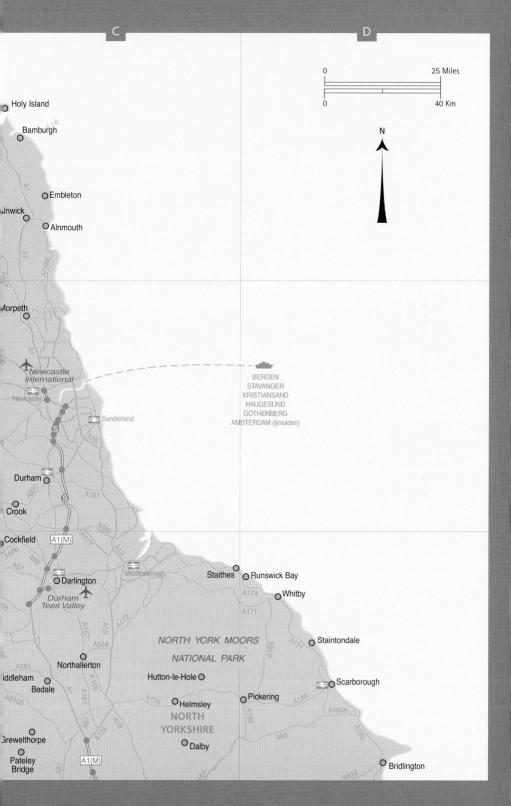

C

D

0   25 Miles

0   40 Km

N

○ Holy Island

○ Bamburgh

A1

○ Embleton

Alnwick ○

A1068

○ Alnmouth

A1

A697

Morpeth ○

A1

Newcastle International

Newcastle

S

Sunderland

A19

Durham ○

A690

S

A181

○ Crook

Cockfield ○

A1(M)

A177

A688

A67

A68

A688

A689

A19

Darlington ○

Middlesbrough

Durham
Tees Valley

Staithes ○   ○ Runswick Bay

A174

○ Whitby

A171

NORTH YORK MOORS

A169

A171

○ Staintondale

A167

A19

A172

A684

Northallerton ○

NATIONAL PARK

Middleham ○

Bedale ○

A684

A1

A168

A167

Hutton-le-Hole ○

A170

○ Scarborough

A1039

A165

A6108

Helmsley ○

○ Pickering

A169

A170

A64

NORTH
YORKSHIRE

Grewelthorpe ○

A6

A1(M)

A168

A19

Dalby ○

A64

Pateley
Bridge ○

A614

○ Bridlington

BERGEN
STAVANGER
KRISTIANSAND
HAUGESUND
GOTHENBERG
AMSTERDAM (Ijmuiden)

Map 6

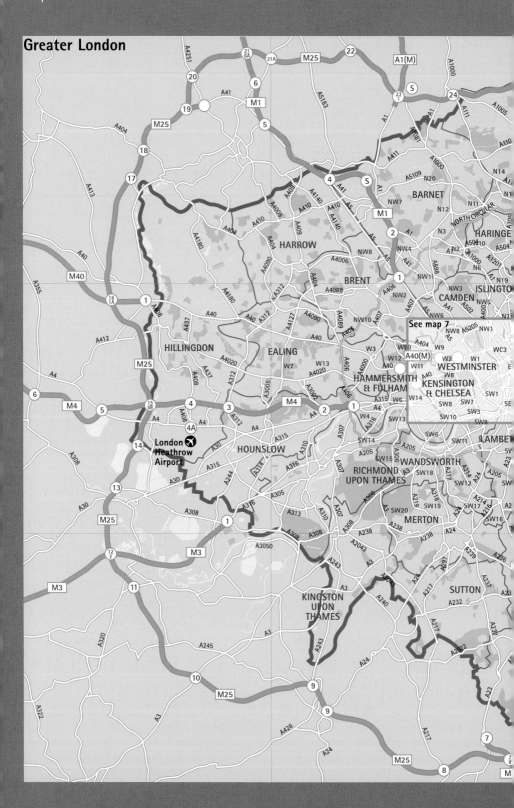

Map 6

Map 7

Central London

enjoyEngland ™

official tourist board guides

Hotels, including country house and town house hotels, metro and budget hotels in England 2008

£10.99

Guest accommodation, B&Bs, guest houses, farmhouses, inns, restaurants with rooms, campus and hostel accommodation in England 2008

£11.99

Self-catering holiday homes, including serviced apartments and approved caravan holiday homes, boat accommodation and holiday cottage agencies in England 2008

£11.99

Touring parks, camping holidays and holiday parks and villages in Britain 2008

£8.99

informative, easy to use and great value for money

Pet-friendly hotels, B&Bs and self-catering accommodation in England 2008

£9.99

Great ideas for places to visit, eat and stay in England

£10.99

Places to stay and visit in South West England

£9.99

Places to stay and visit in Northern England

£9.99

Accessible places to stay in Britain

£9.99

Now available in good bookshops.
For special offers on VisitBritain publications,
please visit **enjoyenglanddirect.com**

England's Northwest

Blackpool and Lancashire, Chester and Cheshire, Cumbria – The Lake District, Liverpool and Merseyside, Manchester

Constant variety and continual delights

England's Northwest is a region of astonishing contrasts. Where else can you travel to four different worlds – from peak to plain, from coast to city – in one short day?

England's Northwest
visitenglandsnorthwest.com

Albert Dock, Liverpool   Tatton Park, Cheshire

The Lowry, Manchester

From the Cumbrian peaks to the Cheshire plain, from the seaside thrills of Blackpool to the buzzing energy of Manchester, England's Northwest is bursting with choice for the holidaymaker. Liverpool celebrated its 800th anniversary in 2007 and is an exciting place to be. Fancy a little R&R? Head for Cumbria. This place is a natural wonderland where plunging lakes and swooshing mountains collide in a perfect marriage. Prefer the bright lights to starry skies? Make Manchester your next stop. This glamorous city is a magnet for every designer label and trendy club out there. Or for a peaceful family break, hire a narrow boat in leafy Cheshire and drift along the waterways of the Cheshire Ring.

Experience a sense of déjà vu at Lyme Park in Cheshire – the setting for BBC's Pride and Prejudice. Another must is a visit to Arley Hall, a magnificent Victorian Jacobean stately home with magical gardens. If you find yourself in Chester, book into The Grosvenor Spa – it's the perfect place to escape the hustle and bustle. And no trip to Manchester would be complete without seeing Imperial War Museum North, a powerful exploration of the impact of war on ordinary lives.

If you love mystical places, you'll adore Alderly Edge in Cheshire. Legend has it that this strange place is linked to King Arthur and Merlin. It's also the setting for the classic children's story The Weirdstone of Brisingamen. If you prefer bargain-hunting to wizard-hunting, there's no more colourful and fascinating market than Affleck's Palace in Manchester. And if you want to experience the great outdoors, it doesn't get much grander that in Cumbria – The Lake District.

Whether it's for a night out, day trip or weekend away with the family, England's Northwest has a wealth of attractions to inspire you.

Destinations

Blackpool

Britain's favourite holiday resort. Feel the thrill on the Pepsi Max Big One at the Pleasure Beach, take high tea in the magnificent Tower Ballroom, or stroll the seven miles of sandy beaches. Blackpool offers you world-class shows, cosmopolitan restaurants, vibrant nightlife, an active sports scene and breathtakingly beautiful scenery on the doorstep – every ingredient, in fact, for an unforgettable, carefree break.

Chester

Experience one of Europe's top heritage cities. Walk the unique city walls, complete with surviving Roman sections, then visit the famous Rows, unique two-tiered galleries in black and white 'magpie' style, to shop for everything from antiques to high fashion. Stroll along the banks of the beautiful River Dee, explore the Roman amphitheatre, and don't miss the Grosvenor and Cheshire Military Museums, the beautiful Grosvenor Park and Chester's famous Roodee Racecourse.

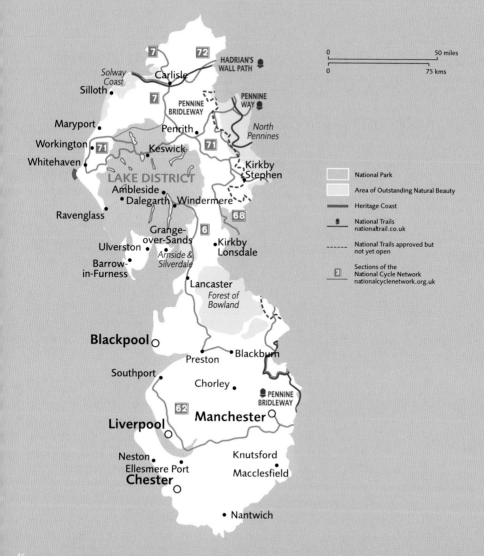

Chester

The Cavern Club, Liverpool

Cumbria – The Lake District

Imperial War Museum North, Manchester

Blackpool

Cumbria – The Lake District

With breathtaking mountains and 16 sparkling lakes, the unsurpassed scenery of Cumbria – The Lake District has inspired writers and poets across the ages. Explore the best walking and climbing routes that England has to offer. Only five peaks in England are over 900m and they are all in Cumbria. Visit the magnificent World Heritage Site at Hadrian's Wall, the most important Roman monument in Britain. Pull off your hiking boots and relax in high-quality accommodation – you'll be thoroughly spoilt for choice.

Liverpool

Experience the unique atmosphere of Liverpool. The birthplace of the Beatles and European Capital of Culture 2008 offers you more theatres, museums and galleries than any UK city outside London. Its history as one of the world's great ports has left a remarkable legacy of art and architecture for you to explore, not forgetting, of course, the city's famous sporting pedigree. So if it's Strawberry Fields, Premiership football or Europe's finest culture you're looking for, it has to be Liverpool.

Manchester

If you haven't been to Manchester, there's never been a better time to visit. Explore a city that has come a long way from its industrial roots and reinvented itself as a truly contemporary metropolis. You'll find modern landmark buildings, a wealth of art and culture, great bars and world-class hospitality. Here there's every experience imaginable, from fine dining and top-class theatre, to major sporting events and year-round festivals. It's a shopping destination in its own right, rivalling that of the capital, with top stores and chic boutiques.

Places to visit

Anderton Boat Lift
Northwich, Cheshire
(01606) 786777
andertonboatlift.co.uk
*Sail through the magnificent
Victorian boat lift*

Arley Hall and Gardens
Northwich, Cheshire
(01565) 777353
arleyhallandgardens.com
*Victorian country house with
splendid gardens*
(grounds only)

Beatles Story
Liverpool, Merseyside
(0151) 709 1963
beatlesstory.com
The history of the Fab Four

Blackwell, The Arts & Crafts House
Windermere, Cumbria
(015394) 46139
blackwell.org.uk
*Elegant Arts and Crafts house and
gardens*

Bowland Wild Boar Park
Preston, Lancashire
(01995) 61554
wildboarpark.co.uk
*Hand-feed animals in a beautiful
wooded park*

Chester Zoo
Cheshire
(01244) 380280
chesterzoo.org.uk
*Black Rhinos and 7,000 other
animals in natural enclosures*

Go Ape! High Wire Forest Adventure
Delamere, Cheshire
0870 444 5562
goape.co.uk
Rope bridges, swings and zip slides
(walkways only)

Imperial War Museum North
Large Visitor
Attraction of the Year
– Silver Winner
Manchester
(0161) 836 4000
iwm.org.uk/north
*Spectacular museum with
innovative display techniques*

Jodrell Bank Visitor Centre
near Macclesfield,
Cheshire
(01477) 571339
jb.man.ac.uk
*Home of the Lovell radio
telescope*
(restricted access)

Lady Lever Art Gallery
Wirral, Merseyside
(0151) 478 4136
ladyleverartgallery.org.uk
*Magnificent collection of fine and
decorative arts*

The Lowry
Salford, Greater
Manchester
(0161) 876 2000
thelowry.com
*Art and entertainment in stunning
21st century landmark*

The Manchester Museum
(0161) 275 2634
manchester.ac.uk/museum
*Displays and exhibitions from
around the world*

Manchester United Museum & Tour
0870 442 1994
manutd.com
*Delve behind the scenes at the
Theatre of Dreams*

Mirehouse Historic House
Keswick, Cumbria
(017687) 72287
mirehouse.com
*Historic house with literary
connections*
(grounds only)

Muncaster Experience
Lake District National Park,
Cumbria
(01229) 717614
muncaster.co.uk
*Historic castle with ghostly
goings-on*
(grounds only)

The Museum of Science and Industry
Manchester
(0161) 832 2244
msim.org.uk
*Historic buildings packed with
fascinating exhibits*

The National Football Museum
Preston, Lancashire
(01772) 908442
nationalfootballmuseum.com
*Amazing journey through football
history*

 Pets Welcome
 Assistance dogs only

Diary dates 2008

National Wildflower Centre
Liverpool, Merseyside
(0151) 738 1913
nwc.org.uk
Wild flowers in a family-friendly environment

Pleasure Beach, Blackpool
Lancashire
0870 444 5566
blackpoolpleasurebeach.co.uk
Thrills and spills featuring Valhalla and the Pepsi Max Big One

Tate Liverpool
Merseyside
(0151) 702 7400
tate.org.uk/liverpool
Modern and contemporary art in historic setting

Tatton Park (NT)
Knutsford, Cheshire
(01625) 534400
tattonpark.org.uk
Historic mansion set in deer park

Urbis
Manchester
(0161) 605 8200
urbis.org.uk
Multi-media exhibitions of city life

Wildfowl & Wetland Trust Martin Mere
Nr Ormskirk, Lancashire
(01704) 895181
wwt.org.uk
Feed endangered species straight from your hand

World Museum Liverpool
Merseyside
(0151) 478 4393
worldmuseumliverpool.org.uk
Treasures from across the world

John Smiths Grand National
Aintree, Merseyside
aintree.co.uk
3 – 5 Apr

Ullswater Walking Festival
ullswater.visitor-centre.co.uk
10 – 18 May

Chester Mystery Plays
Cathedral Green, Chester
chestermysteryplays.com
28 Jun – 19 Jul

The British Open (Golf)
Royal Birkdale, Merseyside
opengolf.com
17 – 20 Jul

RHS Flower Show at Tatton Park
Knutsford, Cheshire
rhs.org.uk
23 – 26 Jul*

Pennine Lancashire Food and Drink Festival
Various locations, Lancashire
penninelancashirefood.co.uk
4 – 7 Sep*

Westmorland County Show
Crooklands, Cumbria
westmorland-county-show.co.uk
11 Sep

Blackpool Illuminations
visitblackpool.com
Sep – Nov*

Manchester Food and Drink Festival
Various locations, Manchester
foodanddrinkfestival.com
10 – 20 Oct*

Muncaster Halloween Week
muncaster.co.uk
27 – 31 Oct

* provisional date at time of going to press

Tourist Information Centres

When you arrive at your destination, visit an Official Partner Tourist Information Centre for quality assured help with accommodation and information about local attractions and events, or email your request before you go. To search for attractions and Tourist Information Centres on the move just text INFO to 62233, and a web link will be sent to your mobile phone.

Accrington	Blackburn Road	(01254) 872595	tourism@hyndburnbc.gov.uk
Altrincham	20 Stamford New Road	(0161) 912 5931	tourist.information@trafford.gov.uk
Ashton-under-Lyne	Wellington Road	(0161) 343 4343	tourist.information@tameside.gov.uk
Barnoldswick	Fernlea Avenue	(01282) 666704	tourist.info@pendle.gov.uk
Barrow-in-Furness	Duke Street	(01229) 876505	touristinfo@barrowbc.gov.uk
Blackburn	50-54 Church Street	(01254) 53277	visit@blackburn.gov.uk
Blackpool	1 Clifton Street	(01253) 478222	tic@blackpool.gov.uk
Bolton	Le Mans Crescent	(01204) 334321	tourist.info@bolton.gov.uk
Bowness	Glebe Road	(015394) 42895	bownesstic@lake-district.gov.uk
Burnley	Croft Street	(01282) 664421	tic@burnley.gov.uk
Bury	Market Street	(0161) 253 5111	touristinformation@bury.gov.uk
Carlisle	Greenmarket	(01228) 625600	tourism@carlisle-city.gov.uk
Chester (Town Hall)	Northgate Street	(01244) 402111	tis@chester.gov.uk
Chester Visitor Centre	Vicars Lane	(01244) 351609	tis@chester.gov.uk
Cleveleys	Victoria Square	(01253) 853378	cleveleystic@wyrebc.gov.uk
Clitheroe	12-14 Market Place	(01200) 425566	tourism@ribblevalley.gov.uk
Congleton	High Street	(01260) 271095	tourism@congleton.gov.uk
Coniston	Ruskin Avenue	(015394) 41533	Conistontic@lake-district.gov.uk
Ellesmere Port	Kinsey Road	(0151) 356 7879	
Fleetwood	The Esplanade	(01253) 773953	fleetwoodtic@btopenworld.com
Garstang	High Street	(01995) 602125	garstangtic@wyrebc.gov.uk
Kendal	Highgate	(01539) 725758	kendaltic@southlakeland.gov.uk
Keswick	Market Square	(017687) 72645	keswicktic@lake-district.gov.uk
Knutsford	Toft Road	(01565) 632611	ktic@macclesfield.gov.uk
Lancaster	29 Castle Hill	(01524) 32878	lancastertic@lancaster.gov.uk
Liverpool 08 Place	Whitechapel	(0151) 233 2459	contact@liverpool.08.com
Liverpool John Lennon Airport	Speke Hall Avenue	0906 680 6886**	info@visitliverpool.com
Lytham St Annes	67 St Annes Road West	(01253) 725610	touristinformation@fylde.gov.uk
Macclesfield	Town Hall	(01625) 504114	informationcentre@macclesfield.gov.uk
Manchester Visitor Information Centre	Lloyd Street	0871 222 8223	touristinformation@marketing-manchester.co.uk
Morecambe	Marine Road Central	(01524) 582808	morecambetic@lancaster.gov.uk
Nantwich	Market Street	(01270) 537359	touristi@crewe-nantwich.gov.uk
Northwich	1 The Arcade	(01606) 353534	tourism@valeroyal.gov.uk
Oldham	12 Albion Street	(0161) 627 1024	ecs.tourist@oldham.gov.uk
Pendle Heritage Centre	Park Hill	(01282) 661701	heritage.centre@pendle.gov.uk

Penrith	Middlegate	(01768) 867466	pen.tic@eden.gov.uk
Preston	Lancaster Road	(01772) 253731	tourism@preston.gov.uk
Rochdale	The Esplanade	(01706) 864928	tic@link4life.org
Saddleworth	High Street	(01457) 870336	ecs.saddleworthtic@oldham.gov.uk
St Helens	Chalon Way East	(01744) 755150	info@sthelenstic.com
Salford	Salford Quays	(0161) 848 8601	tic@salford.gov.uk
Southport	112 Lord Street	(01704) 533333	info@visitsouthport.com
Stockport	30 Market Place	(0161) 474 4444	tourist.information@stockport.gov.uk
Warrington	Horsemarket Street	(01925) 428585	informationcentre@warrington.gov.uk
Whitehaven	Market Place	(01946) 598914	tic@copelandbc.gov.uk
Wigan	62 Wallgate	(01942) 825677	tic@wlct.org
Wilmslow	Rectory Fields	(01625) 522275	i.hillaby@macclesfield.gov.uk
Windermere	Victoria Street	(015394) 46499	windermeretic@southlakeland.gov.uk

** calls to this number are charged at premium rate

River Mersey and Liverpool

Travel info

By road:
Motorways intersect within the region which has the best road network in the country. Travelling north or south use the M6, and east or west the M62.

By air:
Fly into Liverpool John Lennon, Manchester or Blackpool airports.

By rail:
Most Northwest coastal resorts are connected to InterCity routes with trains from many parts of the country, and there are through trains to major cities and towns.

Find out more

Windermere, Cumbria

There are various publications and guides about England's Northwest available from the following Tourist Boards or by logging on to visitenglandsnorthwest.com or calling 0845 600 6040:

Visit Chester and Cheshire
Chester Railway Station, 1st Floor, West Wing Offices, Station Road, Chester CH1 3NT
t (01244) 405600
e info@visitchesterandcheshire.co.uk
w visitchester.com or visitcheshire.com

Cumbria Tourism
Windermere Road, Staveley, Kendal LA8 9PL
t (015398) 22222
e info@cumbriatourism.org
w golakes.co.uk

The Lancashire and Blackpool Tourist Board
St George's House, St George's Street Chorley PR7 2AA
t (01257) 226600 (Brochure request)
e info@visitlancashire.com
w visitlancashire.com

Marketing Manchester – The Tourist Board for Greater Manchester
Churchgate House, 56 Oxford Street Manchester M1 6EU
t (0161) 237 1010
   Brochure request: 0870 609 3013
e touristinformation@marketing-manchester.co.uk
w visitmanchester.com

The Mersey Partnership – The Tourist Board for Liverpool and Merseyside
12 Princes Parade, Liverpool L3 1BG
t (0151) 233 2008 (information enquiries)
t 0844 870 0123 (accommodation booking)
e info@visitliverpool.com (accommodation enquiries)
e 08place@liverpool.gov.uk (information enquiries)
w visitliverpool.com

where to stay in
England's Northwest

All place names in the blue bands are shown on the maps at the front of this guide.

Accommodation symbols
Symbols give useful information about services and facilities. Inside the back-cover flap you can find a key to these symbols. Keep it open for easy reference.

ALLONBY, Cumbria Map ref 5A2   **SELF CATERING**

★★★★
SELF CATERING

Units **1**
Sleeps **2–14**
Low season per wk
£700.00–£740.00
High season per wk
£780.00–£800.00

Crookhurst Farm, Allonby, Maryport
contact Brenda Wilson, Crookhurst Farm, c/o Bowscale Farm, Allonby, Maryport CA15 6RB
t (01900) 881228 & 07773 047591   **e** brenda@crookhurst.com   **w** crookhurst.com

Crookhurst is a working farm set in open countryside, 0.5 miles from the picturesque village on the Solway coast. The farmhouse provides spacious group accommodation in a cosy homely environment.

open All year
payment Cash/cheques

Pets 🐕 £🐈 🐕.   Unit 🏠 📺 📼 📺 📻 📠 🖥 🖨 🔥 🔲 🔳 ✳
General 🛁 🏛 🛠 P ✂ ⬜ Ⓢ   Leisure 🎣 ∪ 🎿   Shop 0.5 miles   Pub 0.5 miles

---

AMBLESIDE, Cumbria Map ref 5A3   **GUEST ACCOMMODATION**

★★★
GUEST ACCOMMODATION

B&B per room per night
s £28.00–£35.00
d £55.00–£70.00

Lyndale Guest House
Low Fold, Lake Road, Ambleside LA22 0DN   **t** (015394) 34244   **e** alison@lyndale-guesthouse.co.uk
w lyndale-guesthouse.co.uk

Victorian guesthouse providing spacious, comfortable accommodation. Hearty breakfasts and excellent services. Located midway between Lake Windermere and Ambleside. Great for touring and walking. Great value for money.

open All year
bedrooms 2 double, 2 single, 2 family
bathrooms 4 en suite, 2 private
payment Credit/debit cards, cash/cheques

Pets 🐕 🐈   Room 📺 ☕ 🍵   General 🛁 🏛 🛠 ✂ 🖥 ✳

AMBLESIDE, Cumbria Map ref 5A3   **GUEST ACCOMMODATION**

★★★★
GUEST ACCOMMODATION

B&B per room per night
s Min £100.00
d £100.00–£150.00

The Old Vicarage
Vicarage Road, Ambleside LA22 9DH   **t** (015394) 33364   **f** (015394) 34734
e info@oldvicarageambleside.co.uk   **w** oldvicarageambleside.co.uk

Quiet central situation. Car park. Pets welcome. Heated indoor swimming pool, sauna and hot tub. Quality accommodation with TV/DVD/VCR, hairdryer, fridge, en suite. Some four-posters, spa baths and some ground-floor rooms.

open All year except Christmas
bedrooms 4 double, 4 twin, 2 family, 4 suites
bathrooms 10 en suite
payment Credit/debit cards, cash/cheques, euros

Pets 🐕 🐈 🐾 🐕.   Room 🛋 📺 ☕ 🍵   General 🛁 🏛 🛠 P ✂ 🖥 🅿 🔥 ⬜ ✳   Leisure 🎣 ♨ ∪ 🚴 🎿

Key to symbols
Open the back flap for a key to symbols.

AMBLESIDE, Cumbria Map ref 5A3 — SELF CATERING

★★★★-★★★★★
SELF CATERING

Units **26**
Sleeps **2-6**

Low season per wk
Min £340.00
High season per wk
Min £495.00

Kirkstone Foot Apartments, Ambleside

contact Mrs J Tunnicliff, Kirkstone Foot Apartments Limited, Kirkstone Pass Road, Ambleside LA22 9EH
t (015394) 32232 **f** (015394) 32805 **e** enquiries@kirkstonefoot.co.uk **w** kirkstonefoot.co.uk

open All year
payment Credit/debit cards, cash/cheques

Superior, luxury holiday cottages and apartments set amongst two acres of beautiful, landscaped grounds, yet only a two-minute stroll from the centre of Ambleside.

⊕ *In Ambleside take Kirkstone Pass road. As road levels out, Kirkstone Foot on right-hand side.*

♥ *Midweek 4 nights for the price of 3. Weekends, Fri and Sat nights subject to availability.*

Pets 🐾 £🐾 Unit 🏠 📺 🌐 🖥 🛏 🍳 🔌 🔥
General ♨ ⌨ ⚲ P ✂ 📶 S Leisure 🚲

APPLEBY-IN-WESTMORLAND, Cumbria Map ref 5B3 — SELF CATERING

★★★
SELF CATERING

Units **7**
Sleeps **2-7**

Low season per wk
£220.00-£450.00
High season per wk
£250.00-£530.00

Milburn Grange Holiday Cottages, Knock, Appleby-in-Westmorland

contact Russell & Debbie Clark, Milburn Grange Holiday Cottages, Milburn Grange, Knock, Appleby-in-Westmorland CA16 6DR
t (01768) 361867 **e** holidays@milburngrange.co.uk **w** milburngrange.co.uk

open All year
payment Credit/debit cards, cash/cheques

Nestling at the foot of the Pennines and enjoying uninterrupted views of the Lakeland fells, our cosy cottages offer a high standard of accommodation and are open all year. The seven cottages can sleep from two to seven people with large groups of up to 29 people accommodated.

⊕ *Exit jct 40 M6. Take the A66 towards Appleby and Scotch Corner. Turn left at Kirkby Thore to Milburn. See website for full directions.*

♥ *Short breaks available Oct-Mar and at other times subject to availability. Minimum 2-night stay. Contact us for prices.*

Pets 🐾 £🐾 🐾 Unit 🏠 📺 🌐 🖥 🛏 🍳 🔌 🔥
General ♨ ⌨ ⚲ P ✂ 📶 S Leisure ⚲ ∪ 🏛 Shop 0.5 miles Pub 2 miles

BASSENTHWAITE, Cumbria Map ref 5A2 — HOTEL

★★★
HOTEL
SILVER AWARD

B&B per room per night
s £75.00-£90.00
d £140.00-£160.00
HB per person per night
£97.00-£115.00

The Pheasant

Bassenthwaite Lake, Cockermouth CA13 9YE **t** (01768) 776234 **f** (01768) 776002
e info@the-pheasant.co.uk **w** the-pheasant.co.uk

open All year except Christmas
bedrooms 8 double, 3 twin, 1 single, 3 suites
bathrooms All en suite
payment Credit/debit cards, cash/cheques

The Pheasant is a charming old coaching inn, with every modern comfort, situated close to Bassenthwaite Lake at the unspoilt northern end of the Lake District. It is one of the last remaining traditional Cumbrian hostelries with its unique period atmosphere, sense of timelessness and peaceful location.

⊕ *Located midway between Keswick and Cockermouth on the A66. Signposted (The Pheasant Inn) from the A66.*

♥ *3-night specials: Sun-Thu from £250 pp DB&B.*

Pets 🐾 £🐾 🐾 🛏 Room 🛏 📺 🔌 🍳 General ♨8 P ✂ 🍽 🛏 ✿ Leisure 🏛

BORROWDALE, Cumbria Map ref 5A3 — HOTEL

★★
COUNTRY HOUSE HOTEL

B&B per room per night
s £34.00–£44.00
d £68.00–£104.00

Mary Mount Hotel

Borrowdale, Keswick CA12 5UU t (017687) 77223 f (017687) 77617 e mawdsley1@aol.com
w marymounthotel.co.uk

Set in 4.5 acres of gardens and woodlands on the shores of Derwentwater, 2.5 miles from Keswick. Views across lake to Catbells and Maiden Moor. Families and pets welcome. Special midweek winter breaks available.

open All year
bedrooms 12 double, 4 twin, 2 single, 2 family
bathrooms All en suite
payment Credit/debit cards, cash/cheques

Pets ♉ ♋ ♓ ♘ ♞ Room ♿ ⊺⊽ ⚲ General ♊ ▥ ♠ P ♀ ⚏ ♙ ✿ Leisure ♻

BRAITHWAITE, Cumbria Map ref 5A3 — GUEST ACCOMMODATION

★★★
INN

B&B per room per night
s £31.00–£37.00
d £62.00–£74.00
Evening meal per person
£7.95–£11.50

Coledale Inn

Braithwaite, Keswick CA12 5TN t (017687) 78272 f (017687) 78416 e info@coledale-inn.com
w coledale-inn.co.uk

Victorian country-house hotel and Georgian inn. Peaceful hillside position away from traffic, with superb mountain views. Families and pets welcome. Fine selection of real ales. Special midweek winter breaks available.

open All year
bedrooms 11 double, 3 twin, 1 single, 5 family
bathrooms All en suite
payment Credit/debit cards, cash/cheques

Pets ♉ ♘ ♞ Room ♿ ⊺⊽ ⚲ General ♊ ▥ ♠ P ♀ ✕ ⚏ ♙ ✿

CARTMEL, Cumbria Map ref 5A3 — SELF CATERING

★★★–★★★★★
SELF CATERING

Units   8
Sleeps 1–18

Low season per wk
£240.00–£350.00
High season per wk
£400.00–£780.00

Longlands at Cartmel, Grange-over-Sands

contact Martin Ainscough, Longlands at Cartmel, Cartmel, Grange-over-Sands LA11 6HG
t (015395) 36475 f (015395) 36172 e longlands@cartmel.com w cartmel.com

open All year
payment Cash/cheques

Extremely well-equipped cottages, furnished to a very high standard, set in a courtyard behind a beautiful Georgian house set in parkland on the side of Hampsfell outside Cartmel. Restored walled garden. Great walks, and superb pubs and restaurants in the village.

⊕ M6 jct 36, follow signs for Barrow (A590) for 12 miles. Left to Cartmel, left at crossroads, left at T-junction. Longlands set back in fields on left.

♥ Short breaks available from Nov-Easter and throughout the year if availability allows.

Pets ♉ Unit ▥ ⊺⊽ ⊡ ⊟ ▣ ♦ ♝ ♖ ⚲ ✿
General ♊ ▥ ♠ ⊙ S Leisure ♦ ∪ Shop 1 mile Pub 1 mile

Accessible needs?

If you have special hearing, visual or mobility needs, there's an index of National Accessible Scheme participants featured in this guide. For more accessible accommodation buy a copy of Easy Access Britain available online at visitbritaindirect.com.

★★★
HOTEL

B&B per room per night
s £90.00–£120.00
d £125.00–£160.00

Grosvenor Pulford Hotel & Spa

Wrexham Road, Pulford, Chester CH4 9DG **t** (01244) 570560 **f** (01244) 570809
e reservations@grosvenorpulfordhotel.co.uk **w** grosvenorpulfordhotel.co.uk

open All year
bedrooms 50 double, 13 twin, 1 single, 8 family, 1 suite
bathrooms All en suite
payment Credit/debit cards

Visit Chester and Cheshire's Large Hotel of the Year 2007. Seventy-three en suite bedrooms, Mediterranean-themed restaurant, stylish gastro bar, Roman-style swimming pool, sauna, steam room, jacuzzi, state-of-the-art Technogym, outdoor tennis court, extensive spa including advanced skin clinic, Turkish Hamman, Arabian Rasul, VIP couples suite, luxurious treatment suites and relaxation rooms.

⊕ Exit M53/A55 at junction signposted A483 Chester, Wrexham and North Wales. Turn left onto B5445 signposted Eccleston and Pulford. Hotel is 2 miles on right.

♥ Romantic Break £175 per deluxe room – £18 dinner allowance per person, Champagne and chocolates, breakfast, use of leisure facilities.

Pets 🐕 🐾 🐾. Room 🛁 📞 📺 💨 🔌 🗝. General 🗞 🎱 ♨ P ☏ 🍴 🖪 ◉ ✳ Leisure 🎿 ⚲ ∪

★★★★
GUEST HOUSE

B&B per room per night
s £45.00–£70.00
d £60.00–£85.00
Evening meal per person
£20.00–£25.00

Rose Cottage

Lorton Road, Cockermouth CA13 9DX **t** (01900) 822189 **f** (01900) 822189
e bookings@rosecottageguest.co.uk **w** rosecottageguest.co.uk

open All year except Christmas and New Year
bedrooms 3 double, 2 twin, 1 single, 2 family
bathrooms All en suite
payment Credit/debit cards, cash/cheques

In a pleasant position and only a ten-minute walk from the town, this family-run guesthouse is within easy reach of the Lakes and coast. Home cooking. Large, private car park. An ideal base for walking or touring.

♥ Midweek or weekend breaks available all year (min 2 nights). Family group packages also available all year (min 12 people).

Pets 🐕 🐾 Room 🛁 📺 💨 General 🗞 🎱 ♨ P ✂ ☏ ✕ 🖪 ◉ ✳

Get on the road

Take yourself on a journey through England's historic towns and villages, past stunning coastlines and beautiful countryside with VisitBritain's series of inspirational touring guides. You can purchase the guides from good bookshops and online at visitbritaindirect.com.

COCKERMOUTH, Cumbria Map ref 5A2   **SELF CATERING**

★★★
SELF CATERING

Units   **1**
Sleeps   **4–6**
Low season per wk
£320.00–£390.00
High season per wk
£450.00–£680.00

The Stables, Dean, Workington

contact Veronica Roper, Sunnyside, Gib Lane, Hoghton PR5 0RS
t (01254) 852027   **e** veronica@vroper.fsnet.co.uk   **w** vholidays.moonfruit.com

open All year
payment Cash/cheques, euros

Delightful 18thC, comfortable, well-equipped cottage with inglenooks, exposed beams and log fires – an excellent base at any time of year. Dean is a peaceful village, ideally situated for exploring the Northern Lakes, West Cumbria, Carlisle and the Scottish Borders. Secluded garden – perfect for a peaceful, relaxing holiday. Walking, cycling, golf, fishing. Ospreys nearby.

⊕ *M6 jct 40, Workington. A66, Cockermouth. At roundabout, left (Egremont A5086), 4 miles right Dean, 1 mile right Dean. Pass Royal Yew. Left after barn conversion.*

♥ *3-night breaks available Oct–Mar. 20% discount for 2 people, depending on season.*

Pets ♙ £♙   Unit ▦ ⊞ ⊟ ▤ ▣ ⊠▢ ⬚▢ ✿
General ⛂ ▥ **P** ✂ **S**   Leisure ☗   Shop 5 miles   Pub < 0.5 miles

CONISTON, Cumbria Map ref 5A3   **GUEST ACCOMMODATION**

★★★
INN

B&B per room per night
s £45.00–£55.00
d £60.00–£85.00
Evening meal per person
£8.00–£18.00

Yewdale Inn

Yewdale Road, Coniston LA21 8DU   **t** (015394) 41280   **f** (015394) 41871   **e** mail@yewdalehotel.com
w yewdalehotel.com

Small, family-run inn situated in the centre of Coniston, within walking distance of the lake. Ideally positioned for walkers and cyclists. Children and pets welcome.

open All year
bedrooms 3 double, 4 family
bathrooms All en suite
payment Credit/debit cards, cash/cheques

Pets ♙ £♙ ♘♙   Room ⊞ ✦   General ⛂ ▥ ♠ **P** ♨ ☷ ✿   Leisure ⚲ ∪ ♿ ⌂

CROSTHWAITE, Cumbria Map ref 5A3   **HOTEL**

★★★
HOTEL

B&B per room per night
s £64.00–£84.00
d £98.00–£128.00
HB per person per night
£69.00–£89.00

Damson Dene Hotel

Crosthwaite, Nr Bowness on Windermere, Kendal LA8 8JE   **t** (015395) 68676   **f** (015395) 68227
e info@damsondene.co.uk   **w** bestlakesbreaks.co.uk

open All year
bedrooms 28 double, 5 twin, 4 family
bathrooms All en suite
payment Credit/debit cards, cash/cheques

This lovely hotel is tucked away in one of the prettiest and most tranquil settings in the Lake District, yet is only a short drive from Lake Windermere. Days may be spent touring the area or relaxing in the comfortable lounge and extensive gardens. Superb leisure facilities.

⊕ *Leave M6 at jct 36. Follow A590 towards Barrow-in-Furness. Turn right onto A5074 signposted Bowness and Windermere. The hotel is about 5 miles on right-hand side.*

♥ *Bargain breaks: 3 nights from £139pp DB&B.*

Pets ♙ ♘♙   Room ♠ ✦ ⊞ ✦ ♘   General ⛂ ▥ ♠ **P** ♨ ☷ ♨ ⊙ ✿   Leisure ⚲ ∪ ♿ ⌂

Place index

If you know where you want to stay, the index at the back of the guide will give you the page number listing accommodation in your chosen town, city or village. Check out the other useful indexes too.

GRASMERE, Cumbria Map ref 5A3 | **HOTEL**

★★
HOTEL
SILVER AWARD

The Grasmere Hotel

Broadgate, Grasmere, Ambleside LA22 9TA **t** (015394) 35277 **f** (015394) 35277
e enquiries@grasmerehotel.co.uk **w** grasmerehotel.co.uk

B&B per room per night
d £95.00–£190.00
HB per person per night
£50.00–£125.00

bedrooms 9 double, 2 twin, 2 single, 1 suite
bathrooms All en suite
payment Credit/debit cards, cash/cheques

Our delightful Victorian hotel offers standards synonymous with larger hotels, providing modern levels of comfort and convenience. Sympathetically refurbished, the hotel boasts an elegant, AA Rosette award-winning restaurant which overlooks our gardens, the River Rothay and fells beyond. The friendly atmosphere encourages many guests to return. Closed January.

⊕ Take A591 from Windermere, through Ambleside to Grasmere. Take 2nd turning signposted Grasmere Village. Hotel is 0.5 miles on the left, next to village hall.

♥ New 'Poets Garden Suite' now available for special occasions. Beautifully furnished, with lounge and bedroom; overlooks garden. From £95pp B&B.

Pets 🐾 ⏰ 🐕 Room 🛏 ☎ 📺 🕯 🍵 General 🛁 10 P 🚫 ♨ 🏋 ⚂ ▣ ❀ Leisure ∪ 🚲 🏊

GRASMERE, Cumbria Map ref 5A3 | **SELF CATERING**

★★★
SELF CATERING

1 Field Foot, Grasmere

contact Mrs J Morrison, 1 Field Foot, Park Crescent, Wigan WN1 1RZ
t (01942) 236350 & (015394) 45305 **e** jean-morrison@hotmail.co.uk

Units **1**
Sleeps **2–5**
Low season per wk
Min £250.00
High season per wk
Max £600.00

A large, cosy cottage in the middle of the village. Heating and electricity included. Top bedroom has wonderful views. Large kitchen/diner, separate TV lounge. Garage. Children and one dog welcome.

open All year
payment Cash/cheques

Pets 🐾 Unit 🏠 📺 🍵 ▣ ⬛ 📲 🍴 ▣ 🔲 🔲 ▣
General 🛁 🏠 🏃 P 🚫 Shop < 0.5 miles Pub < 0.5 miles

GREAT ASBY, Cumbria Map ref 5B3 | **SELF CATERING**

★★★★
SELF CATERING

Scalebeck Holiday Cottages, Great Asby,
Appleby-in-Westmorland

contact Mr K J Budding, Scalebeck Holiday Cottages, Scalebeck, Appleby-in-Westmorland CA16 6TF
t (01768) 351006 **f** (01768) 353532 **e** mail@scalebeckholidaycottages.com
w scalebeckholidaycottages.co.uk

Units **3**
Sleeps **2–5**
Low season per wk
£250.00–£375.00
High season per wk
Max £475.00

open All year
payment Credit/debit cards, cash/cheques

Three well-appointed self-catering cottages sleeping two-five in 17thC barn conversion. Secluded, quiet valley, abundant wildlife. Ideal base to explore Lakes and Dales. Non-smokers, pets welcome, games room with table tennis and pool table. Gas central heating, open all year. Gas, electricity, bed linen and towels included.

⊕ From jct 38 of M6 or Appleby, follow B6260. We are 5 miles south-east of Appleby between villages of Drybeck and Great Asby.

♥ Four nights for the price of three.

Pets 🐾 ⏰ 🐕. Unit 🏠 📺 📲 ▣ ⬛ 📲 🍴 ▣ 🔲 🔲 ❀
General 🛁 🏠 🏃 P 🚫 ▣ ⑤ Leisure ● ∪ 🚲 🏊 Shop 5 miles Pub 1 mile

---

Using map references

Map references refer to the colour maps at the front of this guide.

HIGH LANE, Greater Manchester Map ref 4B2 — **SELF CATERING**

★★★★
SELF CATERING

Units **1**
Sleeps **1–6**
Low season per wk
£275.00–£325.00
High season per wk
£375.00–£425.00

Ty Coch, Stockport

contact Mrs Jane Beard, Ty Coch, 1 Huron Crescent, Lakeside, Cardiff CF23 6DT
t (029) 2076 1888

Two-bedroom bungalow. The kitchen has all facilities with TVs in the lounge and bedrooms. Enclosed rear garden. Good local walks. Close to Lyme Park and Peak District National Park.

open All year
payment Cash/cheques

Pets 🐾 Unit 🏠 📺 ▯▢▤▥ ▦▧▨▩ ▪▫
General ♨ ▥ ⚲ **P** **S** Leisure ∪

HUTTON ROOF, Cumbria Map ref 5A2 — **SELF CATERING**

★★★★★
SELF CATERING

Units **4**
Sleeps **2–20**
Low season per wk
£395.00–£1,595.00
High season per wk
£395.00–£1,595.00

Carrock Cottages, Penrith

contact Malcolm & Gillian Iredale, Carrock Cottages, Carrock House, How Hill, Hutton Roof CA11 0XY
t (01768) 484111 **f** (01768) 488850 **e** info@carrockcottages.co.uk **w** carrockcottages.co.uk

payment Credit/debit cards, cash/cheques

Award-winning luxury cottages in quiet, rural location near lovely villages of Hesket Newmarket, Caldbeck and Greystoke. Explore northern Lake District or head north to historic Carlisle and on to Hadrian's Wall. Restaurants, fell-walking and other activities. Warm welcome guaranteed. Internet access, digital TV. Prices differ at Christmas, New Year and Easter.

⊕ *From M6 jct 41, take B5305 for approx 8 miles; left into Lamonby Village. 1st right at 1st crossroads. Cottages on left, 800m after the wishing well.*

Pets 🐾 🐱 🐕 Unit 🏠 📺 ▯▢▣ ▤▥ ▦▧ ▨▩ ▪▫
General ♨ ▥ ⚲ **P** ✂ **S** Leisure ● ⛰ Shop 5 miles Pub 5 miles

---

KENDAL, Cumbria Map ref 5B3 — **HOTEL**

★★★
HOTEL

B&B per room per night
s £69.00–£89.00
d £108.00–£158.00
HB per person per night
£79.00–£99.00

Riverside Hotel

Stramongate Bridge, Beezon Road, Kendal LA9 6EL **t** (01539) 734861 **f** (01539) 734863
e info@riversidekendal.co.uk **w** bestlakesbreaks.co.uk

open All year
bedrooms 28 double, 2 twin, 16 family, 1 suite
bathrooms All en suite
payment Credit/debit cards, cash/cheques

The Riverside Hotel is on the banks of the River Kent. Dating back to 1626, the building was home to renowned makers of leather for 250 years. Today, the modernised hotel offers comfort and convenience. Situated in the heart of the market town of Kendal, it is an ideal base to explore the Lake District.

⊕ *Leave M6 jct 36. Follow signs for Kendal. Take Kendal North exit into Kendal, over bridge then right at mini-roundabout. 1st right after zebra-crossing.*

♥ *Special 3-night DB&B packages available.*

Pets 🐾 🐕 🦴 Room 🛏 ☎ 📺 ▯▢ ▣ General ♨ ▥ ⚲ **P** ▦ ▧ ▨ Leisure ☂ ● ∪ 🚲

It's all quality-assessed accommodation

Our commitment to quality involves wide-ranging accommodation assessment. Rating and awards were correct at the time of going to press but may change following a new assessment. Please check at time of booking.

KENDAL, Cumbria Map ref 5B3 — GUEST ACCOMMODATION

★★★★
GUEST HOUSE

B&B per room per night
s £35.00–£45.00
d £60.00–£76.00

The Glen

Oxenholme, Kendal LA9 7RF **t** (01539) 726386 & 07743 604599 **f** (01539) 724434
e greenintheglen@btinternet.com **w** glen-kendal.co.uk

open All year
bedrooms 2 double, 1 twin, 2 family, 1 suite
bathrooms All en suite
payment Credit/debit cards, cash/cheques

Visit the Lakes and Beatrix Potter country but miss the crowds and the hassle – stop at The Glen, in a quiet location under Helm (local walk and view point of Lakeland mountains), but within a short walk of inn and restaurant. Relax in the hot tub and walk on Helm after your day touring.

⊕ We are 300m up the hill on the right from Oxenholme Lake District railway station.

Pets 🐕 £🐈 🐾 🐁. Room 🛏 📺 ♨ ☕ General 🍴 P 🚭 ♿ ☀ Leisure 🏊

KING'S MEABURN, Cumbria Map ref 5B3 — SELF CATERING

★★★★
SELF CATERING

Units   4
Sleeps 3–6

Low season per wk
£195.00–£300.00
High season per wk
£305.00–£500.00

Lyvennet Cottages, Penrith

contact Margaret, Wendy & Janet Addison, Lyvennet Cottages, Keld Farm, King's Meaburn, Penrith CA10 3BS
t (01931) 714226 **f** (01931) 714228 **e** wendyaddison@yahoo.com **w** lyvennetcottages.co.uk

open All year
payment Cash/cheques

Attractive, well-furnished cottages in quiet village, overlooking the beautiful Lyvennet Valley and Lakeland hills. Some log fires in winter. Fishing, fuel and linen inclusive. Children and pets welcome. Good pub. Own woodland walks and bird-watching. Bring your own horse – excellent livery or grass. Ideal centre for Lakes, Dales, Hadrian's Wall and Scottish Borders.

⊕ M6 jct 38, 3 miles from the B6260 (Tebay to Appleby).

♥ Short breaks available Oct-Mar (excl Christmas and New Year). Minimum 2 nights.

Pets 🐕 £🐈 Unit 🖥 📺 💻 🔌 🔥 🍳 📷 🎮 ☀
General 🍴 🖿 🌳 P Leisure ∪

KIRKBY LONSDALE, Cumbria Map ref 5B3 — GUEST ACCOMMODATION

★★★★
GUEST ACCOMMODATION

B&B per room per night
s £28.00–£35.00
d £48.00–£54.00

Ullathorns Farm

Middleton, Kirkby Lonsdale, Carnforth LA6 2LZ **t** (015242) 76214 & 07800 990689 **f** (015242) 76214
e pauline@ullathorns.co.uk **w** ullathorns.co.uk

open All year except Christmas and New Year
bedrooms 1 double, 1 family
bathrooms All en suite
payment Cash/cheques

A warm welcome awaits you at Ullathorns, a working farm situated in the unspoilt Lune Valley midway between Sedbergh and Kirkby Lonsdale. An ideal touring base for lakes and dales. Good overnight stopping-off point, situated between junctions of the M6. Refreshments served upon arrival. Individual breakfast tables.

⊕ Ullathorns is set midway between Sedbergh and Kirkby Lonsdale just off the A683.

♥ Stay 3 nights or more and receive a 10% discount (excl Bank Holidays).

Pets 🐕 🐾 🐁 Room 📺 ♨ ☕ General 🍴 🖿 🌳 P 🚭 🍴♿ ☀ Leisure ∪ 🏊

LANGDALE, Cumbria Map ref 5A3 | GUEST ACCOMMODATION

★★★
INN

B&B per room per night
s £45.00–£100.00
d £90.00–£110.00

Britannia Inn

Elterwater, Ambleside LA22 9HP **t** (015394) 37210 **f** (015396) 78075 **e** info@britinn.co.uk
w britinn.co.uk

open All year
bedrooms 7 double, 2 twin
bathrooms 8 en suite, 1 private
payment Credit/debit cards, cash/cheques

Five-hundred-year-old traditional inn nestled in picturesque Elterwater. Relax in front of our cosy log fires or on the sheltered patio with glorious views. Our broad menu comprises home-cooked dishes, many using local produce, complemented by real ales and fine wines. Refurbished, en suite accommodation. Non-smoking.

⊕ From Ambleside, take A593 (Coniston), turning right at Skelwith Bridge onto B5343. Cross cattle grid then turn left into Elterwater. We're on the village green.

♥ Pets most welcome. Ask for special midweek-break prices, and midweek winter offers.

Pets 🐕 🐾 🐈 Room 📞 📺 🛁 🍵 General 🔥 🏛 🅿 🍽 ✕ ⛱ 🎱 ❄ Leisure ∪ 🚲 🏊

MACCLESFIELD, Cheshire Map ref 4B2 | GUEST ACCOMMODATION

★★
FARMHOUSE

B&B per room per night
s £25.00–£35.00
d £45.00–£60.00

Astle Farm East

Chelford, Macclesfield SK10 4TA **t** (01625) 861270 **f** (01625) 861270 **e** gill.farmhouse@virgin.net

open All year
bedrooms 1 double, 1 twin, 1 family
bathrooms All en suite
payment Credit/debit cards, cash/cheques

A warm and friendly welcome awaits you and your family on our picturesque arable farm. Astle Farm East is surrounded by a large garden, down a small rural lane, where we can offer you a quiet stay in an idyllic setting. Farm tours and nature walks available by appointment.

⊕ From Chelford roundabout, take the A537 towards Macclesfield. After 0.5 miles turn right, after lay-by.

Pets 🐕 🐾 🐈 🐾 Room 📺 🛁 General 🔥 🏛 🅿 ✂ ⛱ 🍵 ❄ Leisure 🏊

MANCHESTER AIRPORT

See under Sale

MUNGRISDALE, Cumbria Map ref 5A2 | SELF CATERING

★★★★
SELF CATERING

Units **5**
Sleeps **2–7**

Low season per wk
£300.00–£425.00
High season per wk
£400.00–£625.00

Near Howe Cottages, Penrith

contact Steve & Jill Woolley, Near Howe Hotel and Cottages, Near Howe, Mungrisdale, Penrith CA11 0SH
t (017687) 79678 **f** (017687) 79678 **e** enquiries@nearhowe.co.uk **w** nearhowe.co.uk

open All year
payment Cash/cheques, euros

The ideal answer for a stress-free, away-from-it-all holiday, set amidst 350 acres of open moorland. All cottages have spectacular views over the Cumbrian Fells. Comfortable bar with real fire. Large garden with relaxation areas. Easily accessible, yet isolated enough to ensure peace and tranquillity.

⊕ From M6 jct 40, travel west towards Keswick (A66). Pass Troutbeck after 9 miles. After 1 mile, turn right to Mungrisdale/Caldbeck. Near Howe is 1 mile on the right.

Pets 🐕 £🐈 🐾 Unit 🏠 📺 🍴 🔲 🍳 ❄
General 🔥 🏛 🅿 ✂ 🔲 Leisure ∪ 🚲 🏊 Shop 5 miles Pub 2 miles

NEWBY BRIDGE, Cumbria Map ref 5A3 — **HOTEL**

★★★
HOTEL

B&B per room per night
s £69.00–£89.00
d £108.00–£158.00
HB per person per night
£74.00–£94.00

Newby Bridge Hotel

Newby Bridge, Ulverston LA12 8NA t (015395) 31222 f (015395) 31868
e info@newbybridgehotel.co.uk w bestlakesbreaks.co.uk

open All year
bedrooms 31 double, 3 twin, 4 family
bathrooms All en suite
payment Credit/debit cards, cash/cheques

This elegant Georgian mansion is situated in a commanding position overlooking the southern shores of Lake Windermere. Individually styled bedrooms, many with four-poster beds, jacuzzi bath and lake view. Cosy bar and lounges feature oak panelling and open log fires. Exclusive leisure facilities overlook the mature, Mediterranean-style, five-acre garden.

⊕ M6 jct 36. Follow A590 towards Barrow-in-Furness. On entering Newby Bridge the hotel is on the left-hand side.

♥ Bargain breaks: 3 nights from £139pp DB&B.

Pets 🐕 🐾 ♨ 　Room 🛁 📺 🌸 ♨ 　General 🔥 ▥ ♿ P ⏰ 🍴 ⌕ ♨ ❄ 　Leisure ⚓ ♠ ∪ 🏊

PREESALL, Lancashire Map ref 4A1 — **GUEST ACCOMMODATION**

★★★
BED & BREAKFAST

B&B per room per night
s £20.00–£30.00
d £40.00–£60.00

Grassendale

Green Lane, Preesall, Poulton-le-Fylde FY6 0NS t (01253) 812331 e rondeyo@aol.com

Family home in a quiet location offering bed and breakfast. Three rooms available, ample parking and pets welcome. Only one hour from Southern Lakes and 30 minutes from Blackpool.

open All year
bedrooms 1 double, 1 twin, 1 family
bathrooms 2 en suite, 1 private
payment Cash/cheques

Pets 🐕 🐾 🐾. 　Room 📺 🌸 　General 🔥 P ✂ ❄

SALE, Greater Manchester Map ref 4A2 — **HOTEL**

★★
HOTEL

B&B per room per night
s £39.95–£65.95
d £59.95–£75.95

Lennox Lea Hotel

Irlam Road, Sale M33 2BH t (0161) 973 1764 f (0161) 969 6059 e info@lennoxlea.co.uk
w lennoxlea.co.uk

open All year
bedrooms 15 double, 1 twin, 9 single, 1 suite
bathrooms All en suite
payment Credit/debit cards, cash/cheques

An attractive Victorian building set in its own grounds with ample free parking. Privately run, offering a warm welcome, comfortable accommodation and excellent food. Situated on a peaceful, tree-lined road while conveniently located for many North West attractions. One mile from the motorway network and 0.3 miles from the tram.

⊕ Arriving at Sale Metrolink station, turn right and walk along Northenden Road. Irlam Road is the 3rd road on the left.

Pets 🐕 🐾 　Room 🛁 📺 🌸 ♨ ✋ 　General 🔥 ▥ ♿ P ✂ ⏰ 🍴 ▥ 🖥 　Leisure 🏊

Check the maps

Colour maps at the front pinpoint all the places you will find accommodation entries in the regional sections. Pick your location and then refer to the place index at the back to find the page number.

SAWREY, Cumbria Map ref 5A3 | SELF CATERING

★★★★★
SELF CATERING

Units **1**
Sleeps **1–7**

Low season per wk
£600.00–£755.00
High season per wk
£755.00–£1,020.00

Sawrey Stables, Sawrey

contact Gary Thomason, Lakeland Hideaways, The Square, Hawkshead LA22 0NZ
t (015394) 42435 **f** (015394) 36178 **e** bookings@lakeland-hideaways.co.uk
w lakeland-hideaways.co.uk

open All year
payment Credit/debit cards, cash/cheques

A large, secluded, detached cottage with a sunny garden offering luxurious accommodation for up to seven people, overlooking Lake Windermere. The Aga, open fire and whirlpool bath, four bedrooms (one ground floor) and three bathrooms make this a perfect place to relax and enjoy the tranquillity of this beautiful location.

⊕ Guests to Sawrey Stables collect keys and directions from the Lakeland Hideaways office in the centre of Hawkshead.

Pets 🐾 🐕 🐈 Unit 🏠 📺 📻 🖥 🍽 ■ 🔥🍴 🎱 🔥 🍳 ▫ ✿
General 🐾 🍽 ♨ P ✂ ▫ S Leisure U 🚲 Shop < 0.5 miles Pub < 0.5 miles

SEDBERGH, Cumbria Map ref 5B3 | SELF CATERING

★★★–★★★★★
SELF CATERING

Units **5**
Sleeps **4–6**

Low season per wk
£204.00–£287.00
High season per wk
£331.00–£529.00

Cobble Country Holidays, Sedbergh

contact Mrs R Elizabeth Close, Cobble Country Holidays, 59 Main Street, Sedbergh LA10 5AB
t (015396) 21000 **f** (015396) 21710 **e** cobblesedbergh@yahoo.co.uk **w** cobblecountry.co.uk

open All year
payment Credit/debit cards, cash/cheques

Small self catering development, self-contained units sleeping four to six with a sofa bed, twin and doubles mixed. Flexibility to accommodate groups. Recently refurbished. Centrally situated for easy travel to Yorkshire Dales and Lake District. Two minute walk to shops and pubs. Disabled facilities available in one unit. On-site parking.

⊕ Leave M6 jct 37. Take A684 signposted Sedbergh. Entering town turn left at Dalesman Inn, first right into Bainbridge Road. Apartments on right, 50yds.

♥ Short breaks catered for, minimum of two nights all year round.

Pets 🐾 🐕 Unit 🏠 📺 📻 🖥 🍽 ■ 🔥 🎱 🔥 🍳 ▫ ✿
General 🐾 🍽 ♨ P S Leisure U 🚲

SILVERDALE, Lancashire Map ref 5A3 | SELF CATERING

★★★
SELF CATERING

Units **2**
Sleeps **4–6**

Low season per wk
£200.00–£250.00
High season per wk
£300.00–£520.00

Old Waterslack Farm Cottages and Caravans, Nr
Silverdale, Carnforth

contact Sam Riseborough, Old Waterslack Farm Cottages and Caravans, Silverdale, Carnforth LA5 0UH
t (01524) 701108 & (01524) 720833 **e** bnhevey@tiscali.co.uk

Delightful site set in Arnside/Silverdale Area of Outstanding Natural Beauty. Close to RSPB Reserve. Many superb walks along footpaths including coastal path with views across Morecambe Bay.

open All year
payment Cash/cheques

Pets 🐾 🐕 🐈 Unit 🏠 📺 📻 🖥 ■ 🔥 🎱 🔥 🍳 ▫ ✿
General 🐾 🍽 ♨ P ▫ Leisure U 🚲 🏊 Shop 1 mile Pub 1 mile

It's all in the detail

Please remember that all information in this guide has been supplied by the proprietors well in advance of publication. Since changes do sometimes occur it's a good idea to check details at the time of booking.

SOUTHPORT, Merseyside Map ref 4A1 — HOTEL

★★
HOTEL

B&B per room per night
d £45.00–£75.00

Metropole Hotel

3 Portland Street, Southport PR8 1LL t (01704) 536836 f (01704) 549041
e metropole.southport@btinternet.com w themetropolehotel.com

Fully licensed, centrally located, family-owned
hotel offering traditional standards of comfort and
courtesy. Fifty yards Lord Street shopping
boulevard. Golf breaks a speciality.

open All year
bedrooms 5 double, 4 twin, 10 single, 4 family
bathrooms All en suite
payment Credit/debit cards, cash/cheques

Pets 🐕 £🐾 🍽️ 🏇 Room 📞 📺 💧 General 🔥 ⛱ 🏊 P 🍷 🍴 🎱 Leisure 🎣

TATHAM, Lancashire Map ref 5B3 — SELF CATERING

APPROVED CARAVAN
HOLIDAY HOME

Units   1
Sleeps   6

Low season per wk
£260.00–£295.00
High season per wk
£375.00–£420.00

The Hill Farm Holiday Home, Bentham, Nr Lancaster

t (015242) 62424 e hillfarm@talktalk.net w yorkshire-dales-holiday.co.uk

open All year
payment Cash/cheques

Breathtaking views and relaxation await you at our
luxury caravan. Situated in the Forest of Bowland
Area of Outstanding Natural Beauty on the
Lancashire cycle route with some of the best views
and walks around the Yorkshire Dales and Lake
District. Fully equipped caravan with two bedrooms
(one double, one twin). Enclosed private garden,
barbecue, patio heater and garden furniture.

⊕ M6 jct 34, A683 through Caton. 5 miles, right onto B6480,
signs for Wray then Bridge House Tea Rooms. 2 miles turn
right signed Lowgill. 0.5 miles on left.

♥ Short breaks available from Sep-Jun. Come to see the
lambs in spring.

Pets 🐕 £🐾 🛁 Unit 🛏 📺 📹 📠 💻 🔥 🍳 🔔 🍴 💈 ❄
General 🔥 2 P S Leisure 🚣 Shop 2 miles Pub 2 miles

THORNLEY, Lancashire Map ref 4A1 — SELF CATERING

★★★★
SELF CATERING

Units   2
Sleeps 4–10

Low season per wk
£250.00–£495.00
High season per wk
£405.00–£740.00

Loudview Barn, Preston

contact Mr & Mrs Oliver & Ness Starkey, Loudview Barn, Rams Clough Farm, Thornley,
Preston PR3 2TN
t (01995) 61476 e loudview@ic24.net

open All year
payment Cash/cheques, euros

Stone barn conversion in peaceful location on
fellside in Forest of Bowland, enjoying exceptional
views across unspoilt countryside. Accommodation
in two units that can be combined. Unit 1 comprises
one double, one twin and pair of bunk beds. Unit 2
comprises one double and one twin.

⊕ Easy access from M6, mainline rail and airports
(Manchester and Liverpool in 1 hour).

Pets 🐕 🐾 Unit 🛏 📺 📹 📠 💻 🔥 🍳 🔔 🍴 💈 ❄
General 🔥 ⛱ 🍷 P Leisure 🚲 Shop 4 miles Pub 2 miles

enjoyEngland.com

Big city buzz or peaceful panoramas? Take a fresh look at England and you
may be surprised at what's right on your doorstep. Explore the diversity online
at enjoyengland.com

Horse and Farrier Inn

★★★★
INN

B&B per room per night
s £35.00–£50.00
d £70.00–£100.00
Evening meal per person
£7.00–£16.50

Threlkeld, Keswick CA12 4SQ **t** (017687) 79688 **f** (017687) 79823 **e** info@horseandfarrier.com **w** horseandfarrier.com

open All year
bedrooms 4 double, 1 twin, 6 double/twin
bathrooms 9 en suite, 2 private
payment Credit/debit cards, cash/cheques

The Horse and Farrier Inn is situated beneath Blencathra and is ideally located for walking or touring the Lake District. All bedrooms are en suite, with TV, tea-/coffee-making facilities and hairdryer. Our head chef has recently won the Cumbria Tourist Board's Most Inspiring Chef of the Year 2005/2006.

Pets 🐕 🐾 ℆🐈 🐾 ♨ 🦮 Room 📺 ♨ ☕ General 🛏 🏛 🛎 P 🍽 ✗ ⚑ ✿ Leisure ∪ 🚲 🏊

The Tranquil Otter, Thurstonfield, Carlisle

★★★★–★★★★★★
SELF CATERING

Units   **7**
Sleeps   **2–6**

Low season per wk
£350.00–£650.00
High season per wk
£607.00–£1,190.00

contact Richard & Wendy Wise, The Tranquil Otter Ltd, The Lough, Thurstonfield CA5 6HB **t** (01228) 576661 **f** (01228) 576662 **e** info@thetranquilotter.co.uk **w** thetranquilotter.co.uk

open All year
payment Credit/debit cards, cash/cheques, euros

Well-equipped lodges with picture-book views set in private nature reserve right on the lakeshore in peaceful beauty spot. Log-burner, jacuzzi bath/sauna or hot tub. Wonderful nature (including otters). Private lakeside walks. Own rowing boat. Fly fishing. Outstanding wheelchair access with wheely boat and mobility scooter.

⊕ *Adjacent to the village of Thurstonfield in North Cumbria. Five miles west of Carlisle on the B5307.*

Pets 🐕 🐾 ℆🐈 Unit ▦ 📺 🔲 🍴 🗄 ▣ 🔔 ⚟ 🔽 🍳 ✿
General 🛏 🏛 🛎 P ✂ ☺ S Leisure ∪ 🚲 🏊 Shop < 0.5 miles Pub 2 miles

Ashlack Cottages, Broughton-in-Furness, Kirkby-in-Furness

★★★★
SELF CATERING &
SERVICED APARTMENTS

Units   **5**
Sleeps   **2–17**

Low season per wk
£265.00–£990.00
High season per wk
£499.00–£2,100.00

contact Amanda Keegan, Ashlack Cottages, Ashlack Hall, Grizebeck, Cumbria LA17 7XN **t** (01229) 889888 & 07976 867313 **f** (01229) 889111 **e** enquiries@ashlackcottages.co.uk **w** ashlackcottages.co.uk

open All year
payment Credit/debit cards, cash/cheques

Five luxury holiday cottages, sleeping from 2-17, between Ulverston and Coniston, providing excellent accommodation. All the cottages are beautifully decorated, are surrounded by farmland, have wonderful views overlooking the sea, and breathtaking walks from the door.

⊕ *M6 jct 36, then towards Barrow on A590, through Newby Bridge, then turn right at Greenodd. We are 6 miles on.*

♥ *Winter weekend breaks start at £145 for 2. £780 weekend for 17. Midweek breaks from £120 for 4 nights.*

Pets 🐕 Unit ▦ 📺 🔲 🍴 🗄 ▣ 🔔 ▤ 🍳 ✿
General 🛏 🏛 🛎 P S Leisure ♀ ∪ Shop 2 miles Pub 0.5 miles

Rest assured

All accommodation in this guide has been rated, or is awaiting assessment, by a professional assessor.

WARRINGTON, Cheshire Map ref 4A2 — GUEST ACCOMMODATION

★★★

GUEST ACCOMMODATION

B&B per room per night
s £46.00–£53.00
d £46.00–£53.00

Tall Trees Lodge

Tarporley Road, Lower Whitley, Warrington WA4 4EZ **t** (01928) 790824 & (01928) 715117
f (01928) 791330 **e** booking@talltreeslodge.co.uk **w** talltreeslodge.co.uk

Set in the beautiful Cheshire countryside, a warm welcome awaits you at Tall Trees. The rooms are large, bright and have TV, hairdryer, telephone and coffee-making facilities. All en suite.

open All year except Christmas and New Year
bedrooms 14 double, 1 twin, 5 family
bathrooms All en suite
payment Cash/cheques

Pets 🐈 🐕 🐾 Room 🛏 TV 🍵 General ♨ P ☎

WASDALE, Cumbria Map ref 5A3 — SELF CATERING

★★★★

SELF CATERING

Units   1
Sleeps 1–10
Low season per wk
Min £350.00
High season per wk
Max £550.00

Bleng Barn, Gosforth, Seascale

contact Thomas Ostle, Bleng Farms, Mill House Farm, Wellington, Seascale CA20 1BH
t 07801 862237 & 07775 512918 **f** (01946) 725671 **e** info@blengfarms.co.uk **w** blengfarms.co.uk

This newly converted rural property on a large working farm has many traditional features and modern conveniences, providing a base for a leisurely break or a variety of activity holidays.

open All year
payment Credit/debit cards

Pets 🐈 🐕 Unit 🖼 TV ▦ ▨ ▦ ▨ 🔥 🖥 📺 🖵 ✿
General ♨ P ✂ ◎ S Leisure ∪ 🚴 🏊 Shop 1 mile Pub 0.6 miles

WHINFELL, Cumbria Map ref 5B3 — SELF CATERING

★★★

SELF CATERING

Units   2
Sleeps   6–9
Low season per wk
£300.00–£450.00
High season per wk
£500.00–£750.00

Topthorn Holiday Cottages, Nr Kendal

contact Mrs Diane Barnes, Topthorn Holiday Cottages, Topthorn Farm, Whinfell, Nr Kendal LA8 9EG
t (01539) 824252 **f** (01539) 824386 **e** info.barnes@btconnect.com **w** topthorn.com

Two new 18thC barn conversions. Outstanding views. Peaceful location. Large garden area, patios, BBQ. Wheelchair friendly, children and pets welcome. The Lakes are only 20 minutes away.

open All year
payment Credit/debit cards, cash/cheques

Pets 🐈 🐈 🐕 Unit 🖼 TV ▦ ▨ ▦ ▨ 🔥 🖥 📺 🖵 ✿
General ♨ P ✂ S Leisure ∪ 🏊 Shop 4 miles Pub 4 miles

WIGTON, Cumbria Map ref 5A2 — SELF CATERING

★★★★

SELF CATERING

Units   1
Sleeps 1–8
Low season per wk
£258.00–£299.00
High season per wk
£362.00–£452.00

Foxgloves, Greenrigg Farm, Wigton

contact Mr & Mrs Kerr, Foxgloves, Greenrigg Farm, Westward, Wigton CA7 8AH
t (01697) 342676 **f** (01697) 342676 **e** kerr_greenrigg@hotmail.com **w** foxglovescottagewigton.co.uk

open All year
payment Cash/cheques

Spacious, extremely well-equipped, comfortable cottage with Aga, offering a high standard of accommodation. Superlative setting and views. Large, safe garden. Guests are welcome to explore the farm and fields where a variety of wildlife can be seen. Easy reach Lake District, Scottish Borders, Roman Wall. Children, pets very welcome.

⊕ Travelling north on M6, take jct 41 onto B5305 for 16 miles. Last farm on left before A595. From Carlisle, A595. Left onto B5305, 1st farm on right.

♥ Short breaks and midweek breaks.

Pets 🐈 🐕 Unit 🖼 TV ▦ ▨ ▦ ▨ 🔥 🖥 📺 🖵 ✿
General ♨ P ✂ S Leisure ∪ 🚴 🏊 Shop 1 mile Pub 1 mile

One to five stars

More stars means higher quality accommodation plus a greater range of facilities and services.

WINDERMERE, Cumbria Map ref 5A3 · GUEST ACCOMMODATION

★★★★
GUEST HOUSE

B&B per room per night
s £30.00–£40.00
d £60.00–£98.00

Fairfield Garden Guesthouse

Brantfell Road, Bowness Bay LA23 3AE t (015394) 46565 e relax@the-fairfield.co.uk
w the-fairfield.co.uk

open All year except Christmas
bedrooms 5 double, 2 twin, 1 single, 1 family, 2 suites
bathrooms 10 en suite, 1 private
payment Credit/debit cards, cash/cheques, euros

Secluded Georgian house set in own grounds with beautiful garden and private car park. Informally run B&B with exceptional breakfasts. King-size four-poster bedrooms available. All rooms en suite, some with state-of-the-art, deluxe bathrooms. Guest lounge with Internet access. Located central Bowness – close to Lake Windermere, restaurants, shops and pubs.

⊕ *M6 jct 36. Follow signs Kendal, Windermere. Through Windermere town to Bowness. 1st left after roundabout and left in front of Spinnery restaurant.*

♥ *Reduced prices for 3 nights during weekdays, or extended weekends in low season. DB&B available Nov-Mar.*

Pets 🐕 £🐾 ⛺ 🍴   Room 🛁 📺 👤 🍵   General 🛋6 P ⚡ 🍷 ✗ 🎱 🎬 👥 ✿   Leisure ∪ 🚲

WINDERMERE, Cumbria Map ref 5A3 · SELF CATERING

★★★
SELF CATERING

Units **4**
Sleeps **2–6**

Low season per wk
£190.00–£350.00
High season per wk
£290.00–£490.00

Langdale View Apartments, Windermere

contact Julie Marsh, Langdale View Apartments, 112 Craig Walk, Windermere LA23 3AX
t (015394) 46655 e enquiries@langdale-view.co.uk w langdale-view.co.uk

Attractive, comfortable holiday apartments with car parking. Close to village centre, lake, steamers, shops and restaurants. Fully-equipped kitchens and spacious living areas. Reduced prices for short breaks in low season.

open All year
payment Credit/debit cards, cash/cheques

Pets 🐕 £🐾   Unit 🏠 📺 🍵 📻 💻 🍽 🗑 🍵 🍴 ✿
General 🛋 🎱 🏃 P ⚡ Ⓢ   Leisure ∪ 🚲 ⛵   Shop < 0.5 miles   Pub < 0.5 miles

Help before you go

i

When it comes to your next British break, the first stage of your journey could be closer than you think.

You've probably got a Tourist Information Centre nearby which is there to serve the local community – as well as visitors. Knowledgeable staff will be happy to help you, wherever you're heading.

Many Tourist Information Centres can provide you with maps and guides, and it's often possible to book accommodation and travel tickets too.

You'll find the address of your nearest centre in your local phone book, or look at the beginning of each regional section in this guide for a list of Official Partner Tourist Information Centres.

North East England

County Durham, NewcastleGateshead,
South Tyneside & North Tyneside,
Sunderland, Tees Valley

Natural treasures and a rich history

If dramatic coastlines and wild countryscapes are your thing, you'll be in your element in North East England. Add a turbulent history and warm welcome, and this region has it all.

One NorthEast Tourism Team
visitnortheastengland.com
0870 160 1781

Lindisfarne Castle, Northumberland

High Force, Middleton-in-Teesdale

The Alnwick Garden, Northumberland

NewcastleGateshead

Few regions can compare with North East England for its natural attractions. Ramblers will have a field day in the glorious wilds of the North Pennines, whilst the rolling heather-blue Cheviot Hills in the Northumberland National Park are a picnickers' paradise. The Northumberland coast is another must-see, with its miles of clean sandy beaches such as Spittal and St Aidans. You can't miss the magnificent coastal castles like Bamburgh, but make sure you catch historic Durham Castle and the town's epic cathedral. But it's not all magical landscapes and colourful history. NewcastleGateshead is a vital, modern city with cutting-edge architecture like the Baltic Centre for Contemporary Art and The Sage Gateshead, along with some of the most glamorous shopping in England and vibrant culture.

No visit to the region would be complete without a trip to the Holy Island of Lindisfarne to admire the Castle and Priory. Cut off twice a day by racing tides, you can now visit the heritage centre and 'turn the pages' of the priceless Lindisfarne Gospels on computer. Or try seal spotting around the Farne Islands – just hop on a boat at Seahouses and you'll be enchanted by these wonderful creatures.

While you're in the North East, take a walk to see Hadrian's Wall and explore the Housesteads outpost with its evocative remains including a Roman barracks. In complete contrast, the latest attraction is the Middlesbrough Institute of Modern Art (mima), a gallery of national importance housing works by Emin, Hockney, Frink and many others. Or discover the twin Anglo-Saxon monastery of Wearmouth-Jarrow. It's the UK's nomination for World Heritage Site status in 2009 because of its links to celebrated Christian scholar the Venerable Bede.

Destinations

Berwick-upon-Tweed

England's northernmost town guards the mouth of the River Tweed. Marvel at some of the finest 16th century city walls in Europe, built by Elizabeth I to protect a town that changed hands between England and Scotland 14 times in the medieval era. Nowadays the town is more than part Scottish. Visit the great edifice of Bamburgh Castle and the beautiful gardens at Alnwick. Roam the magnificent Heritage coastline and see Holy Island and the fairytale Lindisfarne Castle.

Darlington

Gateway to the North East and pioneering railway town. Darlington's Railway Centre and Museum displays Stephenson's Locomotion, which opened the Stockton and Darlington Railway in 1825. Discover a civilised town with a pedestrian heart, where medieval 'yards and wynds' link the main streets. Explore the designer Imperial Quarter with over 400 shops to choose from. Culture-lovers will find plenty to occupy them at the Arts Centre and the superb facilities at the Forum Music Centre.

Durham

Described by Bill Bryson as 'a perfect little city.' Its history shows in every cobble. Explore majestic Durham Cathedral, a World Heritage Site, and thought by many to be the finest Norman church architecture in England. Visit the tombs of St Cuthbert and the Venerable Bede. Stroll around a relaxed city centre mainly closed to traffic, take a coffee in the cobbled Market Place and enjoy the stunning floral displays. Take a path to the riverbank and take in the stunning views from the River Wear.

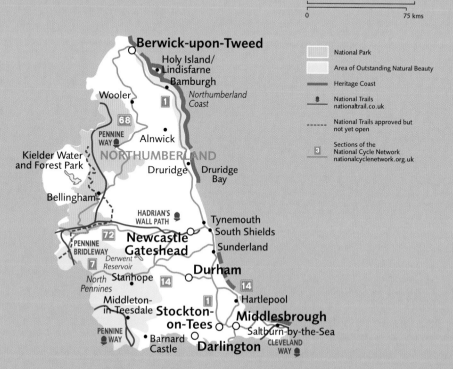

Saltburn-by-the-Sea, Cleveland coast

Darlington Railway Centre and Museum

NewcastleGateshead Quayside

Durham Cathedral

Bamburgh Castle, Northumberland

Stockton-on-Tees

Middlesbrough

Visit the heart of the North East. Middlesbrough was home to Captain Cook whose life is celebrated at the award-winning Captain Cook Birthplace Museum. Learn about the region at The Dorman, the superb museum of local life. Let the historic, floodlit Transporter Bridge convey you across the River Tees. Sports fans can enjoy Premier League football at Middlesbrough, while walkers can explore the North York Moors and the Cleveland coast.

NewcastleGateshead

In the North East of England, Newcastle and Gateshead face each other across the River Tyne coming together at the dazzling Quayside. Must-see attractions including the award-winning Gateshead Millennium Bridge, the Baltic Centre for Contemporary Art and the magnificent new Sage Gateshead, a stunning Sir Norman Foster building, with billowing curves of glass and steel catering for every genre of music. Rich in culture, architecture and history and with a great reputation for style, shopping and nightlife, the variety of life in NewcastleGateshead surprises even the most well travelled visitor.

Stockton-on-Tees

Most famous for its associations with the Stockton & Darlington railway. Discover this friendly town, situated in the heart of the Tees Valley, and surrounded by smaller towns and villages including the charming Georgian town of Yarm. For lovers of outdoor activity, Stockton-on-Tees is fast becoming an impressive international watersports destination, from fishing to white water rafting to river cruising. You'll also find an impressive network of town and country parks.

Places to visit

Alnwick Castle
Large Visitor Attraction of the Year –
Gold Winner
Northumberland
(01665) 510777
alnwickcastle.com

Magnificent medieval castle often used as a film location

The Alnwick Garden
Northumberland
(01665) 511350
alnwickgarden.com
Exciting contemporary garden

BALTIC Centre for Contemporary Art
Gateshead,
Tyne and Wear
(0191) 478 1810
balticmill.com
Diverse international art

Bamburgh Castle
Northumberland
(01668) 214515
bamburghcastle.com
Magnificent coastal castle

Beamish, The North of England Open Air Museum
County Durham
(0191) 370 4000
beamish.org.uk
Let the past come to life

Bede's World
Jarrow, Tyne and Wear
(0191) 489 2106
bedesworld.co.uk
Discover the extraordinary life of the Venerable Bede

Belsay Hall, Castle and Gardens
Newcastle upon Tyne,
Northumberland
(01661) 881636
english-heritage.org.uk
Medieval castle, 17th-century manor and gardens
 (grounds only)

The Bowes Museum
Barnard Castle,
County Durham
(01833) 690606
bowesmuseum.org.uk
Outstanding fine and decorative arts
 (grounds only)

Captain Cook Birthplace Museum
Middlesbrough
(01642) 311211
captcook-ne.co.uk
Explore Cook's early life and seafaring career
 (park only)

Centre for Life
Newcastle upon Tyne,
Tyne and Wear
(0191) 243 8210
life.org.uk
Hands-on science for all

Cragside House, Gardens and Estate
Morpeth, Northumberland
(01669) 620333
nationaltrust.org.uk
Woodland estate and adventure playground
(grounds only)

Discovery Museum
Newcastle upon Tyne,
Tyne and Wear
(0191) 232 6789
twmuseums.org.uk/discovery
Explore world-changing inventions

Dunstanburgh Castle
Craster, Northumberland
(01665) 576231
english-heritage.org.uk
Dramatic ruins of 14th-century castle

Durham Castle
(0191) 334 4106
durhamcastle.com
Fine example of motte and bailey

Durham Cathedral
(0191) 386 4266
durhamcathedral.co.uk
Magnificent Norman architecture

Hartlepool's Maritime Experience
County Durham
(01429) 860077
hartlepoolsmaritimeexperience.com
Authentic reconstruction of an 18th-century seaport

Housesteads Roman Fort (Vercovicium) Hadrian's Wall
near Haydon Bridge,
Northumberland
(01434) 344363
english-heritage.org.uk
Best preserved Roman Fort
(except museum)

Laing Art Gallery
Newcastle upon Tyne,
Tyne and Wear
(0191) 232 7734
twmuseums.org.uk
An important collection of 18th- and 19th-century art

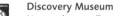

🐾 Pets Welcome
🐾 Assistance dogs only

Diary dates 2008

Locomotion
The National Railway
Museum at Shildon
Shildon, County Durham
(01388) 777999
locomotion.uk.com
Over 100 locomotives

mima, Middlesbrough Institute
of Modern Art
(01642) 726720
visitmima.com
Internationally significant fine and
applied art

Nature's World
Middlesbrough
(01642) 594895
naturesworld.org.uk
A pioneering eco-experience

Raby Castle
Darlington,
County Durham
(01833) 660202
rabycastle.com
Medieval castle with deer park
and gardens
(*grounds only*)

Vindolanda
(Chesterholm)
Hadrian's Wall
near Haydon Bridge,
Northumberland
(01434) 344277
vindolanda.com
Remains of a Roman fort and
settlement

Northern Rocks: The North Pennines Festival
of Geology and Landscape
Weardale
northpennines.org.uk
17 May – 1 Jun*

South Tyneside Summer Festival
Various locations, South Shields
southtyneside.info
1 Jun – 31 Aug*

Durham Regatta
River Wear
durham-regatta.org.uk
Jun*

Alnwick Fair
Market Square
northumberland.gov.uk
9 – 13 Jul*

Sunderland International Friendship Festival
featuring the Kite Festival
Northern Area Playing Fields, Washington
sunderland-kites.co.uk
5 – 6 Jul

Whitley Bay International Jazz Festival
whitleybayjazzfest.org
11 – 13 Jul

Sunderland International Air Show
The promenade
sunderland-airshow.com
26 – 27 Jul

Stockton International Riverside Festival
Various locations, Stockton-on-Tees
sirf.co.uk
30 Jul – 3 Aug

Hexham Abbey Festival
hexhamabbey.org.uk/festival
26 Sep – 4 Oct*

City of Durham Christmas Festival
Various locations, Durham
1 – 2 Dec*

Tourist Information Centres

When you arrive at your destination, visit an Official Partner Tourist Information Centre for quality assured help with accommodation and information about local attractions and events, or email your request before you go. To search for attractions and Tourist Information Centres on the move just text INFO to 62233, and a web link will be sent to your mobile phone.

Alnwick	2 The Shambles	(01665) 511333	alnwicktic@alnwick.gov.uk
Barnard Castle	Flatts Road	(01833) 690909	tourism@teesdale.gov.uk
Darlington	13 Horsemarket	(01325) 388666	tic@darlington.gov.uk
Durham	2 Millennium Place	(0191) 384 3720	touristinfo@durhamcity.gov.uk
Hartlepool	Church Square	(01429) 869706	hpooltic@hartlepool.gov.uk
Hexham	Wentworth Car Park	(01434) 652220	hexham.tic@tynedale.gov.uk
Morpeth	Bridge Street	(01670) 500700	tourism@castlemorpeth.gov.uk
Newcastle upon Tyne	8-9 Central Arcade	(0191) 277 8000	tourist.info@newcastle.gov.uk
Once Brewed*	Military Road	(01434) 344396	tic.oncebrewed@nnpa.org.uk
Sunderland	50 Fawcett Street	(0191) 553 2000	tourist.info@sunderland.gov.uk

* *seasonal opening*

Travel info

By road:
There is excellent motorway access via the A1(M), and the A69 and A66 connect directly to the M6 from the west. North East England is just two hours from Edinburgh, two-and-a-half hours from Manchester and four-and-a-half hours from London by road.

By rail:
Take the train and you're free to unwind all the way, with a tasty meal, your favourite read or just enjoying the view. North East England is easily reached on the East Coast Main Line from the north and south and via many direct connections from the west. Trains between London and Newcastle take just three hours, Birmingham to Darlington in just under three hours and Sheffield to Newcastle in just over three hours.

By air:
North East England has two international airports enabling easy access from UK, Europe and worldwide. Low cost flights fly into the region from a number of UK and European locations. Fly into Durham Tees Valley or Newcastle International airports.

Berwick-upon-Tweed

Hadrian's Wall, Northumberland

Find out more

Log onto the North East England website at **visitnortheastengland.com** for further information on accommodation, attractions, events and special offers throughout the region. A range of free guides are available for you to order online or by calling **0870 160 1781**:

- **Holiday and Short Breaks Guide**
  Information on North East England, including hotels, bed and breakfast, self-catering, caravan and camping parks and accessible accommodation as well as events and attractions throughout the region.

- **Cycling Guide**
  A guide to day rides, traffic-free trails and challenging cycling routes.

- **Gardens Guide**
  A guide to the region's most inspirational gardens.

- **Walking Guide**
  Circular trails and long distance routes through breathtaking countryside.

where to stay in
North East England

All place names in the blue bands are shown on the maps at the front of this guide.

Accommodation symbols
Symbols give useful information about services and facilities. Inside the back-cover flap you can find a key to these symbols. Keep it open for easy reference.

ALLENDALE, Northumberland Map ref 5B2   **GUEST ACCOMMODATION**

★★★★
FARMHOUSE

B&B per room per night
s £25.00–£30.00
d £50.00–£60.00
Evening meal per person
£13.00

Struthers Farm
Catton, Hexham NE47 9LP   t (01434) 683580

Working farm in beautiful countryside near Hadrian's Wall. Well-appointed, en suite rooms, double/twin optional. Evening meal. Nine miles from Hexham. Good parking. A69 Newcastle to Hexham, B6305 to Allendale.

open All year except Christmas
bedrooms 1 double, 1 twin
bathrooms All en suite
payment Cash/cheques

Pets 🐕 🐴   Room 📺 ♨ 🍴   General ⏰ P ✕ 🏠 ✿

ALNMOUTH, Northumberland Map ref 5C1   **HOTEL**

★★
HOTEL

B&B per room per night
s £40.00–£50.00
d £66.00–£80.00

Saddle Hotel
24-25 Northumberland Street, Alnmouth, Alnwick NE66 2RA   t (01665) 830476   f (01665) 830476
e thesaddlehotel@hotmail.co.uk   w saddlehotel.co.uk

The Saddle is a small family-run hotel, offering cosy accommodation and delicious home-cooked food, in one of the most delightful villages in the heart of the beautiful Northumbrian countryside.

open All year except Christmas
bedrooms 4 double, 3 twin, 1 family
bathrooms All en suite
payment Credit/debit cards, cash/cheques

Pets 🐕 🐴 🍽   Room 🔔 📺 ♨ 🍴   General ⏰ 🏛 🅿 🍺 🎱   Leisure ∪ 🚴 ⛵

ALNWICK, Northumberland Map ref 5C1   **SELF CATERING**

★★★
SELF CATERING

Units   **1**
Sleeps   **5**

Low season per wk
£200.00–£330.00
High season per wk
£360.00–£490.00

Juliet Cottage, Alnwick
contact Mrs Louise Sweeney, c/o Juliet Cottage, 11 Woodbine Avenue, Newcastle upon Tyne NE3 1EU
t (0191) 2857794 & 07922 082596   e louise.sweeney@blueyonder.co.uk   w cottageguide.co.uk/juliet

open All year
payment Cash/cheques, euros

Beautiful and charming stone cottage situated in the heart of Alnwick, two minutes' walk from the gates of the castle and gardens. Sleeps four plus. Very cosy, comfortable and clean. Refurbished 2006. Exceptionally well equipped. Original stone fireplace. See website for interior photographs. Private small courtyard backing onto city walls.

♥ *Daily, weekend and weekly charges, together with availability check and online booking, available through the website.*

Pets 🐕   Unit 🛏 📺 ▭ ▣ 🗄 🎛 ▣ ▣ ✿
General ⏰ 🏛 🛁 ⓢ   Leisure 🚴 ⛵   Shop < 0.5 miles   Pub < 0.5 miles

BAMBURGH, Northumberland Map ref 5C1 · HOTEL

★★★
COUNTRY HOUSE HOTEL
SILVER AWARD

Waren House Hotel

Waren Mill, Belford NE70 7EE t (01668) 214581 f (01668) 214484
e enquiries@warenhousehotel.co.uk w warenhousehotel.co.uk

B&B per room per night
d £103.00–£185.00
HB per person per night
£76.00–£120.00

open All year
bedrooms 6 double, 4 twin, 3 suites
bathrooms All en suite
payment Credit/debit cards, cash/cheques, euros

Traditional, beautifully restored and renovated, award-winning country-house hotel in six acres of wooded grounds and walled garden on edge of Budle Bay overlooking Holy Island. Superb accommodation, excellent food, choice of over 250 reasonably priced wines. Two miles Bamburgh Castle, five miles Farne Islands. Children over 14 welcome. Ground-floor suite with wheelchair access.

⊕ *Midway between Belford and Bamburgh on B1342 and 2 miles from the A1 on which we have a sign from both north and south.*

♥ *Short breaks – DB&B from £83.75pppn.*

Pets 🐕🐾🐾 Room 🛏🕯📺🐾🍽 General 🛎14 P🍽🎱🏊🔆 Leisure ∪

BAMBURGH, Northumberland Map ref 5C1 · SELF CATERING

★★★–★★★★★
SELF CATERING

Bradford Country Cottages, Bamburgh

contact Mr L W Robson, Bradford Country Cottages, Bradford House, Bamburgh NE70 7JT
t (01668) 213432 f (01668) 213891 e lwrob@tiscali.co.uk w bradford-leisure.co.uk

Units   **4**
Sleeps   **2–6**
Low season per wk
£200.00–£400.00
High season per wk
£400.00–£600.00

Stone-built cottages in a rural setting, two miles from Bamburgh village, full central heating and facilities, access to swimming pool included in tariff.

open All year
payment Credit/debit cards, cash/cheques

Pets 🐕🐾 Unit 🏠📺📻🍽📺💻🎮📺🔆
General 🛎🍳🅿🔆⊙Ⓢ Leisure 🎣∪ Shop 2 miles Pub 2 miles

BAMBURGH, Northumberland Map ref 5C1 · SELF CATERING

★★★★★
SELF CATERING

Glebe House and Glebe Cottage, Bamburgh

contact Mrs Maria Eliana Robinson, EMR Properties, The Glebe, Radcliffe Road, Bamburgh NE69 7AE
t (01668) 214456 f (01668) 214354 e stay@bamburghglebe.co.uk w bamburghglebe.co.uk

Units   **2**
Sleeps   **2–8**
Low season per wk
£375.00–£895.00
High season per wk
£595.00–£1,495.00

open All year
payment Cash/cheques

This lovely 18thC vicarage has stunning views of church, castle and sea. Spacious and well furnished with full central heating included. First-class kitchen. Children and household pets welcome. Large, peaceful, private gardens. An ideal base for walking and exploring Northumberland's Heritage Coast.

⊕ *From A1, take B1341 10 miles north of Alnwick. Follow signs to Bamburgh, turn left at church (B1342). Glebe is located 300 yds on right.*

♥ *Short breaks available Nov-Mar.*

Pets 🐕🐾🐾 Unit 🏠📺📻🍽📺💻🎮📺🔆
General 🛎🍳🅿⊙Ⓢ Leisure ∪🚲⛵ Shop < 0.5 miles Pub < 0.5 miles

Place index

If you know where you want to stay, the index at the back of the guide will give you the page number listing accommodation in your chosen town, city or village. Check out the other useful indexes too.

BAMBURGH, Northumberland Map ref 5C1 — SELF CATERING

★★★★–★★★★★★
SELF CATERING

Springhill Farm Holiday Accommodation, Seahouses, Bamburgh

Units **7**
Sleeps **2–10**
Low season per wk
£195.00–£720.00
High season per wk
£365.00–£1,600.00

contact Mrs Julie & Miss Sarah Gregory, Springhill Farm Holiday Accommodation, Springhill Farm, Seahouses NE68 7UR
t (01665) 721820 f (01665) 721820 e enquiries@springhill-farm.co.uk w springhill-farm.co.uk

open All year
payment Credit/debit cards, cash/cheques

Beautifully converted traditional barns and original farm cottages. All designed to exceptional standards, decorated and finished with both modern and traditional furniture and appliances, aimed to balance character with functionality for all of your holiday needs. Only half a mile from the outstanding heritage coast running between Bamburgh and Seahouses.

⊕ From Seahouses continue over roundabout towards North Sunderland, in 0.5 miles you reach Longstone Hotel. Turn right then left, continue for 0.5 miles reaching Springhill.

♥ AONB Award for Excellence in Facilities. Short breaks Nov-Mar. Access to Seafield Health and Beauty Club.

Pets ⊁ ⬚⬚ ⬚. Unit ⬚ TV ⬚⬚⬚ ⬚ ⬚⬚ ⬚⬚ ⬚ ⬚ ⬚ ⬚✿
General ⬚ ⬚ ⬚ P ⬚ ⬚ S Leisure ⬚ U ⬚⬚ ⬚ Shop 0.5 miles Pub 0.5 miles

BELLINGHAM, Northumberland Map ref 5B2 — HOTEL

★★
SMALL HOTEL

Riverdale Hall Hotel

B&B per room per night
s £56.00–£72.00
d £98.00–£140.00
HB per person per night
£59.00–£87.00

Bellingham, Hexham NE48 2JT t (01434) 220254 f (01434) 220457
e reservations@riverdalehallhotel.co.uk w riverdalehallhotel.co.uk

open All year
bedrooms 18 double, 9 twin, 5 single, 5 family, 3 suites
bathrooms All en suite
payment Credit/debit cards, cash/cheques

Spacious Victorian country hall in large grounds, on banks of North Tyne river, with splendid views southwards to Dunterley Fell (Pennine Way). All bedrooms en suite with TV, telephone and hospitality tray. Indoor pool, sauna, fishing, cricket and golf nearby. Award-winning restaurant. Kielder Water, Pennine Way, Hadrian's Wall nearby. The Cocker family's 30th year.

♥ Golfing, fishing and cricketing breaks arranged. Free place for organiser for parties of 15 or more.

Pets ⊁ ⬚⬚ ⬚ ⬚. Room ⬚ ⬚ TV ⬚ ⬚ ⬚ General ⬚ ⬚ ⬚ P ⬚ ⬚ ⬚ ⬚✿ Leisure ⬚ ⬚ U ⬚⬚ ⬚

BERWICK-UPON-TWEED, Northumberland Map ref 5B1 — SELF CATERING

★★★
SELF CATERING

Smiddy Cottage, Berwick-upon-Tweed

Units **1**
Sleeps **6**
Low season per wk
£275.00–£391.00
High season per wk
£312.00–£541.00

contact Mrs June Simpson, Smiddy Cottage, Forgeway, Main Street, Horncliffe, Berwick-upon-Tweed TD15 2XW
t (01289) 386411 f (01289) 386411 e june@smiddycottage.co.uk w smiddycottage.co.uk

Converted blacksmith's shop in quiet village on English/Scottish border. Five miles from coast. Ideal for walking and fishing.

open All year
payment Cash/cheques

Pets ⊁ Unit ⬚ TV ⬚⬚⬚ ⬚⬚ ⬚ ⬚ ⬚ ⬚✿
General ⬚ ⬚ ⬚ P ⬚ Shop 4 miles Pub < 0.5 miles

Key to symbols
Open the back flap for a key to symbols.

CHATTON, Northumberland Map ref 5B1   **SELF CATERING**

★★★
SELF CATERING

Units **1**
Sleeps **2**

Low season per wk
£150.00–£240.00
High season per wk
£260.00–£340.00

Percy Cottage, Alnwick

contact Mrs Helen Reed-Jones, The Property Investments, Jamarus Lodge, Kirknewton, Wooler NE71 6XF
t (01668) 216556   **e** tonyreedjones@aol.com   **w** percycottage.co.uk

Attractive stone cottage set in village of Chatton, beautifully refurbished and offering spacious, well-equipped accommodation.

open All year
payment Cash/cheques

Pets 🐾   Unit 🏠 📺 📻 💻 🍽 🔥 ⭕ ▢ 📷 ✿
General P ✂   Shop < 0.5 miles   Pub < 0.5 miles

COCKFIELD, County Durham Map ref 5B3   **SELF CATERING**

★★★★
SELF CATERING

Units **2**
Sleeps **4–5**

Low season per wk
Min £160.00
High season per wk
Max £340.00

Stonecroft and Swallows Nest, Bishop Auckland

contact Mrs Alison Tallentire, Low Lands Farm, Bishop Auckland DL13 5AW
t (01388) 718251   **f** (01388) 718251   **e** info@farmholidaysuk.com   **w** farmholidaysuk.com

open All year
payment Cash/cheques

Award-winning cottages on a working livestock farm. Both cottages beautifully renovated and decorated to an exceptionally high standard. Beams, log fires, gas barbecue, own gardens and parking. Close to Durham City, Northumberland, Lakes, Hadrian's Wall. Pets and children most welcome, childminding available. Children's equipment, fuels, electric, linens and towels all included.

⊕ *Directions on request.*

♥ *Midweek and weekend breaks available out of season. Open Christmas and New Year.*

Pets 🐾 £🐾   Unit 🏠 📺 🍴 📻 💻 🍽 🔥 🔧 ⭕ ▢ 📷 ✿
General 🛏 🏛 🏠 P Ⓢ   Shop 1 mile   Pub 1 mile

CROOK, County Durham Map ref 5C2   **GUEST ACCOMMODATION**

★★★
BED & BREAKFAST

B&B per room per night
s £42.00–£48.00
d £53.00–£66.00

Dowfold House

Low Jobs Hill, Crook DL15 9AB   **t** (01388) 762473   **e** enquiries@dowfoldhouse.co.uk
w dowfoldhouse.co.uk

Dowfold House is in a quiet location overlooking Crook, with stunning views over Weardale and the Pennines. We welcome tourers, cyclists, walkers, dogs and children. People keep coming back!

open All year
bedrooms 1 double, 2 twin
bathrooms 2 en suite, 1 private
payment Cash/cheques, euros

Pets 🐾 £🐾 🐕 🐾 🐾.   Room 📺 🐾 🔧   General 🛏 🏛 🏠 P ✂ 🍴 🔧 🖥 ✿   Leisure ∪ 🚲 🏞

DARLINGTON, Tees Valley Map ref 5C3   **HOTEL**

★★★
COUNTRY HOUSE HOTEL
SILVER AWARD

B&B per room per night
s £90.00–£160.00
d £110.00–£185.00
HB per person per night
£72.00–£105.00

Headlam Hall Hotel, Spa and Golf Course

Headlam, Darlington DL2 3HA   **t** (01325) 730238   **f** (01325) 730790   **e** admin@headlamhall.co.uk
w headlamhall.co.uk

open All year except Christmas
bedrooms 26 double, 6 twin, 4 family, 4 suites
bathrooms All en suite
payment Credit/debit cards, cash/cheques

Charming Jacobean mansion in picturesque hamlet, surrounded by its own 9-hole golf course and farmland. Beautifully appointed, luxurious bedrooms, and restaurant serving freshly prepared food using local ingredients. The superb new spa offers a pool, thermal zone, outdoor spa pool, gym, treatment rooms and informal brasserie bar.

⊕ *Eight miles west of Darlington off A67.*

♥ *Winter, Easter and summer breaks. Plus website offers and golf/spa breaks.*

Pets 🐾 🐕 🐾.   Room 🐾 📺 🐾 🔧 🔧   General 🛏 🏛 🏠 P ✂ 🍴 🖥 ✿   Leisure 🎣 🔍 ∪ 🚲 🏞

DURHAM, County Durham Map ref 5C2 — HOTEL

★★★★
HOTEL
B&B per room per night
s £82.00–£150.00
d £135.00–£180.00
HB per person per night
£80.00–£95.00

Ramside Hall Classic Hotel & Golf Club

Carrville, Durham DH1 1TD t (0191) 386 5282 f (0191) 386 0399 e mail@ramsidehallhotel.co.uk
w ramsidehallhotel.co.uk

open All year
bedrooms 47 double, 30 twin, 2 single, 2 suites
bathrooms All en suite
payment Credit/debit cards, cash/cheques, euros

Ramside Hall Hotel & Golf Club is all about quality, comfort and friendly service. Beautifully presented public areas/lounges, comfortable, spacious bedrooms, two bars, two eating areas, exceptional traditional food at value-for-money prices. Set in attractive gardens and surrounded by 27 holes of challenging scenic golf. Golf clubhouse, shop, floodlit range and Golf Academy.

⊕ Jct 62 off the main A1M. Travel 400m A690 towards Sunderland. Go under the railway bridge, turn right over the dual carriageway. You have arrived.

♥ Golfer's alert! Check out Ramside Hall's special Play & Stay tariffs. 27 holes of great golf.

Pets ♞ ♘ Room 🛏 ℃ 📺 ♨ 🍵 ⚲ General ⌂ 🏔 🍴 P 🍽 ♨ 🍴 ◉ ✿ Leisure ♠ U 🚲 🏊

EMBLETON, Northumberland Map ref 5C1 — SELF CATERING

★★★–★★★★★
SELF CATERING
Units   8
Sleeps   2–7
Low season per wk
£175.00–£225.00
High season per wk
£350.00–£600.00

Doxford Farm Cottages, Chathill

contact Mrs Sarah Shell, Doxford Farm, Doxford, Chathill NE67 5DY
t (01665) 579348 & (01665) 579477 f (01665) 579331 e doxfordfarm@hotmail.com
w doxfordfarmcottages.com

Well equipped cottages on a working farm in wooded countryside four miles from sea. Central heating, open fires. Wildlife trails and woodland walks. Ideal base for Northumberland's castles, coastline and Alnwick Gardens.

open All year
payment Credit/debit cards, cash/cheques

Pets ♞ £♘ Unit 🏠 📺 ☑ ▣ 🖥 🍴 ◉ ⚲
General ⌂ 🏔 🍴 P ◻ S Leisure U 🚲 🏊 Shop 4 miles Pub 4 miles

HAMSTERLEY FOREST

See under Crook

HARBOTTLE, Northumberland Map ref 5B1 — SELF CATERING

★★★
SELF CATERING
Units   1
Sleeps   1–3
Low season per wk
£175.00–£265.00
High season per wk
£256.00–£382.00

Brackenlea Cottage, Rothbury

contact Mr & Mrs John & Helen Dalrymple, 15 Wellway Court, Morpeth NE61 1BW
t (01670) 519629 e john@dalrymple.me.uk w brackenleacottage.co.uk

Charming luxury two bedroom corner terraced stone cottage located in the tiny village of Harbottle in the Northumberland National Park.

open All year
payment Cash/cheques

Pets ♞ Unit 🏠 📺 📱 🖥 ▣ 🍴 🍴 ◉ 🍴
General ⌂ 🏔 P ✂ S Leisure U 🚲 🏊 Shop 10 miles Pub < 0.5 miles

It's all quality-assessed accommodation

Our commitment to quality involves wide-ranging accommodation assessment. Rating and awards were correct at the time of going to press but may change following a new assessment. Please check at time of booking.

HEXHAM, Northumberland Map ref 5B2 — SELF CATERING

★★★★
SELF CATERING

Units **3**
Sleeps **1–5**
Low season per wk
£190.00–£360.00
High season per wk
£260.00–£450.00

Old Church Cottages, Chollerton, Hexham

contact Mrs Marilyn Framrose, Old Church Cottage, Chollerton, Hexham NE46 4TF
t (01434) 681930 **e** oldchurch@supanet.com **w** chollerton-oldchurch.co.uk

Beautiful converted country church: two two-bedroom apartments and double studio apartment. Spacious gardens with patio, seating, pond and barbecue. Local bus. Superb restaurants. Two miles from Hadrian's Wall, convenient for Newcastle, Alnwick, Scottish Borders.

open All year
payment Credit/debit cards, cash/cheques, euros

Pets ♋ ☍ Unit ▥ ㏑ ▣ ▦ ◨ ◙ ◘ ❁
General ❧ ㎜ ♣ P ✂ ☉ Ⓢ Leisure U Shop 1 mile Pub 1 mile

HOLY ISLAND, Northumberland Map ref 5C1 — SELF CATERING

★★★
SELF CATERING

Units **1**
Sleeps **8**
Low season per wk
Min £475.00
High season per wk
Max £920.00

Links View, Holy Island

contact Dr Rachel Pain
e linksviewholyisland@yahoo.co.uk **w** lindisfarne.org.uk/links-view

A Grade II Listed house in Holy Island village offering self-catering holiday accommodation.

open All year
payment Cash/cheques

Pets ♋ ☍ Unit ▥ ㏑ ▣ ▦ ◨ ◘ ◙ ▦ ❁
General ❧ ㎜ ♣ P ✂ Ⓢ Shop < 0.5 miles Pub < 0.5 miles

KIELDER FOREST

See under Bellingham, Wark

MATFEN, Northumberland Map ref 5B2 — GUEST ACCOMMODATION

★★★★
GUEST ACCOMMODATION

B&B per room per night
s Min £35.00
d Min £70.00

Matfen High House

Nr Corbridge, Newcastle upon Tyne NE20 0RG **t** (01661) 886592 **f** (01661) 886847
e struan@struan.enterprise-plc.com

Spacious stone-built former farmhouse, dating from 1735, in quiet rural location one mile north of Hadrian's Wall and Trail. Ideal base for local attractions. 18-hole golf course two miles.

open All year except Christmas
bedrooms 2 double, 2 twin
bathrooms 2 en suite, 2 private
payment Cash/cheques

Pets ♋ ♞ ♣ ♐. Room ㏑ ◔ ♘ General ❧ ㎜ ♣ P ✂ ❁ Leisure ▥

MORPETH, Northumberland Map ref 5C2 — HOTEL

★★★
HOTEL

B&B per room per night
s £75.00–£88.00
d £80.00–£110.00

Longhirst Hall

Longhirst, Morpeth NE61 3LL **t** (01670) 791348 **f** (01670) 791385 **e** enquiries@longhirst.co.uk
w longhirst.co.uk

open All year
bedrooms 56 double, 21 twin
bathrooms All en suite
payment Credit/debit cards, cash/cheques

Nestled in rural Northumberland, Longhirst Hall is an early-19thC, John Dobson-designed building set in 75 acres of woodland and landscaped gardens. All en suite bedrooms in the hall, and 34 dormy houses, each able to accommodate up to eight guests. The perfect blend of business, adventure and tranquillity.

⊕ *Located just off the A1. Take turning marked Hebron, follow road, turn left at T-junction. Longhirst 1 mile along the B1337.*

♥ *Exclusive Alnwick Garden breaks, including tickets and brochure, £118 (£59pp).*

Pets ♋ ♞ ♐. Room ♨ ✆ ㏑ ♘ ♜ ♬ General ❧ ㎜ ♣ P ✂ ♟ ⛾ ◪ ◙ ❁ Leisure ⚲ U ⚵

WARK, Northumberland Map ref 5B2
HOTEL

Rating Applied For
HOTEL

B&B per room per night
s £45.00–£60.00
d £80.00–£120.00

Battlesteads Hotel

Wark, Hexham NE48 3LS **t** (01434) 230209 **f** (01434) 230039 **e** info@battlesteads.com
w battlesteads.com

open All year
bedrooms 7 double, 7 twin, 1 single, 2 family
bathrooms All en suite
payment Credit/debit cards, cash/cheques

18thC inn, formerly a farmhouse, in the heart of rural Northumberland, close to the Roman Wall and Kielder Water. An ideal centre for exploring Border country and for relaxing, walking or cycling. Ground-floor bedrooms available. Excellent restaurant using fresh, local produce. Three cask ales.

⊕ Wark village is on the B6320 Bellingham road, 10 miles north of Hexham from the A69. Battlesteads is immediately to your left as you enter Wark.

♥ Changing offers throughout the year. Please see website.

Pets 🐕 £🐴🐷🐑🐾 Room 🛏🕯📺🍵🍽🔥 General 🛎🏛🎹♿🅿🍴📶🎱🖥✳ Leisure ⛳🏊

Walkers and cyclists welcome

Look out for quality-assessed accommodation displaying the Walkers Welcome and Cyclists Welcome signs.

Participants in these schemes actively encourage and support walking and cycling. In addition to special meal arrangements and helpful information, they'll provide a water supply to wash off the mud, an area for drying wet clothing and footwear, maps and books to look up cycling and walking routes and even an emergency puncture-repair kit! Bikes can also be locked up securely undercover.

The standards for these schemes have been developed in partnership with the tourist boards in Northern Ireland, Scotland and Wales, so wherever you're travelling in the UK you'll receive the same welcome.

Finding accommodation
is as easy as 1 2 3

VisitBritain's official guides to quality accommodation make it quick and easy to find a place to stay. There are several ways to use this guide.

1

PROPERTY INDEX

If you know the name of the establishment you wish to book, turn to the property index at the back where the relevant page number is shown.

2

PLACE INDEX

The place index at the back lists all locations with accommodation featured in the regional sections. A page number is shown where you can find full accommodation and contact details.

3

COLOUR MAPS

All the place names in black on the colour maps at the front have an entry in the regional sections. Refer to the place index for the page number where you will find one or more establishments offering accommodation in your chosen town or village.

Yorkshire

East Yorkshire, North Yorkshire,
South Yorkshire, West Yorkshire

The land of romantic moors and vibrant cities

Yorkshire is the country's largest region, and it packs plenty in. From its three national parks brimming with breathtaking countryside to its stylish cosmopolitan cities, Yorkshire is big, beautiful and welcoming.

Yorkshire Tourist Board
yorkshire.com
0870 609 0000

Cow and Calf Rock, Ilkley

Boulby Cliffs

Millennium Galleries, Sheffield

York Minster

Yorkshire is blessed with some of England's wildest, most rugged countryside, including the vast expanse of the North York Moors and the dramatic carved valleys of the Peak District. Prefer your landscape a little lusher? Take a relaxing stroll across the rolling Yorkshire Dales or pretty Herriot Country. And you'll fall in love with the Yorkshire seaside whether it's lively resorts or the fossil-filled Heritage Coast. You'll also be in your element if you are into the urban scene. Vibrant cities like Leeds, Bradford, Hull and Sheffield offer designer shopping, Michelin-starred eateries and a buzzing cultural life. And then there's York. It may boast world-famous Viking roots and masses of medieval appeal, but today it also oozes contemporary chic with its continental café bar culture.

One place you won't want to miss is Fountains Abbey and Studley Royal Water Garden. This World Heritage Site features the impressive remains of a Cistercian abbey and elegant ornamental lakes. Or discover the Forbidden Corner, a unique labyrinth of tunnels, chambers and follies in the Dales. It's an unforgettable day out for the whole family. And you can while away a pleasant afternoon exploring the antique shops of historic Harrogate or the Victorian village of Saltaire. Don't miss York Minster, one of Europe's greatest gothic cathedrals, and while you're in York why not stop off at the National Railway Museum?

Yorkshire is a unique mix of influences and inspirational places. It's restful and zestful, forward looking yet founded on a bedrock of traditional values. The people are a friendly, straight-talking lot and take great pride in introducing visitors to Yorkshire's many and varied faces. Plain speaking may be part of Yorkshire's character, but there's nothing plain about this captivating part of Britain. Country or city, trendy or traditional, ancient history or cutting-edge – Yorkshire has it all.

Destinations

Barnsley

Barnsley, gateway to Pennine Yorkshire, boasts a rich industrial heritage. You'll also find an exciting mix of entertainment to suit all tastes. Shop for bargains at the 700-year-old indoor/outdoor market, then sample the famous 'Barnsley Chop'. Close by is the RSPB Old Moor, a 250-acre wetlands nature reserve and a superb place to watch wildlife. The surrounding rural villages offer quiet, cosy restaurants and pubs.

Halifax

If you appreciate outstanding architecture and a thriving cultural life, Halifax is for you. Visit the superb Borough Market, the galleried Piece Hall, and Eureka! the fascinating Museum for Children. Take in a series of exciting galleries including the Henry Moore Studio and the Dean Clough and find a full programme of great acts at the Victoria Theatre.

Hull

Enjoy the invigorating yet relaxing atmosphere that only a waterfront city can offer. Visit the Museum Quarter linking four of Hull's eight free museums including the interactive Streetlife Museum. Don't miss the £40 million aquarium, 'The Deep', home to 40 sharks and one of the most spectacular sea-life attractions in the world. Marvel at the engineering of the Humber Bridge and, after dark, experience Hull's very own café bar culture and take in a show at Hull Truck or Hull New Theatre.

| 0 | | 50 miles |
| 0 | | 75 kms |

National Park

Area of Outstanding Natural Beauty

Heritage Coast

National Trails
nationaltrail.co.uk

National Trails approved but
not yet open

Sections of the
National Cycle Network
nationalcyclenetwork.org.uk

The Deep, Hull

Leeds

Eureka! Museum for Children, Halifax

Village in the Pennines

The Shambles, York

Whitby Abbey

Leeds

Experience a combination of fast-paced, buzzing city centre with the serenity of the Yorkshire Dales on the doorstep. Rich local history, world-class sport and diverse year-round entertainment make Leeds a great place for everyone to enjoy. You'll find a shopaholic's dream, from the elegant Corn Exchange to the exquisite Victoria Quarter, not to mention the only Harvey Nichols outside London. See opera and dance at the internationally acclaimed Opera North and Northern Ballet, jousting at the Royal Armouries and outstanding collections in the many museums and galleries.

Whitby

Visit one of Britain's finest stretches of coastline with cliffs, bays, sandy beaches and attractive villages. Follow Whitby's quaint cobbled streets and climb the steps to the parish church of St Mary, whose churchyard inspired Bram Stocker's 'Dracula'. Then down to the historic quayside of this 1,000-year-old port and celebrate the town's seafaring tradition at the Captain Cook Festival, named in honour of Whitby's most famous son.

York

The history of York is the history of England. Visit award-winning attractions including the magnificent York Minster, and the world's biggest and best railway museum. Let 21st-century technology transport you back to the Viking age at Jorvik, and wander through the terrifying York Dungeon. Pedestrianised streets make York an ideal city to explore on foot. Follow the city's specialist shopping trails '5 Routes to Shopping Heaven', or browse the specialist antique and book dealers. Then take the weight off your feet in one of the many quaint teashops.

Places to visit

Bolton Abbey Estate
Skipton, North Yorkshire
(01756) 718009
boltonabbey.com
Priory ruins in beautiful setting

**Brodsworth Hall
and Gardens**
Doncaster, South Yorkshire
(01302) 722598
english-heritage.org.uk
Country home of Victorian gentry

Brontë Parsonage Museum
Haworth, West Yorkshire
(01535) 642323
bronte.org.uk
Home of the famous literary sisters

Castle Howard
York, North Yorkshire
(01653) 648444
castlehoward.co.uk
*Majestic 18th century house in
breathtaking parkland*
(grounds only)

The Deep
Hull, East Yorkshire
(01482) 381000
thedeep.co.uk
*One of the most spectacular
aquariums in the world*

**Eureka! The Museum
for Children**
Halifax, West Yorkshire
(01422) 330069
eureka.org.uk
*Britain's leading interactive
museum for children*

**Fountains Abbey and
Studley Royal**
Ripon, North Yorkshire
(01765) 608888
fountainsabbey.org.uk
*Outstanding 800-acre World
Heritage Site*

Harewood House
West Yorkshire
(0113) 218 1010
harewood.org
*Exquisite Adams interiors and
Chippendale furniture*

The Henry Moore Institute
Leeds, West Yorkshire
(0113) 246 7467
henry-moore-fdn.co.uk
*Beautiful exhibition space housing
four sculpture galleries*

Jorvik - The Viking City
York, North Yorkshire
(01904) 543400
vikingjorvik.com
Viking history comes to life

**Magna Science
Adventure Centre**
Rotherham,
South Yorkshire
(01709) 720002
visitmagna.co.uk
Extraordinary science adventure

**National Coal Mining
Museum for England**
Wakefield, West Yorkshire
(01924) 844560
ncm.org.uk
Unique museum of coalfields

National Media Museum
Bradford, West Yorkshire
0870 701 0200
nmpft.org.uk
*With spectacular 3D IMAX cinema
and interactive television gallery*

**National Railway
Museum**
York, North Yorkshire
0870 421 4001
nrm.org.uk
*See the Flying Scotsman at the
world's largest railway museum*

**North Yorkshire
Moors Railway**
Pickering
(01751) 472508
nymr.co.uk
*Heritage railway steaming through
stunning scenery*

**The Norwich Union Yorkshire
Wheel**
York, North Yorkshire
(01904) 686263
nrm.org.uk
York's new landmark aerial attraction

**RHS Garden
Harlow Carr**
Harrogate,
North Yorkshire
(01423) 565418
rhs.org.uk
*Stunning garden with year-round
events*

**Royal Armouries
Museum**
Leeds, West Yorkshire
(0113) 220 1916
armouries.org.uk
*Jousting tournaments and
fabulous exhibitions*

🐕 Pets Welcome
🐕 Assistance dogs only

Diary dates 2008

**Sewerby Hall
and Gardens**

Bridlington,
East Yorkshire
(01262) 673769
eastriding.gov.uk/sewerby
*Country house in dramatic cliff-
top location*
🐕 *(grounds only)* 🐾

Skipton Castle

North Yorkshire
(01756) 792442
skiptoncastle.co.uk
Fine preserved medieval castle
🐕 🐾

Whitby Abbey

North Yorkshire
(01904) 601974
english-heritage.org.uk
Moody and magnificent ruins
🐕 🐾

**The World of
James Herriot**

Thirsk, North Yorkshire
(01845) 524234
worldofjamesherriot.org
*Restored home of the famous vet
and author*
🐾

York Castle Museum

North Yorkshire
(01904) 687687
yorkcastlemuseum.org.uk
*England's most popular museum
of everyday life*
🐾

York Minster
North Yorkshire
(01904) 557216
yorkminster.org
*One of the great cathedrals
of the world*
🐾

Yorkshire Sculpture Park
Wakefield, West Yorkshire
(01924) 832631
ysp.co.uk
*Open-air gallery in beautiful
grounds*
🐕 *(grounds only)* 🐾

Family History Festival
Kings Hall & Winter Gardens, Ilkley
familyhistoryfestival.co.uk
13 January

Jorvik Viking Festival
Various locations, York
jorvik-viking-centre.co.uk
13 – 17 Feb

**Wakefield Festival of Food, Drink and
Rhubarb**
Various locations, Wakefield
wakefield.gov.uk
29 Feb – 1 Mar

Dales Festival of Food and Drink
Leyburn
dalesfestivaloffood.org
3 – 5 May

The Great Yorkshire Show
Harrogate
greatyorkshireshow.com
8 – 10 Jul

Kettlewell Scarecrow Festival
kettlewell.info
9 – 17 Aug

York Festival of Food and Drink
Various locations, York
yorkfestivaloffoodanddrink.com
19 – 28 Sep

Hull Fair
Walton Street, Hull
hullfair.net
10 – 18 Oct

Dickensian Christmas Fayre
Various locations, Grassington
grassington.net
First three Saturdays in Dec

Tourist Information Centres

When you arrive at your destination, visit an Official Partner Tourist Information Centre for quality assured help with accommodation and information about local attractions and events, or email your request before you go. To search for attractions and Tourist Information Centres on the move just text INFO to 62233, and a web link will be sent to your mobile phone.

Aysgarth Falls	Aysgarth Falls National Park	(01969) 662910	aysgarth@ytbtic.co.uk
Beverley	34 Butcher Row	(01482) 391672	beverley.tic@eastriding .gov.uk
Bradford	Centenary Square	(01274) 433678	tourist.information@bradford.gov.uk
Bridlington	25 Prince Street	(01262) 673474	bridlington.tic@eastriding.gov.uk
Brigg	Market Place	(01652) 657053	brigg.tic@northlincs.gov.uk
Cleethorpes	42-43 Alexandra Road	(01472) 323111	cleetic@nelincs.gov.uk
Danby*	Lodge Lane	(01439) 772737	moorscentre@northyorkmoors-npa.gov.uk
Filey*	John Street	(01723) 383637	fileytic@scarborough.gov.uk
Grassington	Hebden Road	(01756) 751690	grassington@ytbtic.co.uk
Guisborough	Church Street	(01287) 633801	guisborough_tic@redcar-cleveland.gov.uk
Halifax	Piece Hall	(01422) 368725	halifax@ytbtic.co.uk
Harrogate	Crescent Road	(01423) 537300	tic@harrogate.gov.uk
Haworth	2/4 West Lane	(01535) 642329	haworth@ytbtic.co.uk
Hebden Bridge	New Road	(01422) 843831	hebdenbridge@ytbtic.co.uk
Holmfirth	49-51 Huddersfield Road	(01484) 222444	holmfirth.tic@kirklees.gov.uk
Hornsea*	120 Newbegin	(01964) 536404	hornsea.tic@eastriding.gov.uk
Huddersfield	3 Albion Street	(01484) 223200	huddersfield.tic@kirklees.gov.uk
Hull	1 Paragon Street	(01482) 223559	tourist.information@hullcc.gov.uk
Humber Bridge	Ferriby Road	(01482) 640852	humberbridge.tic@eastriding.gov.uk
Ilkley	Station Rd	(01943) 602319	ilkley@ytbtic.co.uk
Knaresborough	Market Place	0845 389 0177	kntic@harrogate.gov.uk
Leeds	The Arcade, City Station	(0113) 242 5242	touristinfo@leeds.gov.uk
Leyburn	Railway Street	(01969) 623069	leyburn@ytbtic.co.uk
Malham	National Park Centre	(01969) 652380	malham@ytbtic.co.uk
Malton	Malton Museum	(01653) 600048	maltontic@btconnect.com
Pateley Bridge*	18 High Street	0845 389 0177	pbtic@harrogate.gov.uk
Pickering	The Ropery	(01751) 473791	pickering@ytbtic.co.uk
Redcar	Esplanade	(01642) 471921	redcar_tic@redcar-cleveland.gov.uk
Reeth	The Green	(01748) 884059	reeth@ytbtic.co.uk
Richmond	Victoria Road	(01748) 850252	richmond@ytbtic.co.uk
Ripon	Minster Road	(01765) 604625	ripontic@harrogate.gov.uk
Rotherham	40 Bridgegate	(01709) 835904	tic@rotherham.gov.uk
Scarborough	Brunswick Shopping Centre	(01723) 383636	tourismbureau@scarborough.gov.uk
Scarborough (Harbourside)	Sandside	(01723) 383636	harboursidetic@scarborough.gov.uk

Selby	52 Micklegate	(01757) 212181	selby@ytbtic.co.uk
Settle	Cheapside	(01729) 825192	settle@ytbtic.co.uk
Sheffield	14 Norfolk Row	(0114) 221 1900	visitor@sheffield.gov.uk
Skipton	35 Coach Street	(01756) 792809	skipton@ytbtic.co.uk
Sutton Bank	Sutton Bank	(01845) 597426	suttonbank@ytbtic.co.uk
Thirsk	49 Market Place	(01845) 522755	thirsktic@hambleton.gov.uk
Wakefield	9 The Bull Ring	0845 601 8353	tic@wakefield.gov.uk
Whitby	Langborne Road	(01723) 383637	whitbytic@scarborough.gov.uk
Withernsea*	131 Queen Street	(01964) 615683	withernsea.tic@eastriding.gov.uk
York **(De Grey Rooms)**	Exhibition Square	(01904) 550099	tic@visityork.org
York **(Railway Station)**	Station Road	(01904) 550099	kg@visityork.org

* seasonal opening

Semer Water, near Bainbridge

Find out more

The following publications are available from Yorkshire Tourist Board by logging on to yorkshire.com or calling 0870 609 0000:

- **Yorkshire Accommodation Guide 2008**
  Information on Yorkshire, including hotels, self catering, camping and caravan parks.

- **Make Yorkshire Yours Magazine**
  This entertaining magazine is full of articles and features about what's happening in Yorkshire, including where to go and what to do.

Travel info

By road:
Motorways: M1, M62, M606, M621, M18, M180, M181, A1(M).
Trunk roads: A1, A19, A57, A58, A59, A61, A62, A64, A65, A66.

By rail:
InterCity services to Bradford, Doncaster, Harrogate, Kingston upon Hull, Leeds, Sheffield, Wakefield and York. Frequent regional railway services city centre to city centre, including Manchester Airport service to Scarborough, York and Leeds.

By air:
Fly into Durham Tees Valley, Humberside, Leeds/Bradford International or Robin Hood, Doncaster, Sheffield.

where to stay in
Yorkshire

All place names in the blue bands are shown on the maps at the front of this guide.

Accommodation symbols
Symbols give useful information about services and facilities. Inside the back-cover flap you can find a key to these symbols. Keep it open for easy reference.

BARMBY MOOR, East Riding of Yorkshire Map ref 4C1   **SELF CATERING**

★★★★
SELF CATERING

Units **1**
Sleeps **1–6**
Low season per wk
£375.00–£400.00
High season per wk
£440.00–£600.00

Northwood Coach House, York

contact Ann Gregory, Northwood Coach House, St Helens Square, Barmby Moor YO42 4HF
t (01759) 302305   **e** annjgregory@hotmail.com   **w** northwoodcoachhouse.co.uk

open All year
payment Cash/cheques, euros

This pretty, three-bedroomed, converted Victorian coach house overlooks open countryside. Warm and cosy in winter, it is ideally situated in a picturesque village on the edge of the Wolds, only 12 miles from York and convenient for the coast and moors. Pubs, shops and restaurants nearby.

⊕ At main crossroads in village take road between the pub and general store. House is up a long drive after sharp bend before school field.

♥ Short breaks (3 days), bookable 28 days in advance, 60% normal weekly rate.

Pets 🐕 🐈 🐾   Unit ▦ 📺 🔲 🔲 🔲 🔲 🔲 🔲 🔲 🔲 🔲 🔲 ❄
General 🛏 ▦ 🅿 🅿 🅂   Leisure ∪ 🚲   Shop < 0.5 miles   Pub < 0.5 miles

---

BEDALE, North Yorkshire Map ref 5C3   **GUEST ACCOMMODATION**

★★★★
INN

B&B per room per night
s £50.00–£60.00
d £65.00–£75.00

The Castle Arms Inn

Bedale DL8 2TB   **t** (01677) 470270   **f** (01677) 470837   **e** castlearms@aol.com   **w** thecastlearms.co.uk

open All year
bedrooms 6 double, 3 twin
bathrooms All en suite
payment Credit/debit cards, cash/cheques

A family-run, 14thC inn which has been completely refurbished. All twin and double bedrooms are en suite, and have been furnished to an exceptional standard, and include TV and tea-/coffee-making facilities. A warm welcome awaits you, with open fires, traditional ales and real home cooking.

⊕ From A1 Leeming Bar take A684 to Bedale. Follow B6268 to Masham for 2 miles. Turn left to Arboretum. One mile after Arboretum turn left to Snape.

♥ Special seasonal rates available Oct-Mar.

Pets 🐕 🐈 🐾 🛏   Room 🛏 📺 💧   General 🛏 5 🅿 ❗ ✕ ❄

BRIDLINGTON, East Riding of Yorkshire Map ref 5D3 — **SELF CATERING**

★★★★
SELF CATERING

Units	**1**
Sleeps	**5**

Low season per wk
£195.00–£275.00
High season per wk
£350.00–£550.00

Smithy Cottage, Grindale

contact Karen Coman, 29 Braithegayte, Wheldrake, York YO19 6TB
t (01904) 448933 & 07709 273250 **e** enquiries@thesmithy.info **w** thesmithy.info

open All year
payment Cash/cheques

Set in the small rural hamlet of Grindale, close to the Heritage coast, this unique 200-year-old detached, single-storey, spacious former blacksmiths' has been lovingly restored to a high standard. It boasts a large inglenook fireplace, wood-burning stove, beams, period features, four-poster bed and secluded patio garden.

⊕ Set in the scenic Yorkshire Wolds, close to the Heritage coast and a short drive from Scarborough, Filey and Flamborough. Just off the A165.

♥ Short breaks available. Private parking. All quality bed linen and towels provided. Heating included, no smoking.

Pets ♉ ⚘. Unit ▥ ▣ ⊡ ⊟ ▣ ▤ ▨ ⚌ ▨ ▨ ▨ ✿
General ⚏ ▥ ♣ P ✂ S Leisure ∪ Shop 3 miles Pub 3 miles

BURNSALL, North Yorkshire Map ref 5B3 — **HOTEL**

★★
SMALL HOTEL
SILVER AWARD

B&B per room per night
s £79.00–£139.00
d £145.00–£205.00
HB per person per night
£82.50–£112.50

The Devonshire Fell Hotel and Restaurant

Burnsall, Skipton BD23 6BT **t** (01756) 729000 **f** (01756) 729009 **e** res@devonshirehotels.co.uk
w devonshirehotels.co.uk

open All year
bedrooms 6 double, 4 twin, 2 family
bathrooms All en suite
payment Credit/debit cards, cash/cheques, euros

Unique city-chic hotel in the countryside with stunning views across the Yorkshire Dales. Bright, squishy sofas, vibrant decor, contemporary art, huge wood-burning stove, really-well-equipped bedrooms and bathrooms, delicious, freshly prepared food with the best of local and estate produce – plus free access to The Devonshire Health Spa and Bolton Abbey Estate.

⊕ At the junction with the B6160 and the A59, travel north for 6 miles. Located on the left-hand side as you enter Burnsall.

♥ Sun-night sleepover in a double room, including champagne, spa entry, Yorkshire breakfast and a delicious dinner, from £160 per couple.

Pets ♉ ⚐ ⚘ Room ☏ ▣ ☕ ⚌ General ⚏ ▥ ♣ P ♨ ⛊ ▣ ✿ Leisure ∪ ⚲ ⛵

Country Code

always follow the Country Code

- Be safe – plan ahead and follow any signs
- Leave gates and property as you find them
- Protect plants and animals, and take your litter home
- Keep dogs under close control
- Consider other people

★★★★
FARMHOUSE

B&B per room per night
d £54.00–£65.00
Evening meal per person
£10.00–£20.00

South Moor Farm

Dalby Forest Drive, Scarborough YO13 0LW t (01751) 460285 e vb@southmoorfarm.co.uk
w southmoorfarm.co.uk

open All year
bedrooms 1 double, 1 twin, 1 single, 1 family
bathrooms 3 en suite, 1 private
payment Credit/debit cards, cash/cheques

Quiet rural location on Dalby Forest Drive between Pickering and Scarborough. An excellent base to explore Dalby Forest on foot, bike or horse after a full English breakfast. Packed lunches and evening meals by arrangement. Children's play area, orienteering courses, quad bikes, 4x4 driving and astronomy in Dalby Forest.

⊕ *Follow Dalby Forest Drive (look for brown tourism signs). We are 10 miles from Thornton-le-Dale, 6 miles from Hackness. Grid Ref SE905905.*

♥ *Reduced rates for children under 14 years. Discounts on stays of 5 nights or more.*

Pets 🐾 🐱 🐴 Room 📺 ♨ 🐾 General 🛏 🏠 🕴 P ⚡ ✕ 🍴 🔥 Leisure ∪ 🚲 ⛵

★★★★
SELF CATERING

Units　　2
Sleeps　2–4
Low season per wk
£200.00–£350.00
High season per wk
£300.00–£750.00

Yellowtop Country Park, Foggathorpe

contact Paula Jessop, Yellowtop Country Park, Foggathorpe, York YO8 6PZ
t (01430) 860461 e yellowtopcountry@aol.com w yellowtopcountry.co.uk

open All year
payment Credit/debit cards, cash/cheques, euros

Situated at the foot of the Yorkshire Wolds between York and beautiful Beverley, surrounded by attractive market towns. Offering famous Yorkshire hospitality. Excellent coarse fishing. Lovely walks on and off-site. Wi-Fi hot spot. Pretty local village, just two miles away, hosts a good selection of pubs and eateries.

Pets 🐾 🐱 🐴 Unit 🏠 📺 🍴 ■ 📱
General 🛏 🏠 🕴 P ⚡ ⊙ Ⓢ Leisure ∪ ⛵ Shop 2 miles Pub 2 miles

★★★★
SELF CATERING

Units　　1
Sleeps　　4
Low season per wk
£233.00–£329.00
High season per wk
£356.00–£548.00

Fir Tree Farm Holiday Homes, Grewelthorpe, Ripon

contact Eric & Jane Simpson, Fir Tree Farm Holiday Homes, High Bramley, Grewelthorpe,
Ripon HG4 3DL
t (01765) 658727 f (01765) 658600 e firtreefarmhouse@aol.com w firtree-farm-holidayhomes.co.uk

open All year
payment Cash/cheques, euros

Willow Tree Lodge is situated in beautiful woodland amongst rolling hills and is ideally situated for exploring the Dales. Superbly finished on a privately-owned 100-acre farm. We are ten miles from the cathedral city of Ripon and four miles from the old market town of Masham.

♥ *3-night stays available Oct-Jan (excl Christmas and New Year) and occasionally at other times.*

Pets 🐾 Unit 🏠 📺 🍴 ■ 🍴 🐾 ⊙ 📱 ✿
General 🛏 🕴 P ⚡ Ⓢ Leisure ∪ 🚲 ⛵ Shop 4 miles Pub 4 miles

SELF CATERING

★★★★
SELF CATERING

Units **2**
Sleeps **2–4**

Low season per wk
£270.00–£290.00
High season per wk
£380.00–£435.00

Cherry Tree Cottages, Barkisland, Nr Halifax

contact Stan & Elaine Shaw, Cherry Tree Cottages, Wall Nook, Barkisland, Halifax HX4 0BL
t (01422) 372662 **f** (01422) 372662 **e** cherrytree@yorkshire-cottages.co.uk
w yorkshire-cottages.co.uk

open All year
payment Credit/debit cards, cash/cheques

Warm, comfortable, stone-built cottages set in two acres of natural woodland/heather garden with superb Pennine views and direct access to open countryside and footpaths. Close to a quiet Calderdale village with good pubs and restaurants nearby. Ideal location for exploring Brontë Country and Pennine Yorkshire. Pets and children welcome. Wireless internet access.

⊕ *Ten-minute drive from either jct 22 or 24 on M62. Two miles from Ripponden on B6113, and 400yds from the Spring Rock Tavern.*

♥ *Short breaks available, minimum 3 nights. Check our website for late availability.*

Pets ♞ ♨. Unit ▥ ﹐TV﹐ ⬚ ⬚ ▪ ⬚ ⬚ ⬚ ⬚ ❋
General ⬚ ﹐▥ ♔ P ⤬ ▣ ⑤ Leisure ∪ ⬚ Shop 1 mile Pub < 0.5 miles

GUEST ACCOMMODATION

★★★
BED & BREAKFAST

B&B per room per night
d £50.00–£70.00

Court Croft

Church Lane, Hebden, Skipton BD23 5DX **t** (01756) 753406

Five-hundred-acre livestock farm. Farmhouse in village location close to the Dales Way. Ideal for touring the Dales, Nidderdale and Ribblesdale.

open All year
bedrooms 3 twin
bathrooms 2 en suite, 1 private
payment Cash/cheques

Pets ♞ ⬚ ♨ ♨. Room ﹐TV﹐ ⬚ ⬚ General ⬚ ♔ P ⬚ ⬚ ❋ Leisure ∪ ⬚

SELF CATERING

★★★★
SELF CATERING

Units **1**
Sleeps **1–4**

Low season per wk
Min £210.00
High season per wk
£305.00–£385.00

Townend Cottage, Beadlam

contact Mrs Margaret Begg, Townend Farmhouse, High Lane, Beadlam, Nawton, York YO62 7SY
t (01439) 770103 **e** margaret.begg@ukgateway.net **w** visityorkshire.com

open All year
payment Cash/cheques

Originally part of an 18thC farmhouse, this is a very warm, comfortable, two-bedroomed stone cottage with oak beams. Situated off the main road in a village three miles from the charming market town of Helmsley. Ideal for walking or touring Moors, coast and York. Central heating and log fire included in price.

⊕ *Enter Beadlam on the A170 from Helmsley. Take 1st left turning into High Lane and then 1st right turning into Townend Cottage Drive.*

Pets ♞ Unit ▥ ﹐TV﹐ ⬚ ⬚ ▪ ⬚ ⬚ ⬚ ⬚ ⬚ ❋
General ⬚ ▥ ♔ P Leisure ⬚ Shop 3 miles Pub < 0.5 miles

Place index

If you know where you want to stay, the index at the back of the guide will give you the page number listing accommodation in your chosen town, city or village. Check out the other useful indexes too.

★★★★
SELF CATERING

Units **1**
Sleeps **2–5**

Low season per wk
£250.00–£325.00
High season per wk
£250.00–£325.00

Cottage In The Pond, Garton

contact Mr Adrian Fisher, Middle Keld Countryside Experience, North Field Farm, Garton HU11 4QB
t (01964) 527256   **f** (01964) 529029   **e** info@middlekeld.co.uk   **w** middlekeld.co.uk

The cottage is located on a farm in a quiet location. Completely refurbished to a high standard, this 300-year-old cottage still retains its original character. Woodland and paddock walk on site.

open All year
payment Credit/debit cards, cash/cheques

Pets 🐕 🐈 🐾   Unit 🏠 📺 🔲 🔳 ♨ 🛢 🍴 🍶 🛋 🏷 ✿
General 🛏 🖼 🚶 P ✂ Ⓢ   Leisure ∪ 🚲 🏛   Shop 2 miles   Pub 2 miles

★★★★
SELF CATERING

Units **2**
Sleeps **2–6**

Low season per wk
Min £295.00
High season per wk
Max £495.00

The Green, Hutton-le-Hole, York

t (020) 8892 9132   **f** (020) 8400 1545   **e** info@thegreen.eu   **w** thegreen.eu

open All year
payment Cash/cheques

With views over the village green from every bedroom and sitting room, this unique holiday home is ideal for exploring the Yorkshire moors and coastal towns with Castle Howard and York a short drive away. Our spacious, newly refurbished apartments sleep between two and ten people in comfort. Dogs welcome.

✦ *One mile east of Kirkbymoorside on the A170 is the road heading north to Hutton-le-Hole. The Green is opposite the pub and Ryedale Folk Museum.*

Pets 🐕   Unit 🏠 📺 🔲 🔳 ♨ 🛢 🍶 🛋 🏷
General 🛏 P ✂ ▢   Leisure ∪ 🏛   Shop 3 miles   Pub < 0.5 miles

★★★★
SELF CATERING

Units **1**
Sleeps **1–5**

Low season per wk
Min £322.00
High season per wk
Min £491.00

Middle Cottage, Middleham, Leyburn

contact Mrs Jennie Perren, 2 North Park Grove, Leeds LS8 1JJ
t (0113) 237 1817   **f** (0113) 237 1817   **e** jennifer.perren@btinternet.com
w yorkshire-dales-holiday-cottage.co.uk

Sitting room with dining area, kitchen, three bedrooms, bathroom with shower. Electric heating, garden to the rear, parking 200yds.

open All year
payment Cash/cheques

Pets 🐕 🐈 🐾   Unit 🏠 📺 🔲 🔳 ♨ 🛢 🍴 🍶 🛋 🏷 ✿
General 🛏 ✂ Ⓢ   Leisure ∪ 🏛   Shop < 0.5 miles   Pub < 0.5 miles

★★★
SELF CATERING

Units **1**
Sleeps **3–4**

Low season per wk
£190.00–£300.00
High season per wk
£340.00–£410.00

Old Cobbler's Cottage, Driffield, North Dalton

contact Chris Wade, Waterfront Cottages, 2 Star Row, North Dalton, Driffield YO25 9UX
t (01377) 217662 & 07801 124264   **f** (01377) 217754   **e** chris.wade@adastra-music.co.uk
w waterfrontcottages.co.uk

open All year
payment Credit/debit cards, cash/cheques

19thC, mid-terraced, oak-beamed cottage overlooking picturesque pond in a peaceful and friendly farming village, between York and Yorkshire's Heritage Coast. Ideally located for walking, visiting the coast, historic houses, races at York and Beverley or just relaxing. Excellent inn/restaurant adjacent, shops 1.5 miles. Pets welcome.

✦ *On entering North Dalton, take narrow lane up the side of The Star pub car park. Old Cobbler's is a mid-terraced cottage in the row.*

♥ *Short breaks available, 2 nights (excl Christmas, New Year, Easter and Bank Holidays).*

Pets 🐕 🐾   Unit 🏠 📺 🔲 🔳 🍴 🍶 🛋 🏷 ✿
General 🛏 🖼 🚶 P ✂ Ⓢ   Leisure 🏛   Shop 1.5 miles   Pub < 0.5 miles

NORTHALLERTON, North Yorkshire Map ref 5C3 — SELF CATERING

★★★★
SELF CATERING

Units **4**
Sleeps **2–4**
Low season per wk
£175.00–£280.00
High season per wk
£290.00–£440.00

Hill House Farm Cottages, Little Langton, Northallerton

contact Julie & James Griffith, Hill House Farm, Little Langton, Northallerton DL7 0PZ
t (01609) 770643 **e** info@hillhousefarmcottages.com **w** hillhousefarmcottages.com

open All year
payment Credit/debit cards, cash/cheques

These four well-equipped cottages, converted from former farm buildings, are set around a lawned courtyard garden, in a peaceful rural setting with magnificent views. Situated three miles from the market town of Northallerton, they are ideal for exploring both the Yorkshire Dales and the North York Moors.

Pets 🐕 🐾 Unit 🛏 📺 🎮 💻 ⬜ 🔌 📻 🍽 🔥 ⬜ ❄
General ⬜ 🏠 ♿ P Leisure ∪ 🎣 Shop 3 miles Pub 1.5 miles

PATELEY BRIDGE, North Yorkshire Map ref 5C3 — SELF CATERING

★★★★
SELF CATERING &
SERVICED APARTMENTS

Units **4**
Sleeps **2–10**
Low season per wk
£195.00–£385.00
High season per wk
£335.00–£710.00

Helme Pasture, Old Spring Wood, Harrogate

contact Mrs Rosemary Helme, Hartwith Bank, Summerbridge, Harrogate HG3 4DR
t (01423) 780279 **f** (01423) 780994 **e** helmepasture@btinternet.com **w** helmepasture.co.uk

open All year
payment Credit/debit cards, cash/cheques, euros

Scandinavian lodges and converted Dales barn. Award-winning conservation woodland. Holiday in tranquil surroundings. Country walks. Close to a multitude of attractions including Fountains Abbey, castles, Yorkshire villages and floral towns – Harrogate, Skipton, Ripon, York. Traditional markets. Pet-friendly, laundry facilities, and a warm family welcome.

⊕ *Harrogate, B6165 towards Pateley Bridge. At Summerbridge (Flying Dutchman pub), turn up Hartwith Bank. Helme Pasture is 0.3 miles on left.*

♥ *Short breaks available.*

Pets 🐕 🐈 🐾 Unit 🛏 📺 💻 🎮 📠 ⬜ 🔌 📻 🔥 ❄
General ⬜ P ✂ 🖨 S Leisure ∪ Shop < 0.5 miles Pub < 0.5 miles

PICKERING, North Yorkshire Map ref 5D3 — HOTEL

 ★★
SMALL HOTEL
SILVER AWARD

B&B per room per night
s £38.00–£50.00
d £70.00–£85.00
HB per person per night
Min £57.50

The Old Manse

Middleton Road, Pickering YO18 8AL **t** (01751) 476484 **f** (01751) 477124
e info@oldmansepickering.co.uk **w** oldmansepickering.co.uk

Fine Edwardian house in one acre of garden/ orchard. A short walk to steam railway and town centre. All rooms en suite, car parking on site.

open All year
bedrooms 4 double, 2 twin, 1 single, 3 family
bathrooms All en suite
payment Credit/debit cards, cash/cheques

Pets 🐕 🐈 🐾 Room 🛏 ☕ 📺 💧 🔌 ✂ General ⬜1 🏠 ♿ ✂ 🍽 🎱 ❄ Leisure 🚲 🎣

It's all quality-assessed accommodation

Our commitment to quality involves wide-ranging accommodation assessment. Rating and awards were correct at the time of going to press but may change following a new assessment. Please check at time of booking.

PICKERING, North Yorkshire Map ref 5D3 **SELF CATERING**

★★★★
SELF CATERING

Units 1
Sleeps 2–6
Low season per wk
Min £400.00
High season per wk
Max £900.00

Kirklea Cottage, Pickering

contact Mrs Carol Hill, Kirklea Cottage, 23 Hungate, Pickering YO18 7DL
t (01751) 477202 **e** info@pickeringholidaycottage.co.uk **w** pickeringholidaycottage.co.uk

Detached three-bedroom, two-bathroom cottage located in the centre of Pickering, complete with private hot tub and situated in an enclosed 0.25 acre landscaped garden. Private parking.

open All year
payment Cash/cheques

Pets 🐕 😼 🐾 Unit ▥ 📺 🖭 🖳 🖩 🖨 ❖
General 🛋 🏠 ♿ P ✂ Ⓢ Leisure 🚴 Shop < 0.5 miles Pub < 0.5 miles

PICKERING, North Yorkshire Map ref 5D3 **SELF CATERING**

★★★★
SELF CATERING

Units 4
Sleeps 4–6
Low season per wk
£295.00–£360.00
High season per wk
£635.00–£820.00

Let's Holiday, Pickering

contact John and Penny Wicks, Let's Holiday, Pickering YO18 8QA
t (01751) 475396 **e** holiday@letsholiday.com **w** letsholiday.com

open All year
payment Credit/debit cards, cash/cheques

Comfortable and fully equipped offering indoor pool, spa and sauna, and set in extensive level grounds at the heart of our National Park village. Paddocks and stabling for DIY livery. Village pub, play area and duck pond nearby. Perfect for exploring North York Moors, the coast and City of York.

⊕ *In Pickering turn left at roundabout along A170. After approx 300m turn right at traffic lights. Follow road for approx 4 miles to reach Newton-on-Rawcliffe.*

♥ *Low season short breaks: 2 or 3 nights over the weekend and 4 nights for the price of 3 midweek.*

Pets 🐕 🐾 Unit ▥ 📺 🖭 🖳 🖨 ❖
General 🛋 🏠 ♿ P ✂ Ⓢ Leisure ♨ ∪ 🏊 Shop 4 miles Pub < 0.5 miles

RUNSWICK BAY, North Yorkshire Map ref 5D3 **GUEST ACCOMMODATION**

★★★★
GUEST HOUSE

B&B per room per night
s £45.00–£55.00
d £70.00–£80.00
Evening meal per person
Min £18.50

The Firs

26 Hinderwell Lane, Runswick Bay, Nr Whitby TS13 5HR **t** (01947) 840433 **f** (01947) 841616
e mandy.shackleton@talk21.com **w** the-firs.co.uk

In a coastal village, eight miles north of Whitby. All rooms en suite with colour TV, tea/coffee facilities. Private parking. Children and dogs welcome. Open April to October.

bedrooms 3 double, 2 twin, 1 single, 5 family
bathrooms All en suite
payment Cash/cheques, euros

Pets 🐕 😼 🐾 Room 🛋 📺 ❖ 🍵 General 🛋 P ✕ 🍴 🍺 🔥 ❖ Leisure 🏊

SCARBOROUGH, North Yorkshire Map ref 5D3 **HOTEL**

COUNTRY HOUSE HOTEL

B&B per room per night
s £60.00–£100.00
d £120.00–£160.00
HB per person per night
£65.00–£100.00

Ox Pasture Hall

Lady Edith's Drive, Throxenby, Scarborough YO12 5TD **t** (01723) 365295 **f** (01723) 355156
w oxpasturehall.com

Ox Pasture Hall offers quiet luxury in beautiful rural surroundings with comfortable and spacious accommodation and extensive and imaginative menus.

open All year
bedrooms 15 double, 2 twin, 3 single, 2 family
bathrooms All en suite
payment Credit/debit cards, cash/cheques

Pets 🐕 😼 🐾 Room 🛋 📺 ❖ 🍵 General 🛋 🏠 ♿ P 🍽 🍴 ❖ Leisure ∪

Key to symbols
Open the back flap for a key to symbols.

SCARBOROUGH, North Yorkshire Map ref 5D3 — GUEST ACCOMMODATION

★★★★
GUEST HOUSE

B&B per room per night
s £30.00
d £52.00–£54.00

Sylvern House

25 New Queen Street, Scarborough YO12 7HJ **t** (01723) 360952 **e** sylvernhouse@aol.com
w smoothhound.co.uk/hotels/sylvern.html

open All year
bedrooms 3 double, 1 twin, 2 single, 3 family
bathrooms All en suite
payment Credit/debit cards, cash/cheques

Enjoy a warm welcome, good home cooking and a friendly atmosphere with Vicki and Richard at Sylvern House. We are ideally situated close to both bays and the town centre. All rooms en suite, children and pets welcome. Internet access. Open all year, including Christmas and New Year.

⊕ Directions to the hotel will be included with your booking acknowledgement.

Pets 🐾 🐕 🐱 Room TV 🍵 General 🛏 🏠 🍽 ♨ 🐾 ✿

SCARBOROUGH, North Yorkshire Map ref 5D3 — SELF CATERING

★★★
SELF CATERING

Units **1**
Sleeps **2–7**
Low season per wk
£250.00–£300.00
High season per wk
£450.00–£600.00

Driftwood, Scarborough

contact Mrs Diane Crampton, Filey Road, Gristhorpe YO14 9PH
t (01723) 516700 **e** info@bedwyns.co.uk **w** bedwyns.co.uk

Detached three-bedroomed dormer bungalow overlooking Scarborough Mere. In country park near Oliver's Mount. Great base for Yorkshire coast and North York Moors. Four adults, three children. Pet friendly.

open All year
payment Credit/debit cards, cash/cheques

Pets 🐾 🐱 Unit 🛏 TV 🍳 🍽 📺 🔔 📻 🔌
General 🛏 P Shop 0.5 miles Pub 0.75 miles

SCARBOROUGH, North Yorkshire Map ref 5D3 — SELF CATERING

★★★
SELF CATERING

Units **3**
Sleeps **2–4**
Low season per wk
£195.00–£300.00
High season per wk
£300.00–£485.00

East Farm Country Cottages, Scalby, Scarborough

contact Mrs Joanne Ireland, East Farm Country Cottages, 31 Woodland Ravine, Scarborough YO12 6TA
t (01723) 353635 **e** joeastfarmcottages@hotmail.co.uk **w** eastfarmcountrycottages.co.uk

open All year
payment Cash/cheques

Three delightful two-bedroomed, single-storey stone cottages. Situated in the area's prettiest location just outside the village of Scalby, within the North York Moors National Park, yet only five minutes away from Scarborough. Ideal for walking, cycling or touring. Pets welcome in two cottages. All non-smoking. Parking, garden.

⊕ Travel along A171 northwards from Scarborough, approx 2 miles. Turn left onto Hackness Road, along Hay Lane, left onto private lane at National Park sign.

♥ Short breaks in the winter months or at short notice in high season.

Pets 🐾 £🐾 🐱 Unit 🛏 TV 📺 🔔 📻 🔌 ✿
General 🛏 🍽 P Leisure 🚴 Shop 1 mile Pub 1 mile

A holiday on two wheels

For a fabulous freewheeling break, seek out accommodation participating in our Cyclists Welcome scheme. Look out for the symbol and plan your route online at nationalcyclenetwork.org.

SCARBOROUGH, North Yorkshire Map ref 5D3 — SELF CATERING

★★★★
SELF CATERING

Units **3**
Sleeps **1-5**

Low season per wk
£195.00
High season per wk
£250.00–£495.00

Honeysuckle Cottage, Scarborough

contact David and Jane Beeley, Forge Valley Cottages, Thompson's Rigg Farm, Crosscliff, Langdale End, Scarborough YO13 0LN
t (01723) 882284 **e** enquiries@forgevalleycottages.co.uk **w** forgevalleycottages.co.uk

open All year
payment Cash/cheques

Lovely stone-built cottage in delightful village close to Scarborough. Great days out in Whitby, Filey, York, Helmsley and Pickering. Two bedrooms (double and twin) sleeping 2-5. Modern, highly equipped kitchen. Patio garden with gas BBQ. Lovely walks and cycle rides. Non-smoking. Pets welcome. Open all year.

⊕ *East Ayton is approx 4 miles west of Scarborough.*

♥ *Low season short breaks from £125 for 1-3 nights.*

Pets 🐕 🐈 Unit 🛏 📺 📱 🍳 🧺 🔥 🔌 General 🛏 📶 🏃 P ✂ Leisure ∪ 🏊 Shop < 0.5 miles Pub < 0.5 miles

SETTLE, North Yorkshire Map ref 5B3 — GUEST ACCOMMODATION

★★★
INN

B&B per room per night
s £34.00–£39.00
d £60.00–£65.00
Evening meal per person
£7.95–£13.95

Maypole Inn

Maypole Green, Long Preston, Skipton BD23 4PH **t** (01729) 840219 **f** (01729) 840727
e robert@maypole.co.uk **w** maypole.co.uk

open All year
bedrooms 2 double, 1 twin, 1 single, 2 family
bathrooms All en suite
payment Credit/debit cards, cash/cheques, euros

Traditional 17thC village inn on the Maypole Green, situated within the Yorkshire Dales and close to the Trough of Bowland and the Lake District. Restaurant serving home-made food with a good local reputation. Traditional beers – we are four-times winner of the CAMRA Pub of the Season.

⊕ *We are on the main A65 road, between the market towns of Skipton and Settle. 45 mins from the M6 motorway.*

♥ *Midweek and winter breaks available – please telephone for details.*

Pets 🐕 🐈 🐩 🐾 Room 🍵 📺 🛁 General 🛏 📶 🏃 P ✂ 🍽 🎱 💻 Leisure ♠ ♦ ∪ 🚲 🏊

SHEFFIELD, South Yorkshire Map ref 4B2 — GUEST ACCOMMODATION

★★★
GUEST ACCOMMODATION

B&B per room per night
s £45.00
d £45.00
Evening meal per person
£5.00–£15.00

Parson House Farm

Longshaw, Sheffield S11 7TZ **t** (01433) 631017 **f** (01433) 630794 **e** debbel@btconnect.com
w parsonhouse.co.uk

Quality comfortable rooms with private bathroom. Set in Peak District, great for families/couples, breakfast, half or full board available. Pets welcome. Outdoor activities available.

open All year
bedrooms 2 family
bathrooms 2 private
payment Cash/cheques

Pets 🐕 🐈 🐩 🐾 Room 🛁 📺 🛁 General 🛏 📶 🏃 P X 💻 Leisure ♠ ∪ 🚲 🏊

Take a break

Look out for special promotions and themed breaks. This could be your chance to indulge an interest, find a new one, or just relax and enjoy exceptional value. Offers (highlighted in colour) are subject to availability.

★★★
SELF CATERING

Units **4**
Sleeps **1–6**

Low season per wk
£165.00–£240.00
High season per wk
£280.00–£450.00

White Hall Farm Holiday Cottages, Scarborough

contact Mr & Mrs James and Celia White, White Hall Farm Holiday Cottages, White Hall Farm, Scarborough YO13 0EY
t (01723) 870234   **e** celia@white66.fsbusiness.co.uk   **w** whitehallcottages.co.uk

open All year
payment Cash/cheques

Peace and tranquillity found on our 130-acre sheep farm with stunning coastal and rural views. Walks from your door amid woodland, streams and coastal path. Home from home, well-equipped, welcoming cottages, which are separate from the farm. Ideally located to explore North Yorkshire. Dogs/horses made welcome.

⊕ *Scarborough to Whitby (A171). At Cloughton, right turn to Shire Horse Farm. Go straight on for 1 mile on country lane. Cottages at end of lane.*

Pets 🐕 🐾   Unit 🗒️ 📺 ▣ ▣ ▣ ▣ ▤   🔒 🔲 🔳 ✿
General 🛋️ 🏠 🅿 ⊡ ⓢ   Leisure ∪   Shop 6 miles   Pub 4 miles

★★★
SELF CATERING

Units **1**
Sleeps **5**

Low season per wk
£240.00–£360.00
High season per wk
£345.00–£570.00

Pennysteel Cottage, Staithes

contact Chris Wade, Waterfront Cottages, 2 Star Row, North Dalton, Driffield YO25 9UX
t (01377) 217662 & 07801 124264   **f** (01377) 217754   **e** chris.wade@adastra-music.co.uk
w waterfrontcottages.co.uk

open All year
payment Credit/debit cards, cash/cheques

Old fisherman's cottage of unique character with beamed ceilings, wood-panelled walls and wood-burning stove. All windows and terrace overlook the picturesque harbour of Staithes. Ideal for the coast and walking. Top-quality restaurant, pub serving food, cafes, art gallery and craft and local shops all within a few yards.

⊕ *Go down hill into the old village. Bear right at the bottom. Take the 2nd passage on the left after the pub. Take left fork.*

Pets 🐕   Unit 🗒️ 📺 ▣ ▣ ▣ ▣ ▤   🔒 🔲 🔳 ✿
General 🛋️ 🏠 ✂   Shop < 0.5 miles   Pub < 0.5 miles

★★★★
HOTEL

B&B per room per night
s £95.00–£145.00
d £95.00–£145.00

Cedar Court Hotel

Denby Dale Road, Wakefield WF4 3QZ   **t** (01924) 276310   **f** (01924) 280221
e conf@cedarcourthotels.co.uk   **w** cedarcourthotels.co.uk

International hotel, designed and built to high specifications. Suitable for the business person, private functions, conferences and holidaymakers. Two double rooms designed for disabled persons.

open All year
bedrooms 120 double, 27 twin, 2 family
bathrooms All en suite
payment Credit/debit cards, cash/cheques, euros

Pets 🐕 🐾 🐟 🐾   Room 🛏️ 📞 📺 👆 🔳   General 🛋️ 🏠 🅿 ✂ 🍽 ♨ 🛜 ⧆ ▣ ✿   Leisure 🎣 🔥

★★★
GUEST ACCOMMODATION

B&B per room per night
s £22.00–£40.00
d £42.00–£52.00

The Old Star

Main Street, West Witton, Leyburn DL8 4LU   **t** (01969) 622949   **e** enquiries@theoldstar.com
w theoldstar.com

17thC, stone-built former coaching inn. Set in a farming community with uninterrupted views of Wensleydale from the rear of the property. Oak beams, log fire and a friendly atmosphere.

open All year except Christmas
bedrooms 4 double, 1 twin, 2 family
bathrooms 5 en suite
payment Cash/cheques

Pets 🐕 🐾 🐟 🐾   Room 🛏️ 📺 👆 🔳   General 🛋️ 🏠 🅿 🍽 ▣ ✿   Leisure 🚲 🏞️

WHITBY, North Yorkshire Map ref 5D3 **SELF CATERING**

★★★
SELF CATERING

Units	**1**
Sleeps	**2**

Low season per wk
£200.00–£250.00
High season per wk
£300.00–£400.00

Bolthole Cottage, Whitby

contact Kaaren Noble, Stormville, Robin Hood's Bay, Whitby YO22 4RA
t (01947) 880063 **e** kaaren@noble47.freeserve.co.uk **w** boltholecottage.co.uk

Quiet, warm, comfortable cottage. Two minutes
from harbour. Good base for walking. Bath,
shower, TV, DVD and modern kitchen.

open All year
payment Cash/cheques

Pets 🐕 🐈 🐾. Unit ▥ 📺 📧 ▨ 🖥 🖳 💿 ✿
General ✄ Ⓢ Leisure 🚲 ⛵ Shop < 0.5 miles   Pub < 0.5 miles

YORK, North Yorkshire Map ref 4C1 **GUEST ACCOMMODATION**

★★★★
GUEST ACCOMMODATION
SILVER AWARD

B&B per room per night
s £30.00–£65.00
d £60.00–£75.00

Ascot House

80 East Parade, York YO31 7YH **t** (01904) 426826 **f** (01904) 431077 **e** admin@ascothouseyork.com
w ascothouseyork.com

open All year except Christmas
bedrooms 8 double, 3 twin, 1 single, 3 family
bathrooms 12 en suite, 1 private
payment Credit/debit cards, cash/cheques

A family-run Victorian villa, built in 1869, with en
suite rooms of character and many four-poster or
canopy beds. Delicious English, continental and
vegetarian breakfasts served. Fifteen minutes' walk
to historic walled city centre, castle museum or York
Minster. Residential licence and residents' lounge,
sauna and private, enclosed car park.

⊕ *From A1/M1 take A64 then A1036 from the east into York.*
About 100yds past 30mph signs, take 2nd exit off
roundabout. Right at traffic lights into East Parade.

Pets 🐕 🐾 🐈 Room 🛏 📺 👜 ✎ General ▦ 🕯 **P** ⽟ 🍵 ℍ

YORK, North Yorkshire Map ref 4C1 **GUEST ACCOMMODATION**

★★★
GUEST HOUSE

B&B per room per night
s £28.00–£30.00
d £44.00–£60.00

Bull Lodge Guest House

37 Bull Lane, Lawrence Street, York YO10 3EN **t** (01904) 415522 **f** (01904) 415522
e stay@bulllodge.co.uk **w** bulllodge.co.uk

open All year except Christmas and New Year
bedrooms 4 double, 1 twin, 1 single
bathrooms 3 en suite
payment Credit/debit cards, cash/cheques

Modern, detached property in quiet, tree-lined side-
street location off A1079, 0.75 miles to centre. Close
to bus route, University of York, business/science
park, nature park/cycleway. En suites include
ground-floor double ideal for mobility-impaired
guests. Dogs welcome by arrangement. Freshly-
cooked, full-choice breakfast. Private on-site parking,
bicycle/motorbike garaging.

⊕ *Bull Lane is off Lawrence Street (A1079 Hull Road), 2 miles*
A64, 500yds city walls at Walmgate Bar. Local bus (no 10)
from rail station.

♥ *Quote advert for discount when booking, 5% 3/4 nights,*
10% 5 or more nights (excl Bank Holidays and special
events).

Pets 🐕 🐾 Room 🛏 📺 👜 ✎ General ♺5 **P** ✄ ℍ Leisure 🚲 ⛵

Using map references

Map references refer to the colour maps at the front of this guide.

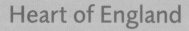

Heart of England

Herefordshire, Shropshire, Staffordshire,
Warwickshire, West Midlands,
Worcestershire

Wholesome fun and a whole lot more

When it comes to good food
and simple pleasures,
people make a bee-line for
the Heart of England.
Whether it's dining out,
gliding along a canal or
catching a nerve-jangling
rollercoaster, there's
nowhere better.

visittheheart.com

Wrekin Reservoir, Shropshire

Malvern Hills, Worcestershire

Charlecote Park, Warwickshire

Symonds Yat, Herefordshire

From Vale of Evesham asparagus to Herefordshire Beef, this region's rich soil and lush pastureland produces some of the UK's finest ingredients. Small wonder that from village pubs to Michelin-starred restaurants, your eating experience will be a highlight of your stay. Great family days out are a speciality, too. Whether it's throwing pots at the famous Wedgwood factory, braving the rides at Drayton Manor Theme Park or unwinding on a narrow boat, there are simply attractions galore. And if you like picnics, take a spread along to Symond's Yat RSPB Nature Reserve overlooking the gorgeous Wye Valley.

Want to get the most from your stay? Pick up a Thrill Hopper ticket that gives you great value access to four top theme park attractions – Drayton Manor Theme Park, Alton Towers, SnowDome and Waterworld. And don't miss Trentham's splendid Italian Garden and the Eastern Pleasure Garden restoration at one of the 19th century's most celebrated gardens. Then there's the National Cold War Exhibition at RAF Museum Cosford, an illuminating and exciting look at the tensions that tormented the superpowers during the 20th century (prepare to be amazed by Britain's three V-Bombers – Vulcan, Valiant and Victor). And Walsall Illuminations transform the town's arboretum into an enchanting wonderland of lakeside lights, laser shows and floodlit gardens.

The region is also famous as the cradle of the Industrial Revolution, so make a pilgrimage to Ironbridge Gorge World Heritage Site and catch ten fantastic museums in one truly spectacular setting.

The Heart of England's appeal lies in both its timelessness and modernity. The cultural diversity and vibrancy of Birmingham reflects a very different England to the one of Shakespeare's Stratford-upon-Avon, the sleepy villages of Warwickshire and Herefordshire and beauty of the Cotswolds.

Destinations

Birmingham

Birmingham is a dynamic city combining a fascinating history with a world-class cultural scene. Lose yourself in shopping heaven in the stunningly remodelled Bullring, wander through the historic Jewellery Quarter then sit back and enjoy the Symphony Orchestra in the magnificent Symphony Hall. Indulge your sweet tooth at Cadbury World, or take in a major event at the NEC or NIA. You'll also find yourself at the heart of a region full of history and heritage, beautiful quaint villages and access to lush rolling countryside – Birmingham really is a gateway to the heart of England!

Coventry

Discover the city that is re-inventing itself. Coventry, the setting for myth and legend, famous for Lady Godiva and St George the dragon-slayer, is now an ideal visitor destination building on its rich heritage with up-to-the-minute shopping, bars and restaurants. Browse one of the oldest indoor markets in Europe, gaze at the beauty of St Mary's Guildhall, visit the late 20th century cathedral standing amid the ruins of its predecessor, and don't miss the Transport Museum for the largest collection of British road transport in the world.

Hereford

Visit this ancient city on the banks of the River Wye. You'll find historic buildings housing modern shops and modern buildings holding historic treasures. Don't miss Hereford Cathedral with its priceless Mappa Mundi and Chained Library. Wander through the spacious High Town and intriguing side streets. The ancient and modern grace the banks of the beautiful River Wye – including the new Left Bank Village, while the Cider Museum tells a fascinating story and bolsters Hereford's claim to be 'The Apple of England's Eye'.

Hereford Cider Museum

Bullring Shopping Centre, Birmingham

Coventry Cathedral

Wedgewood Visitor Centre, Stoke-on-Trent

Bancroft Gardens, Stratford-upon-Avon

River Severn, Shrewsbury

Ludlow

Ludlow

Discover the place Betjemen described as 'the loveliest town in England.' With over 500 listed buildings, Ludlow is a feast for the eyes. Britain's first 'slow' town is also a gastronomic capital and host to the renowned Ludlow Marches Food & Drink Festival. You'll find a host of speciality food shops, and more restaurants and inns than you can shake a cocktail stick at. To walk off lunch, stroll in the enchanting Angel Gardens, or take in a performance at the open-air theatre in the stunning medieval ruin of Ludlow Castle.

Shrewsbury

This charming county town boasts over 660 listed buildings. Wander the Shuts and Passages – a medieval maze of narrow alleys criss-crossing the town, and admire the Norman abbey, medieval castle, and Shrewsbury Museum and Art Gallery housed in Rowley's House. Interesting, independent shops are plentiful, with food a speciality. Track the evolution of Charles Darwin, Shrewsbury's famous son, and, for a summer treat, breathe the scent of more than three million blooms at the internationally famous Shrewsbury Flower Show in August.

Stoke-on-Trent

Visit the UK's capital of china, 'The Potteries'. Award-winning museums tell the full story and the opportunity to throw your own pot. Take in a show at the magnificent Regent Theatre and Victoria Hall with their star-studded programmes of West End shows. Given its close proximity to Alton Towers and its excellent shopping and leisure facilities, Stoke-on-Trent is sure to fire your imagination.

Stratford-upon-Avon

Unearth a magical blend of heritage and drama in and around Shakespeare's home town. Explore five houses with Shakespeare connections including Anne Hathaway's Cottage and Shakespeare's Birthplace. Visit one of England's most beautiful parish churches at Holy Trinity to see Shakespeare's grave and enjoy some of his great works performed by the world's largest classical theatre company, the RSC. Take a boat out on the River Avon, wander the boutiques, specialist stores and gift shops, and discover some of Britain's finest historic houses and gardens.

Places to visit

**Birmingham Museum
& Art Gallery**
(0121) 303 2834
bmag.org.uk
*Fine and applied art, archaeology
and local history collections*

**Black Country
Living Museum**
Dudley, West Midlands
(0121) 557 9643
bclm.co.uk
*Twenty-six acres of fascinating
living history*

**Brockhampton Estate
National Trust**
near Bromyard, Herefordshire
(01885) 482077
nationaltrust.org.uk
*14th-century moated manor
house*
 (grounds only)

Cadbury World
Bournville, West Midlands
0845 450 3599
cadburyworld.co.uk
*Chocolate-making
demonstrations and samples*

**Cider Museum and
King Offa Distillery**
Hereford
(01432) 354207
cidermuseum.co.uk
*Be sure to sample a free tasting of
distillery products*

The Commandery
Worcester
(01905) 361821
worcestercity-
museums.org.uk
*Exciting stories of power, greed,
war, wealth and romance*

**The Complete
Working Historic Estate
of Shugborough
(The National Trust)**
Milford, Staffordshire
(01889) 881388
shugborough.org.uk
*Explore 900 acres of historic
parkland with working Georgian
buildings*
 (grounds only)

Compton Verney House
Stratford-upon-Avon,
Warwickshire
(01926) 645500
comptonverney.org.uk
Art collection in a listed building

Coventry Cathedral
West Midlands
(024) 7652 1200
coventrycathedral.org.uk
*Unique 20th-century architecture
to both inspire and enthral*

Coventry Transport Museum
West Midlands
(024) 7623 4270
transport-museum.com
*Fascinating collection of vehicles
spanning all the ages*

Drayton Manor Theme Park
near Tamworth, Staffordshire
0870 872 5252
draytonmanor.co.uk
*Great rides and attractions set in
280 acres of parkland*

Hampton Court Gardens
Leominster, Herefordshire
(01568) 797777
hamptoncourt.org.uk
Stunning organic gardens

**Ironbridge Gorge
Museums**
Ironbridge, Shropshire
(01952) 432405
ironbridge.org.uk
*Revolutionary inventions in
inspiring museums*

Kenilworth Castle
Warwickshire
(01926) 852078
english-heritage.org.uk
*A vast complex of ruined
fortifications and palatial apartments*

National Motorcycle Museum
Solihull, West Midlands
(01675) 443311
nationalmotorcyclemuseum.co.uk
Largest of its kind in the world

National Sea Life Centre
Birmingham, West Midlands
(0121) 643 6777
sealifeeurope.com
*Features tubular underwater walk-
though tunnel*

Royal Air Force Museum
Cosford, Shropshire
(01902) 376200
rafmuseum.org
*One of the largest aviation
collections in the UK*
(grounds only)

Royal Worcester Visitor Centre
(01905) 746000
royalworcester.co.uk
See craftmanship at work

 Pets Welcome
Assistance dogs only

Diary dates 2008

Severn Valley Railway
Bewdley, Worcestershire
(01299) 403816
svr.co.uk
*Steam trains running along the
beautiful Severn Valley*
🐕 🐾

Shakespeare's Birthplace
Stratford-upon-Avon,
Warwickshire
(01789) 204016
shakespeare.org.uk
The bard's inspiring dwelling place
🐾

Shakespearience
Stratford-upon-Avon,
Warwickshire
(01789) 290111
shakespearience.co.uk
Shakespeare's lifestory
🐾

Thinktank – Birmingham
Science Museum
 (0121) 202 2222
thinktank.ac
Hands on interactive fun
🐾

Trentham Leisure Ltd
Stoke-on-Trent,
Staffordshire
(01782) 657341
trenthamleisure.co.uk
Garden restoration project
🐕 🐾

The Wedgwood
Visitor Centre
Stoke-on-Trent,
Staffordshire
0870 606 1759
thewedgwoodvisitorcentre.com
*Displays, factory tours and
sweeping parkland*
🐾

The National Boat, Caravan & Outdoor Show
NEC, Birmingham
boatandcaravan.co.uk
19 – 24 Feb

Crufts
NEC, Birmingham
thekennelclub.org.uk
6 – 9 Mar

The Ordnance Survey Outdoors Show
NEC, Birmingham
theoutdoorsshow.co.uk
14 – 16 Mar

The Cosford Air Show
cosfordairshow.co.uk
1 Jun

Three Counties Countryside Show
The Malvern Showground, Worcestershire
threecounties.co.uk
13 – 15 Jun

Godiva Festival
Memorial Park, Coventry
godivafestival.co.uk
11 – 13 Jul*

The Big Chill
Eastnor Castle, Ledbury
bigchill.net
1 – 3 Aug

Ludlow Marches Food and Drink Festival
foodfestival.co.uk
12 – 14 Sep

Worcester Christmas Fayre
worcestershire.gov.uk
27 – 30 Nov

Frankfurt Christmas Market
Victoria Square/New Street, Birmingham
birmingham.gov.uk
13 Nov – 23 Dec*

* provisional date at time of going to press

Tourist Information Centres

When you arrive at your destination, visit an Official Partner Tourist Information Centre for quality assured help with accommodation and information about local attractions and events, or email your request before you go.

Bewdley	Load Street	(01299) 404740	bewdleytic@wyreforestdc.gov.uk
Birmingham Rotunda	150 New Street	0870 225 0127	callcentre@marketingbirmingham.com
Bridgnorth	Listley Street	(01746) 763257	bridgnorth.tourism@shropshire-cc.gov.uk
Burton upon Trent	Coors Visitor Centre	(01283) 508111	tic@eaststaffsbc.gov.uk
Coventry Airport	Coventry Airport South	(024) 7622 7264	tic@cvone.co.uk
Coventry Cathedral	Cathedral Ruins	(024) 7622 7264	tic@cvone.co.uk
Coventry Ricoh Arena	Phoenix Way	0870 111 6397	tic@cvone.co.uk
Coventry Transport Museum	Hales Street	(024) 7622 7264	tic@cvone.co.uk
Hereford	1 King Street	(01432) 268430	tic-hereford@herefordshire.gov.uk
Ironbridge	Ironbridge Gorge Museum Trust	(01952) 884391	tic@ironbridge.org.uk
Leamington Spa	The Parade	0870 160 7930	info@shakespeare-country.co.uk
Leek	1 Market Place	(01538) 483741	tourism.services@staffsmoorlands.gov.uk
Lichfield	Lichfield Garrick	(01543) 412112	info@visitlichfield.com
Ludlow	Castle Street	(01584) 875053	ludlow.tourism@shropshire-cc.gov.uk
Malvern	21 Church Street	(01684) 892289	malvern.tic@malvernhills.gov.uk
Oswestry	Mile End	(01691) 662488	tic@oswestry-bc.gov.uk
Ross-on-Wye	Edde Cross Street	(01989) 562768	tic-ross@herefordshire.gov.uk
Rugby	Little Elborow Street	(01788) 534970	visitor.centre@rugby.gov.uk
Shrewsbury	The Square	(01743) 281200	visitorinfo@shrewsbury.gov.uk
Stafford	Market Street	(01785) 619619	tic@staffordbc.gov.uk
Stoke-on-Trent	Victoria Hall	(01782) 236000	stoke.tic@stoke.gov.uk
Stratford-upon-Avon	Bridgefoot	0870 160 7930	info@shakespeare-country.co.uk
Tamworth	29 Market Street	(01827) 709581	tic@tamworth.gov.uk
Warwick	Jury Street	(01926) 492212	touristinfo@warwick-uk.co.uk
Worcester	High Street	(01905) 726311	touristinfo@cityofworcester.gov.uk

Travel info

By road:
Britain's main motorways (M1/M6/M5) meet in the Heart of England; the M40 links with the M42 south of Birmingham while the M4 provides fast access from London to the south of the region. These road links ensure that the Heart of England is more accessible by road than any other region in the UK.

By rail:
The Heart of England is served by an excellent rail network. InterCity rail services are fast and frequent from London and other major cities into the region. Trains run from Euston to Birmingham, Coventry and Rugby; from Paddington to the Cotswolds, Stratford-upon-Avon and Worcester; and from Marylebone to Birmingham and Stourbridge. From the main stations a network of regional routes take you around the Heart of England.

By air:
Fly into Birmingham, Coventry or Nottingham East Midlands.

Brindleyplace, Birmingham

Find out more

Further information is available from the following organisations:

Marketing Birmingham
(0121) 202 5115
visitbirmingham.com

Black Country Tourism
blackcountrytourism.co.uk

Visit Coventry & Warwickshire
(024) 7622 7264
visitcoventryandwarwickshire.co.uk

Visit Herefordshire
(01432) 260621
visitherefordshire.co.uk

Shakespeare Country
0870 160 7930
shakespeare-country.co.uk

Shropshire Tourism
(01743) 462462
shropshiretourism.info

Destination Staffordshire
0870 500 4444
enjoystaffordshire.com

Stoke-on-Trent
(01782) 236000
visitstoke.co.uk

Destination Worcestershire
(01905) 728787
visitworcestershire.org

Help before you go

To search for attractions and Tourist Information Centres on the move just text INFO to 62233, and a web link will be sent to your mobile phone.

where to stay in
Heart of England

All place names in the blue bands are shown on the maps at the front of this guide.

Accommodation symbols
Symbols give useful information about services and facilities. Inside the back-cover flap you can find a key to these symbols. Keep it open for easy reference.

BISHOP'S CASTLE, Shropshire Map ref 4A3 | **SELF CATERING**

★★★★
SELF CATERING

Units **1**
Sleeps **4**
Low season per wk
£200.00–£275.00
High season per wk
£275.00–£350.00

Mount Cottage, Bishop's Castle

contact Mrs Heather Willis, Mount Cottage, Bull Lane, Bishop's Castle SY9 5DA
t (01588) 638288 f (01588) 638288 e heather@mountcottage.co.uk w mountcottage.co.uk

Converted 17thC barn. Very short walk to town. Well-equipped, modern fitted kitchen. Bathroom/wc with over-bath shower and second wc. Beams throughout.

open All year
payment Cash/cheques

Pets 🐾 ⚡🐾 Unit 🛏 📺 🎛 💻 🗄 🔌 🔲 🌀 🕯❄
General 🛋 🎱 🏋 P ✂ ⑤ Leisure ∪ 🚲 ⛰ Shop < 0.5 miles Pub < 0.5 miles

---

BRIDGNORTH, Shropshire Map ref 4A3 | **SELF CATERING**

★★★
SELF CATERING

Units **1**
Sleeps **1–2**
Low season per wk
Min £140.00
High season per wk
Min £180.00

The Granary, Bridgnorth

contact Mrs Sarah Allen, The Granary, The Old Vicarage, Vicarage Road, Dittons Priors, Bridgnorth WV16 6SP
t (01746) 712272 f (01746) 712288 e allens@oldvicditton.freeserve.co.uk

Farm granary in unspoilt South Shropshire countryside. Bridgnorth within easy reach, Ludlow 16 miles. Studio sitting room, bedroom, kitchen, bathroom. Excellent walking.

open All year
payment Cash/cheques

Pets 🐾 🐾 Unit 🛏 📺 💻 🔌 🔲 ❄
General 🛋 P Leisure ⚲ ⛰ Shop 0.5 miles Pub 0.5 miles

CASTLEMORTON, Worcestershire Map ref 2B1 | **SELF CATERING**

★★★★
SELF CATERING

Units **1**
Sleeps **1–5**
Low season per wk
£227.00–£333.00
High season per wk
£427.00–£502.00

Notts Farm Cottage, Nr Malvern

contact Ms Sarah Limbrick, Druggers End, Castlemorton, Nr Malvern WR13 6JD
t (01684) 833380 f (01684) 833150 e sarah.limbrick@highcourt.demon.co.uk
w malvernholidaycottage.co.uk

Charming detached cottage created from barn conversion in peaceful countryside. Two bedrooms, four-poster bed, two bathrooms, comfortable, spacious and welcoming. Well behaved dogs welcome. Stabling available for horses.

open All year
payment Cash/cheques

Pets 🐾 Unit 🛏 📺 🎛 🗄 💻 🔌 🔲 🌀 🕯❄
General 🛋 🎱 🏋 P ✂ Leisure ∪ ⛰ Shop 1 mile Pub 1 mile

ELLESMERE, Shropshire Map ref 4A2 — SELF CATERING

★★★★
SELF CATERING

Units **1**
Sleeps **2**
Low season per wk
£191.00–£211.00
High season per wk
£263.00–£304.00

The Byre, Ellesmere, Welsh Frankton

contact Mr Frank Lauriello, 4 Onnen Gardens, Trefonen, Oswestry SY10 9FA
t (01691) 662280 **e** frank@myddle.net **w** byre-holiday-cottage.co.uk

The Byre is a one-bedroom self-catering 19thC barn conversion situated in Welsh Frankton, near Ellesmere, Shropshire. A perfect base for an active holiday or romantic break.

open All year
payment Cash/cheques

Pets 🐕 🐾 Unit 📺 📷 📠 🔌 📻 📶 💿 ✳
General **P** **S** Leisure 🏊 Shop 3 miles Pub 1 mile

IRONBRIDGE, Shropshire Map ref 4A3 — SELF CATERING

★★★
SELF CATERING

Units **1**
Sleeps **1–3**
Low season per wk
£185.00–£195.00
High season per wk
£375.00–£430.00

Victoria Cottage, Ironbridge

contact Mr Colin Thompson, 4 Village Court, Priorslee, Telford TF2 9QH
t 07970 417497 **e** cthompson@bcs.org.uk **w** ironbridgegorge.co.uk

Two-bedroom Victorian cottage in Ironbridge. Restored and comfortably furnished with modern amenities. Within easy walking distance of the world's first Iron Bridge and close to all museums.

open All year
payment Credit/debit cards, cash/cheques

Pets 🐕 £🐕 🐾 Unit 🛏 📺 📷 📠 📷 🔌 📻 📶 💿 ✳
General 🍳 📶 **S** Shop 0.5 miles Pub < 0.5 miles

KENLEY, Shropshire Map ref 4A3 — SELF CATERING

★★★★
SELF CATERING

Units **2**
Sleeps **2–4**
Low season per wk
£180.00–£220.00
High season per wk
£280.00–£350.00

Courtyard Cottages, Shrewsbury

contact Mrs Annabel Gill, No 1 & 2 Courtyard Cottages, Lower Springs Farm, Kenley, Shrewsbury SY5 6PA
t (01952) 510841 **f** (01952) 510841 **e** afgill@hotmail.co.uk **w** stmem.com/courtyardcottages

Immaculate, recently converted cottages with exposed oak beams. Large garden and stocked trout pools in lovely, peaceful valley with panoramic views of Wenlock Edge.

open All year
payment Cash/cheques

Pets 🐕 £🐕 🐾 Unit 🛏 📺 📷 📠 📷 📻 📶 💿 ✳
General 🍳 📶 � **P** ✂ **S** Leisure ∪ 🚲 🏊 Shop 3 miles Pub 3 miles

LEAMINGTON SPA, Warwickshire Map ref 4B3 — HOTEL

★★★
HOTEL

B&B per room per night
s £65.00–£75.00
d £80.00–£95.00

Eaton Court Hotel

1-7 St Marks Road, Leamington Spa CV32 6DL **t** (01926) 885848 **f** (01926) 882798
e info@eatoncourt.co.uk **w** eatoncourt.co.uk

Friendly, privately owned and run hotel near town and Warwick Castle. Spacious en suite rooms with comfortable facilities, function rooms, licensed restaurant and secluded garden. Excellent central location.

open All year except Christmas and New Year
bedrooms 12 double, 12 twin, 8 single, 4 family
bathrooms All en suite
payment Credit/debit cards, cash/cheques

Pets 🐕 🐾 🐾 Room 🛏 📞 📺 🔌 📻 🎵 General 🍳 📶 � **P** 🍽 📺 ☀ ✳ Leisure 🎣

Place index

If you know where you want to stay, the index at the back of the guide will give you the page number listing accommodation in your chosen town, city or village. Check out the other useful indexes too.

★★★–★★★★★
SELF CATERING

Units   **5**
Sleeps   **2–5**
Low season per wk
£195.00–£380.00
High season per wk
£250.00–£499.00

White House Cottages, Ledbury

contact Mrs Marianne Hills, The White House, Aylton, Ledbury HR8 2RQ
t (01531) 670349   **e** bookings@whitehousecottages.co.uk   **w** whitehousecottages.co.uk

open All year
payment Cash/cheques

Well-equipped, self-catering cottages situated in a small hamlet four miles west of Ledbury. Surrounded by Herefordshire's idyllic countryside, these former farm buildings have been carefully adapted to create very comfortable and individual holiday accommodation. Perfect for exploring the Wye Valley, the Malverns and surrounding area. Resident owners.

⊕ *From Ledbury take A438 to Hereford. At the Trumpet crossroads turn left onto A4172. After 1 mile turn right to Aylton, White House approx 0.25 miles on left.*

♥ *3-night short breaks available all year, subject to certain booking restrictions. Please ring for details.*

Pets ⌁ ⌁   Unit [TV] ▣ ◫ ◳ ▢ ◫ ✿
General ⌁ ⩩ ⌁ P ✂ ◎ Ⓢ   Leisure ∪   Shop 4 miles   Pub 2 miles

★★★
GUEST ACCOMMODATION

B&B per room per night
s £45.00–£65.00
d £65.00

The Bull

14 The Bull Ring, Ludlow SY8 1AD   **t** (01584) 873611   **f** (01584) 873666   **e** info@bull-ludlow.co.uk
w bull-ludlow.co.uk

open All year
bedrooms 2 double, 1 twin, 1 family
bathrooms All en suite
payment Credit/debit cards, cash/cheques

Situated in the town centre. The oldest pub in Ludlow, (earliest mention c1343). It was known as Peter of Proctor's house and probably dates back to c1199.

Pets ⌁ ⌁   Room [TV] ◖   General ⌁ ⩩ P ⌁   Leisure ∪ ⛅ ⌂

★★★★
GUEST HOUSE

B&B per room per night
s £35.00–£45.00
d £60.00–£75.00

Cannara Guest House

147 Barnards Green Road, Malvern WR14 3LT   **t** (01684) 564418   **f** (01684) 564418
e info@cannara.co.uk   **w** cannara.co.uk

Feel at home at Cannara, where style, ambience, attention to detail and guest comfort is of paramount importance to us.

open All year
bedrooms 2 double, 2 twin, 1 family
bathrooms All en suite
payment Credit/debit cards, cash/cheques

Pets ⌁ ⌁ ⩩ ⌁   Room ◖ [TV] ◖ ◳   General ⌁ P ⌁ ⩩ ◫ ◉ ✿   Leisure ⌂

★★★
BED & BREAKFAST

B&B per room per night
s £30.00–£40.00
d £58.00–£65.00

Harmony House Malvern

184 West Malvern Road, Malvern WR14 4AZ   **t** (01684) 891650   **e** catherine@harmonymalvern.com
w harmonyhousemalvern.com

A warm and spacious home set on the western slopes of the Malvern Hills. Close to footpaths and bus route. Wonderful views. Double/twin bed option. Organic/local food.

open All year
bedrooms 2 double, 1 family
bathrooms All en suite
payment Cash/cheques

Pets ⌁ ⩩ ⌁   Room ◖ ◳   General ⩩ ◫ ◉

PEMBRIDGE, Herefordshire Map ref 2A1 **SELF CATERING**

★★★
SELF CATERING

Units **2**
Sleeps **1–4**

Low season per wk
£185.00–£280.00
High season per wk
£280.00–£325.00

The Granary and The Dairy, Leominster

contact Mrs Nancy Owens, The Granary and The Dairy, The Grove, Noke Lane, Pembridge, Leominster HR6 9HP
t (01544) 388268 **f** (01544) 388154 **e** nancy@grovedesign.co.uk

open All year
payment Cash/cheques

Set in spectacular, peaceful Herefordshire countryside. Ideal for walks on Offa's Dyke, Mortimer Trail or around the farm itself. Many interesting places to visit, eg Mappa Mundi, Hereford and National Trust properties. Local horse-riding, fishing, go-karting. Warm welcome with tea tray and home bakes.

Pets 🐕 £🐾 Unit 🛏 TV ▣ 📶 🗑 🍳 ⚙
General 🔥 ♨ ♿ P S Leisure ∪ 🚵 Shop 3 miles Pub 3 miles

RUDYARD, Staffordshire Map ref 4B2 **SELF CATERING**

★★★★
SELF CATERING

Units **1**
Sleeps **5**

Low season per wk
£525.00–£595.00
High season per wk
£630.00–£665.00

The Bothy, Rudyard, Leek

contact Mr Andrew Mount and Miss Michelle Ash
t 07771 702949 & 07957 856629 **e** info@thebothy-rudyard.co.uk **w** thebothy-rudyard.co.uk

open All year
payment Cash/cheques

The Bothy is a secluded retreat nestling on the banks of Rudyard Lake. The perfect escape for couples and families alike. Tastefully furnished and fully equipped, no detail has been overlooked. Relax on the stunning waterfront terrace with hot tub. Complete with private pontoon and boating and fishing rights.

⊕ *Take A523 for two miles north of Leek. Turn onto B5331 to Rudyard village. At mini-roundabout turn right following signs for yacht club.*

Pets 🐕 Unit 🛏 TV ▣ 🗑 📶 🍳 ⚙
General 🔥 ♨ ♿ P S Leisure ∪ 🚵 Shop 10 miles Pub 3 miles

RUGBY, Warwickshire Map ref 4C3 **GUEST ACCOMMODATION**

★★★★
FARMHOUSE
SILVER AWARD

B&B per room per night
s £35.00–£40.00
d £55.00–£60.00

Lawford Hill Farm

Lawford Heath Lane, Lawford Heath, Rugby CV23 9HG **t** (01788) 542001 **f** (01788) 537880
e lawford.hill@talk21.com **w** lawfordhill.co.uk

Bed and breakfast all the year round in our spacious Georgian farmhouse and converted stables. Close to Warwick, Stratford, NEC, NAC and Ryton Gardens.

open All year except Christmas and New Year
bedrooms 2 double, 2 twin, 1 single, 1 family
bathrooms All en suite
payment Credit/debit cards, cash/cheques

Pets 🐕 £🐾 🐴 🐾 Room 🛏 TV 🐕 🍳 General 🔥 ♨ ♿ P ✂ 🖥 🍴 📷 ⚙ Leisure 🏰

RUGBY, Warwickshire Map ref 4C3 **SELF CATERING**

★★★★
SELF CATERING

Units **3**
Sleeps **4–8**

Low season per wk
£400.00–£450.00
High season per wk
£450.00–£600.00

Lawford Hill Farm, Rugby

contact Mr & Mrs Susan Moses, Lawford Hill Farm, Lawford Heath Lane, Rugby CV23 9HG
t (01788) 542001 **f** (01788) 537880 **e** lawford.hill@talk21.com **w** lawfordhill.co.uk

Attractive converted barns set within a farmyard. Fully equipped to ensure you are cosy and comfortable. Short breaks by arrangement. Located three miles from Rugby on Lawford Heath Lane.

open All year
payment Credit/debit cards, cash/cheques

Pets 🐕 £🐾 🐾 Unit 🛏 TV ▣ 🗑 📶 🍳 ⚙
General 🔥 ♨ ♿ P ✂ 📷 Shop 1.5 miles Pub 1 mile

STAFFORD, Staffordshire Map ref 4B3 — GUEST ACCOMMODATION

★★
GUEST HOUSE

B&B per room per night
s £29.00–£36.00
d £52.00–£60.00
Evening meal per person
£6.00–£14.00

Wyndale Guest House

199 Corporation Street, Stafford ST16 3LQ t (01785) 223069

The Wyndale is a comfortable Victorian house conveniently situated 0.25 miles from the town centre and en route to the county showground, hospital, university and technology park.

open All year except Christmas
bedrooms 2 double, 2 twin, 2 single, 2 family
bathrooms 5 en suite
payment Credit/debit cards, cash/cheques

Pets ⛩ 🐾 Room 🛏 📺 🍵 🍷 General ♿ ▥ ♨ P ✗ 🎱 🕯 ☼

STOKE-ON-TRENT, Staffordshire Map ref 4B2 — GUEST ACCOMMODATION

★★
GUEST HOUSE

B&B per room per night
s Min £24.00
d £40.00–£44.00

Verdon Guest House

44 Charles Street, Stoke-on-Trent ST1 3JY t (01782) 264244 f (01782) 264244
w verdonguesthouse.co.uk

Large, friendly guesthouse in town centre, close to bus station. Convenient for the Potteries and museums. Alton Towers 20 minutes, M6 ten minutes. All rooms with Sky TV. Excellent value.

open All year
bedrooms 4 double, 3 twin, 1 single, 5 family
bathrooms 5 en suite
payment Credit/debit cards, cash/cheques

Pets ⛩ 🐾 🐕 Room 🛏 📺 🍵 General ♿ P

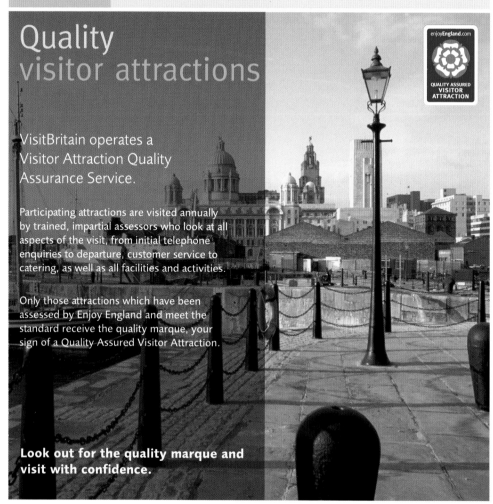

Quality
visitor attractions

VisitBritain operates a Visitor Attraction Quality Assurance Service.

Participating attractions are visited annually by trained, impartial assessors who look at all aspects of the visit, from initial telephone enquiries to departure, customer service to catering, as well as all facilities and activities.

Only those attractions which have been assessed by Enjoy England and meet the standard receive the quality marque, your sign of a Quality Assured Visitor Attraction.

enjoyEngland.com

QUALITY ASSURED
VISITOR
ATTRACTION

Look out for the quality marque and visit with confidence.

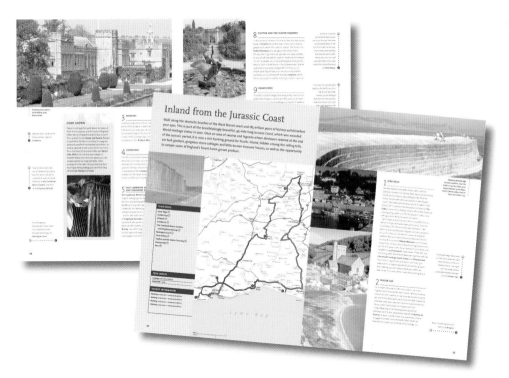

Take a tour of England

VisitBritain presents a series of **three** inspirational touring guides to the regions of England: South and South West, Northern England and Central England.

Each guide takes you on a fascinating journey through stunning countryside and coastlines, picturesque villages and lively market towns, historic houses and gardens.

- Easy-to-use maps
- Clear directions to follow the route
- Lively descriptions of all the places for you to discover
- Stunning photographs bring each area to life

Touring Central England – £14.99
Touring Northern England – £14.99
Touring South and South West England – £14.99
plus postage and handling

East Midlands

Leicestershire & Rutland, Lincolnshire,
Northamptonshire, Nottinghamshire,
Peak District & Derbyshire

Fresh air, fabulous countryside and festivals galore

If you love getting out into the open air, you'll adore the East Midlands. Whether you're the sporty type or just a fresh air addict, the East Midlands has lots in store for the whole family.

East Midlands Tourism
discovereastmidlands.com

National Space Centre, Leicester

Sherwood Forest Country Park

Chatsworth House, Derbyshire

Walkers be warned: you'll never want to leave. The idyllic River Dove is surrounded by the remains of ancient coral reefs which form Dovedale, and it's reckoned to be the ultimate ramble. Then there's the Pennine Way with its towering mountain plateau of Kinder Scout, not to mention the wild High Peak Trail. Cycling's big in these parts too. Take on the 'Black Death Challenge' and spin into seven medieval plague villages; or tackle the terrifying slalom descent at Sherwood Pines. Feeling adventurous? Try your hand at dragon boat racing at Carsington Water, or water-skiing at the National Watersports Centre. And then there are golf courses galore, the British Grand Prix at Silverstone, the famous Burghley Horse Trials...not forgetting the World Conker Championship in Ashton.

The East Midlands is home to many arts festivals, so be sure to keep an eye out for the Stamford Shakespeare Festival at Tolethorpe Hall and Buxton's Gilbert and Sullivan Festival. With heritage in mind, there are a whole host of dramatic castles such as Bosworth and Peveril to explore. And if you want to be swept off your feet, you won't want to miss the National Space Centre where you can test your ability to survive a perilous voyage into deep space by taking the interactive Human Spaceflight.

Discover Creswell Crags, a limestone gorge honeycombed with caves that were home to Ice Age man. Or lose yourself in the maze at Chatsworth House. And don't miss Snibston Discovery Park in the heart the National Forest, an award-winning family attraction exploring the impact of technology on our everyday lives.

Prefer to live it up? Make for historic Lincoln, Nottingham, Derby or Leicester where fine Asian cuisine is spicily sumptuous. Seek out traditional local fare too – delicious cheeses, gingerbread and the famous Melton Mowbray pork pies.

Destinations

Derby

This multi-cultural city bursts with entertainment venues, attractions, shopping experiences and open green spaces. The compact city centre makes exploring easy. Visit the indoor market housed in the wonderful Victorian Market Hall and take advantage of free attractions including the Museum and Art Gallery where you'll find work by famous local artist, Joseph Wright. Don't miss the cathedral, which has the second highest church tower in England, Royal Crown Derby and Pride Park football stadium.

Leicester

A cosmopolitan and cultured city, Leicester offers unusual shops, fine restaurants, a vibrant nightlife and a strong cultural diversity. Discover designer labels in the Leicester Lanes, and exquisitely embroidered silks along the Golden Mile. Travel to infinity and beyond at the National Space Centre and experience live music at De Montfort Hall. Witness top class action from Leicester's sporting teams and savour a glass of champagne at one of the city's stylish café bars.

Lincoln

Possessing magnificent architectural heritage, Lincoln is a blend of history, cultural variety, shopping and lively entertainment. Approach the city from any direction and you are drawn to the magnificent outline of the cathedral, one of the finest Gothic buildings in Europe. From the cobbled streets and antiques to the modern art scattered throughout the city, the past and present is all around. Events throughout the year make Lincoln irresistible – the famous Christmas Market, the Brayford Waterfront Festival, and the weekend that most attractions open for free – Lincoln weekend.

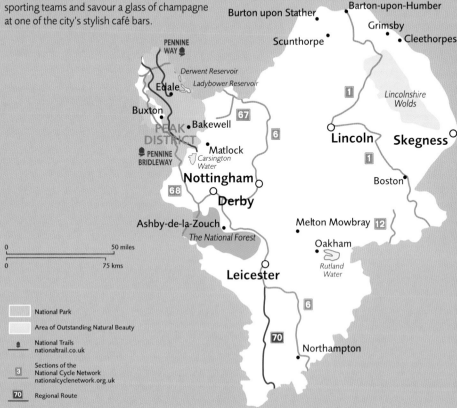

National Park

Area of Outstanding Natural Beauty

National Trails
nationaltrail.co.uk

Sections of the
National Cycle Network
nationalcyclenetwork.org.uk

Regional Route

Lincoln Castle

Gibralter Point, near Skegness

The National Forest, near Derby

Peak District

Rutland Water

Leicester

Nottingham

Nottingham

Nottingham is the undisputed capital of the East Midlands, boasting a sophisticated urban environment with an enviable reputation for clubs, theatres, cinemas and galleries, not to mention a deserved reputation as one of the top retail centres in the country. History is never far away, though, with reminders of Nottingham's legendary hero Robin Hood and his adversary the Sheriff of Nottingham. Explore the Castle Museum and Art Gallery, and Wollaton Hall, one of the most ornate Tudor buildings in Britain, complete with 500-acre deer park.

Peak District

The Peak District is Britain's first and most popular National Park. Roam on open moorland to the north and take in the magnificent views over the Derwent Dams. Further south, stroll alongside sparkling rivers in wildlife-rich valleys far from the hustle and bustle of town. The Peak Park Rangers lead regular guided walks – choose from long hikes to village tours. Take in the grandeur of Chatsworth House or Haddon Hall, and sample the local oatcakes with Hartington Stilton, followed by a delicious Bakewell pudding.

Rutland

Tiny Rutland, less than 20 miles across, may be the smallest county in England, but it's packed with hidden treasures. Explore the castle in the historic county town of Oakham, browse the antiquarian bookshops of Uppingham and choose from more than 50 picturesque villages of thatched stone-built cottages. Rutland Water is a must – a giant reservoir where you can fish, walk, cycle and sail. Enjoy Shakespeare at Rutland Open Air Theatre or ride the locomotives at the Rutland Railway Museum. Discover the natural beauty of Rutland – England's best-kept secret!

Skegness

Take time to explore some of the UK's finest seaside resorts. The Lincolnshire coastline, stretching from Skegness to Mablethorpe offers you sun, fun, excitement and laughter, but also tranquillity, clean beaches, and glorious fresh air. Skegness, Lincolnshire's premier resort, features an award-winning six-mile-long beach. Enjoy the seafront illuminations from mid-summer, indulge in family fun at the Pleasure Beach, and visit the seals at the Natureland Sanctuary.

Places to visit

78 Derngate
Northampton
(01604) 603407
78derngate.org.uk
Terraced house transformed by
Charles Rennie Mackintosh

Alford Manor House
Alford, Lincolnshire
(01507) 463073
alfordmanorhouse.co.uk
Large thatched manor house

Althorp
Northampton
(01604) 770107
althorp.com
Spencer family home since 1508

Belton House,
Park and Gardens
Grantham, Lincolnshire
(01476) 566116
nationaltrust.org.uk
Restoration-period country house

Bolsover Castle
Bolsover, Derbyshire
(01246) 822844
english-heritage.org.uk
17th-century house on the site of
a Norman fortress

Burghley House
Stamford, Lincolnshire
(01780) 752451
burghley.co.uk
The largest and grandest
Elizabethan house
(grounds only)

Chatsworth House, Garden,
Farmyard & Adventure
Playground
Bakewell, Derbyshire
(01246) 582204
chatsworth.org
Beautiful house, garden and
fountains
(grounds only)

Clumber Park
Worksop, Nottinghamshire
(01909) 476592
nationaltrust.org.uk
Year-round colour and interest
(grounds only)

Creswell Crags Museum and
Education Centre, Picnic site,
Caves & Gorge
Worksop, Derbyshire
(01909) 720378
creswell-crags.org.uk
Limestone gorge, caves and lake
(gorge only)

Gainsborough
Old Hall
Gainsborough,
Lincolnshire
(01427) 612669
lincolnshire.gov.uk
Medieval manor house

Go Ape! High Wire
Forest Adventure
near Edwinstowe,
Nottinghamshire
0870 444 5562
goape.co.uk
Rope bridges, swings and zip slides
(walkways only)

Grimsthorpe Castle,
Park and Gardens
near Bourne, Lincolnshire
(01778) 591205
grimsthorpe.co.uk
Castle covering four periods of
architecture
(parkland only)

Haddon Hall
Bakewell, Derbyshire
(01629) 812855
haddonhall.co.uk
Medieval and Tudor manor house

Hardwick Hall
Chesterfield, Derbyshire
(01246) 850430
nationaltrust.org.uk
Elizabethan country house and
parkland
(grounds only)

Kirby Hall
Corby, Northamptonshire
(01536) 203230
english-heritage.org.uk
Elizabethan and 17th-century
house
(grounds only)

Lincoln Castle
(01522) 511068
lincolnshire.gov.uk/
lincolncastle
Historic former court and prison

Lincoln Cathedral
(01522) 561600
lincolncathedral.com
One of the finest gothic buildings
in Europe

National Space Centre
Leicester
0870 607 7223
spacecentre.co.uk
The UK's largest space attraction

Newstead Abbey
near Nottingham
(01623) 455900
newsteadabbey.org.uk
800-year-old remains of a priory church

Nottingham Castle Museum and Gallery
(0115) 915 3700
nottinghamcity.gov.uk/museums
17th-century mansion on medieval-castle site

Peveril Castle
Castleton, Derbyshire
(01433) 620613
english-heritage.org.uk
Ruined Norman castle

Rockingham Castle
Corby, Northamptonshire
(01536) 770240
rockinghamcastle.com
Rose gardens and exquisite art

Sherwood Forest Country Park
near Mansfield, Nottinghamshire
(01623) 823202
sherwood-forest.org.uk
Native woodland packed with adventure

Silverstone Circuit
Northamptonshire
0870 458 8260
silverstone-circuits.co.uk
The home of British motor racing

Tattershall Castle
Lincoln
(01526) 342543
nationaltrust.org.uk
Dramatic 15th-century red-brick tower

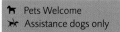
🐴 Pets Welcome
🐕 Assistance dogs only

Diary dates 2008

Peak District Walking Festival
Various locations, Peak District
visitpeakdistrict.com
Apr – May*

Lincolnshire Wolds Walking Festival
Various locations, Lincolnshire
visitlincolnshire.com
17 May – 1 Jun

Stamford Shakespeare Festival
Rutland Open Air Theatre, Stamford
stamfordshakespeare.co.uk
Jun – Aug*

Althorp Literary Festival
Althorp House, Northamptonshire
althorp.com/literaryfestival
14 – 15 Jun

Buxton Festival
Various locations, Buxton
buxtonfestival.co.uk
4 – 20 Jul*

Robin Hood Festival
Sherwood Forest Visitor Centre, Edwinstowe
sherwoodforest.org.uk
First week in Aug*

Festival of History
Kelmarsh Hall, Northamptonshire
kelmarsh.com
9 – 10 Aug

DH Lawrence Festival
Eastwood, Nottinghamshire
broxtowe.gov.uk/festival
Mid-Aug – mid-Sep*

East Midlands Food Festival
Melton Mowbray, Leicestershire
eastmidlandsfoodfestival.co.uk
4 – 5 Oct

Lincoln Christmas Market
lincoln.gov.uk
4 – 7 Dec

Tourist Information Centres

When you arrive at your destination, visit an Official Partner Tourist Information Centre for quality assured help with accommodation and information about local attractions and events, or email your request before you go. To search for attractions and Tourist Information Centres on the move just text INFO to 62233, and a web link will be sent to your mobile phone.

Ashbourne	13 Market Place	(01335) 343666	ashbourneinfo@derbyshiredales.gov.uk
Bakewell	Bridge Street	(01629) 816558	bakewell@peakdistrict-npa.gov.uk
Buxton	The Crescent	(01298) 25106	tourism@highpeak.gov.uk
Castleton	Buxton Road	(01433) 620679	castleton@peakdistrict-npa.gov.uk
Chesterfield	Rykneld Square	(01246) 345777	tourism@chesterfield.gov.uk
Derby	Market Place	(01332) 255802	tourism@derby.gov.uk
Leicester	7/9 Every Street	0906 294 1113**	info@goleicestershire.com
Lincoln Castle Hill	9 Castle Hill	(01522) 873213	tourism@lincoln.gov.uk
Matlock	Crown Square	(01629) 583388	matlockinfo@derbyshiredales.gov.uk
Matlock Bath	The Pavillion	(01629) 55082	matlockbathinfo@derbyshiredales.gov.uk
Ripley	Market Place	(01773) 841488	touristinformation@ambervalley.gov.uk
Sleaford	Carre Street	(01529) 414294	tic@n-kesteven.gov.uk
Swadlincote	West Street	(01283) 222848	tic@sharpespotterymuseum.org.uk

** *calls to this number are charged at premium rate*

Travel info

The central location of the East Midlands makes it easily accessible from all parts of the UK.

By road:
From the north and south, the M1 bisects the East Midlands with access to the region from junctions 14 through to 31. The A1 offers better access to the eastern part of the region, particularly Lincolnshire and Rutland. From the west, the M69, M/A42 and A50 provide easy access.

By rail:
The region is well served by InterCity services, offering direct routes from London, the north of England and Scotland to the East Midlands' major cities and towns. East/west links offer not only access to the region but also travel within it.

By air:
East Midlands Airport (Nottingham, Leicester, Derby) is located centrally in the region, with scheduled domestic flights from Aberdeen, Belfast, Edinburgh, Glasgow, Isle of Man and the Channel Islands. Manchester, Birmingham, Luton, Stansted and Humberside airports also offer domestic scheduled routes, with easy access to the region by road and rail.

Find out more

Whinstone Lee Tor, Peak District

Further publications are available from the following organisations:

East Midlands Tourism
w discovereastmidlands.com
• Discover East Midlands

Experience Nottinghamshire
t (0115) 915 5330
w visitnotts.com
• Nottinghamshire Essential Guide,
  Where to Stay Guide, Stay Somewhere Different,
  City Breaks, Attractions – A Family Day Out
• Robin Hood Breaks
• Pilgrim Fathers

Peak District and Derbyshire
t 0870 444 7275
w visitpeakdistrict.com
• Peak District Visitor Guide
• Savour the Flavour of the Peak District
• Derbyshire – the Peak District Visitor Guide
• Derbyshire – the Peak District Attractions Guide
• Camping and Caravanning Guide
• What's on Guide

Lincolnshire
t (01522) 873213
w visitlincolnshire.com
• Visit Lincolnshire – Destination Guide,
  Great days out, Gardens & Nurseries,
  Aviation Heritage, Good Taste
• Go with the flow

Explore Northamptonshire
t (01604) 838800
w explorenorthamptonshire.co.uk
• Explore Northamptonshire Visitor Guide,
  County Map, Food and Drink

Leicestershire and Rutland
t 0906 294 1113
w goleicestershire.com
• Rutland Visitor Guide
• Market Harborough & Lutterworth Guide
• Ashby de la Zouch and The National Forest Guide
• Melton Mowbray and the Vale of Belvoir
• Loughborough and Charnwood Forest
• GoLeicestershire
• Must See 3

Whinstone Lee Tor, Peak District

where to stay in
East Midlands

All place names in the blue bands are shown on the maps at the front of this guide.

Accommodation symbols
Symbols give useful information about services and facilities. Inside the back-cover flap you can find a key to these symbols. Keep it open for easy reference.

ALFORD, Lincolnshire Map ref 4D2 — **SELF CATERING**

★★★★
SELF CATERING

Units **4**
Sleeps **2–6**

Low season per wk
£130.00–£240.00
High season per wk
£260.00–£470.00

Woodthorpe Hall Country Cottage, Alford

contact Mrs Stubbs, Woodthorpe Hall Country Cottage, Woodthorpe, Alford LN13 0DD
t (01507) 450294 **f** (01507) 450885 **e** enquiries@woodthorpehallleisure.co.uk
w woodthorpehallleisure.co.uk

Cottages overlooking golf course. Central heating, TV and video, dishwasher, washer/dryer, fridge/freezer, microwave and telephone. Fishing, garden and aquatic centre, restaurant and bar etc.

open All year
payment Credit/debit cards, cash/cheques

Pets 🛏 🐾 🐕. Unit ▦ TV ⬚ ▣ 📦 🍽 ♨ 📺 🖳 ❄
General 🅿 ♿ ⊙ Leisure ♣ Shop < 0.5 miles Pub < 0.5 miles

ASHBOURNE, Derbyshire Map ref 4B2 — **HOTEL**

★★
HOTEL

B&B per room per night
s £40.00–£90.00
d £55.00–£100.00
HB per person per night
£40.00–£80.00

The Dog and Partridge Country Inn

Ashbourne DE6 2HS **t** (01335) 343183 **f** (01335) 342742 **e** info@dogandpartridge.co.uk
w dogandpartridge.co.uk

Family-run,17thC inn with purpose-built rooms in the grounds. Log fires, real ales, good food. Wi-Fi Internet. Pets and children welcome. Ideal Peak District location. Very close to Alton Towers.

open All year
bedrooms 8 double, 4 twin, 2 single, 15 family
bathrooms All en suite
payment Credit/debit cards, cash/cheques

Pets 🛏 🐕 🐾 🐈. Room 🛋 📞 TV 👜 🍵 ⚷ General 🅿 🛏 🅿 🍴 ⚑ ❄ Leisure ∪ 🚲

Don't forget www.

Web addresses throughout this guide are shown without the prefix www. Please include www. in the address line of your browser. If a web address does not follow this style it is shown in full.

ASHBOURNE, Derbyshire Map ref 4B2 — SELF CATERING

★★★★
SELF CATERING

Units **5**
Sleeps **2-6**

Low season per wk
£234.00-£430.00
High season per wk
£430.00-£677.00

Paddock House Farm Holiday Cottages, Alstonefield, Ashbourne

contact Mr & Mrs Mark & Melissa Redfern, Paddock House Farm Holiday Cottages, Alstonefield, Ashbourne DE6 2FT
t (01335) 310282 e info@paddockhousefarm.co.uk w paddockhousefarm.co.uk

open All year
payment Cash/cheques

Luxury holiday cottages in the heart of the Peak District National Park. Cottages have either three bedrooms, two bedrooms or one bedroom. Wonderful views of the open countryside in a very peaceful location. Excellent attractions, including Alton Towers, Chatsworth and Dovedale. Pets allowed in three cottages.

⊕ From Alstonefield village head for Hulme End, 1.5 miles on the left. At the end of our drive turn left to the main courtyard.

♥ 20% reduction for 2 adults booking a 3-bedroom cottage only using 1 bedroom (off-peak only).

Pets 🐕 🐈 Unit 🏠 📺 ▣ ▣ ▣ ▣ ▣ ▣ ▣ ▣ ▣ ✻ General 🛒 ▥ ⚐ P ⚒ ◎ S Leisure 🔍 ∪ 🚲 ⌂ Shop 1.5 miles Pub 1.5 miles

BARNOLDBY LE BECK, North East Lincolnshire Map ref 4D1 — SELF CATERING

★★★-★★★★★
SELF CATERING

Units **3**
Sleeps **2-6**

Low season per wk
£175.00-£200.00
High season per wk
£250.00-£320.00

Grange Farm Cottages & Riding School, Grimsby

contact Jo & Sue Jenkins, Grange Farm Cottages & Riding School, Waltham Road, Barnoldby le Beck DN37 0AR
t (01472) 822216 e sueuk4000@netscape.net w grangefarmcottages.com

Even non-horse riders can appreciate the tranquillity of Grange Farm Cottages. Each highly-equipped cottage has one twin and one double bedroom – a real home from home. Riding can be arranged.

open All year
payment Cash/cheques

Pets 🐕 🐈 Unit 🏠 📺 ▣ ▣ ▣ ▣ ▣ ▣ ✻ General 🛒 ▥ ⚐ P ⚒ S Leisure ∪ ⌂ Shop 2 miles Pub 0.5 miles

BEESTON, Nottinghamshire Map ref 4C2 — GUEST ACCOMMODATION

★★★
GUEST HOUSE

B&B per room per night
s £25.00-£50.00
d £50.00-£60.00
Evening meal per person
£7.95-£15.00

Hylands

Queens Road, Beeston, Nottingham NG9 1JB t (0115) 925 5472 f (0115) 922 5574
e hyland.hotel@btconnect.com w s-h-systems.co.uk/hotels/hylands.html

open All year except Christmas
bedrooms 6 double, 7 twin, 17 single, 8 family
bathrooms 23 en suite
payment Credit/debit cards, cash

A family-run hotel offering comfortable, clean accommodation with a warm and friendly atmosphere. Situated close to Nottingham University, the city indoor tennis centre and Attenborough nature reserve. Within easy walking distance of an award-winning pub and several excellent restaurants, and with frequent transport links to the city centre.

⊕ Leave M1 at jct 25. Follow A52 towards Nottingham. At roundabout take B6003 (Long Eaton). At T-junction follow A6005 (Nottingham). Hylands is 2.5 miles along on right.

♥ Discounts available for groups and stays of 4 nights or longer. Extra discounts during winter. Please contact for details.

Pets 🐕 🐾 Room 🛏 ✆ 📺 ☕ 🍽 General 🛒 ▥ ⚐ P ♟ ✗ ▤ 🎣 ✻ Leisure 🔍 ⌂

Key to symbols
Open the back flap for a key to symbols.

BOSTON, Lincolnshire Map ref 3A1 · **SELF CATERING**

Elms Farm Cottages, Boston

★★★★–★★★★★
SELF CATERING

Units **8**
Sleeps **1–5**

Low season per wk
£290.00–£320.00
High season per wk
£395.00–£450.00

contact Carol Emerson, Elms Farm Cottages, The Elms, Hubberts Bridge, Boston PE20 3QP
t (01205) 290840 & 07887 652021 f (01205) 290840 e carol@elmsfarmcottages.co.uk
w elmsfarmcottages.co.uk

open All year
payment Credit/debit cards, cash/cheques

Award-winning barn conversion of high-quality cottages, some with wood-burning stoves. Private patio with picnic bench. All cottages are accessible, four with disabled shower rooms especially suitable for wheelchair users. Grass field with wild-flower meadow for guests to enjoy. Communal laundry and built-in barbecue.

⊕ On A1121 (Boston side), 250m from Hubberts Bridge crossroads.

♥ Tastes of Lincolnshire welcome pack on weekly stays.

Pets 🐕 £🐕 🐾. Unit 🛏 📺 ▣ 🖥 🍽 ❖
General ⛏ 🗐 ♿ P ⚡ 🖼 S Leisure 🚲 ⛳ Shop 2 miles Pub < 0.5 miles

BRADWELL, Derbyshire Map ref 4B2 · **GUEST ACCOMMODATION**

Stoney Ridge

★★★★
GUEST ACCOMMODATION

B&B per room per night
s £40.00–£46.00
d £68.00–£72.00

Granby Road, Bradwell, Hope Valley S33 9HU t (01433) 620538 e toneyridge@aol.com
w stoneyridge.org.uk

open All year
bedrooms 3 double, 1 twin
bathrooms 3 en suite, 1 private
payment Credit/debit cards, cash/cheques

Large private bungalow, set in established gardens, enjoying wonderful views over Hope Valley. The friendly village of Bradwell is three miles east of Castleton. Enjoy a swim at no extra charge in our 28ft indoor heated pool. Three double en suite rooms and one twin with private facilities. Plus legendary breakfasts.

⊕ Take directions to Bowling Green Inn. Carry on uphill for 200m. Turn sharp left onto Granby Road, Stoney Ridge is 4th on right.

♥ Winter and midweek offers. See website for details.

Pets 🐕 🐾 🐾 Room 📺 ❖ 🍽 General ⛏ 10 P 🖼 🛏 🎿 ❖ Leisure 🎿 ∪

BUXTON, Derbyshire Map ref 4B2 · **HOTEL**

Alison Park Hotel

★★
SMALL HOTEL

B&B per room per night
s £45.00–£50.00
d £90.00–£100.00
HB per person per night
£62.50–£68.50

3 Temple Road, Buxton SK17 9BA t (01298) 22473 f (01298) 72709
e reservations@alison-park-hotel.co.uk w alison-park-hotel.co.uk

An Edwardian arts and crafts house, set within its own grounds in quiet location, just out of the town centre. The family management of the hotel ensures a warm welcome.

open All year
bedrooms 7 double, 4 twin, 4 single, 3 family
bathrooms 14 en suite, 4 private
payment Credit/debit cards, cash/cheques

Pets 🐕 🐾 🐾 Room 🛏 📞 📺 ❖ 🍽 General ⛏ 🗐 ♿ P ❤ 🖼 🛏 ❖ Leisure 🚲 ⛳

Place index

If you know where you want to stay, the index at the back of the guide will give you the page number listing accommodation in your chosen town, city or village. Check out the other useful indexes too.

BUXTON, Derbyshire Map ref 4B2 | **GUEST ACCOMMODATION**

★★★
INN

B&B per room per night
s Min £45.00
d Min £55.00
Evening meal per person
£7.50–£12.50

Devonshire Arms

Peak Forest, Buxton SK17 8EJ **t** (01298) 23875 **f** (01298) 23598 **e** fiona.clough@virgin.net
w devarms.com

open All year except Christmas
bedrooms 4 double, 2 family
bathrooms All en suite
payment Credit/debit cards, cash/cheques

Traditional Peak District inn. High-standard, en suite rooms with TV and coffee facilities. Excellent food, traditional ales, coal fire. Dogs and children free. Guaranteed warm welcome.

Pets 🐕 ♞🐾🏠. Room 📺 ♨🍵 General 🛏🔥P🍽✕♨⚡ Leisure ∪ 🚲

CURBAR, Derbyshire Map ref 4B2 | **SELF CATERING**

★★★
SELF CATERING

Units **2**
Sleeps **2–6**

Low season per wk
£200.00–£250.00
High season per wk
£250.00–£320.00

Upper Barn and Lower Barn, Hope Valley

contact Dr J Morrissy & Dr P Cox, Upper Barn and Lower Barn, Orchard House, The Hillock, Curbar, Calver, Hope Valley S32 3YJ
t (01433) 631885 **w** curbarcottages.com

A recent conversion of a 200-year-old barn into cottages. Linked to let as one if required.

open All year
payment Cash/cheques, euros

Pets 🐕 Unit 🖼 📺 🔲 🔳 🗄 📻 🔌⚡
General 🛏🏠🔥P Ⓢ Leisure ∪ Shop 1 mile Pub < 0.5 miles

LAMBLEY, Nottinghamshire Map ref 4C2 | **SELF CATERING**

★★★
SELF CATERING &
SERVICED APARTMENTS

Units **1**
Sleeps **4**

Low season per wk
£180.00–£200.00
High season per wk
£245.00–£265.00

Dickman's Cottage, Lambley, Nottingham

contact Mr William Marshall Smith, Springsyde, Birdcage Walk, Otley LS21 3HB
t (01943) 462719 **f** (01943) 850925 **e** marshallsmithuk@hotmail.com
w mywebpage.netscape.com/wmarshallsmith/default.html

open All year
payment Cash/cheques, euros

Five miles north-east of Nottingham. Beamed cottage with garden. Two bedrooms – one double, one twin. TV/video, dishwasher, washer/dryer. Private parking.

⊕ M1 jct 26. Follow the signs for Arnold and from there for Lambley then turn into Mill Lane from Main Street.

♥ Short and weekend breaks available. Prices on application.

Pets 🐕 £🐕 Unit 🖼 📺 🔲🔳 🗄📻 🔌⚡
General 🛏🏠P⚬ Ⓢ Shop < 0.5 miles Pub < 0.5 miles

LEICESTER, Leicestershire Map ref 4C3 | **GUEST ACCOMMODATION**

★★★
BED & BREAKFAST

B&B per room per night
s £35.00
d £50.00

Wondai B&B

47-49 Main Street, Newtown Linford, Leicester LE6 0AE **t** (01530) 242728

Our bed and breakfast is located in the village just a short walk from Bradgate Park which was home to Lady Jane Grey, Queen of England for nine days in 1553.

open All year except Christmas
bedrooms 1 twin, 1 family
bathrooms All en suite
payment Cash/cheques

Pets 🐕 ♞🐾 Room ♨ General 🛏🏠🔥P⚬ ♨🎣 Leisure 🎣

MUMBY, Lincolnshire Map ref 4D2 — GUEST ACCOMMODATION

★★★
GUEST ACCOMMODATION

B&B per room per night
s £25.00–£30.00
d £50.00–£70.00
Evening meal per person
£5.00–£15.00

Brambles

Occupation Lane, Alford LN13 9JU t (01507) 490174 e suescrimshaw@btinternet.com

Newly built rural bungalow, quiet scenic setting, close to the costal resorts. Two en suite double rooms for bed and breakfast.

open All year
bedrooms 1 double, 1 family
bathrooms All en suite
payment Cash/cheques

Pets 🛏 £🛏 🖳 🐾. Room 🛏 📺 💆 🍷 General 🕮 🛧 P ✕ 🍴 🕮 ☀ ☼ Leisure ♦ ∪ 🏤

NORTHAMPTON, Northamptonshire Map ref 2C1 — GUEST ACCOMMODATION

★★★★
GUEST ACCOMMODATION

B&B per room per night
s Min £34.00
d Min £62.50
Evening meal per person
Min £12.50

The Poplars

Cross Street, Moulton NN3 7RZ t (01604) 643983 f (01604) 790233 e info@thepoplarshotel.com
w thepoplarshotel.com

open All year except Christmas and New Year
bedrooms 6 double, 1 twin, 6 single, 4 family
bathrooms 13 en suite
payment Credit/debit cards, cash/cheques

A small, comfortable, family-run country hotel of character, situated in picturesque village of Moulton. Perfect location for visiting family, friends and local attractions. Special weekend rates. Quality food provided, sourced locally whenever possible.

Pets 🛏 🍷 Room 🛏 📺 💆 🍷 General ⌛ 🕮 🛧 P ⚥ 💡 ✕ 🍴 🕮 🔍 ☼ Leisure ∪ 🚲 🏤

NORTON DISNEY, Lincolnshire Map ref 4C2 — GUEST ACCOMMODATION

★★★★
FARMHOUSE

B&B per room per night
s £51.00
d £82.00
Evening meal per person
£15.50–£25.00

Brills Farm

Brills Hill, Norton Disney, Lincoln LN6 9JN t (01636) 892311
e admin@brillsfarm-bedandbreakfast.co.uk w brillsfarm-bedandbreakfast.co.uk

open All year except Christmas and New Year
bedrooms 2 double, 1 twin/double
bathrooms All en suite
payment Credit/debit cards, cash/cheques

This beautifully renovated 1720 Georgian farmhouse with fabulous views, provides warm hospitality, luxurious bedrooms, open fireplaces and a lovely drawing room for relaxation. Dine under the crystal chandelier or in the gardens under the stars. Gourmet breakfasts use home-grown and home-made produce. Ideally located for Newark and Swinderby antiques fairs.

⊕ From A1/A46/A17 junction, take A46 towards Lincoln. Take exit signed Brough, Stapleford and Norton Disney. Right at T-junction. Follow approx 0.75 miles. 1st left, 1 mile, wide gravel entrance on right.

♥ 15% discount for stays of 3 nights or more between 1 Nov and 28 Feb, excl Christmas and New Year.

Pets 🛏 🖳 🐾. Room 📺 💆 🍷 General ⌛12 P ⚥ 💡 ✕ 🍴 🕮 ☼ Leisure ∪ 🏤

It's all quality-assessed accommodation

Our commitment to quality involves wide-ranging accommodation assessment. Rating and awards were correct at the time of going to press but may change following a new assessment. Please check at time of booking.

OAKHAM, Rutland Map ref 4C3 — **HOTEL**

★★★
HOTEL
SILVER AWARD

Barnsdale Lodge Hotel

The Avenue, Rutland Water, Oakham LE15 8AH **t** (01572) 724678 **f** (01572) 724961
e enquiries@barnsdalelodge.co.uk **w** barnsdalelodge.co.uk

B&B per room per night
s £65.00–£85.00
d £80.00–£115.00

open All year
bedrooms 21 double, 8 twin, 7 single, 2 family,
6 suites
bathrooms All en suite
payment Credit/debit cards, cash/cheques

Enjoy a relaxing break on the beautiful north shore of Rutland Water. We can offer you anything from a wedding to an intimate dinner for two. Our informal dining areas are reflected in our seasonal bistro menu. Our bedrooms are all comfortably and individually decorated and have garden or countryside views.

Pets 🐕 £🐾 🐾🐾🐾 Room 🛏🕯📺♨🍴♿ General 🛋🎱⚓P♟🍽♦🅿⚙ Leisure ∪🚵⚓

OLD BOLINGBROKE, Lincolnshire Map ref 4D2 — **SELF CATERING**

★★★★
SELF CATERING

Units 2
Sleeps 3

Low season per wk
£190.00–£205.00
High season per wk
£280.00–£325.00

1 & 2 Hope Cottages, Old Bolingbroke

contact Mr & Mrs Taylor, Clowery Cottage, Craypool Lane, Scothern, Lincoln LN2 2UU
t (01673) 861412 **f** (01673) 863336 **e** hopecottages@aol.com **w** hopecottages.co.uk

open All year
payment Cash/cheques

Enjoy visiting these well-appointed country cottages, located in a quiet, royal village complete with castle ruins. Explore rolling Lincolnshire Wolds, nearby seaside or historic Lincoln and a host of market towns. Walking, cycling, fishing, nature reserves nearby – or just enjoy the peace and quiet!

⊕ *From A158 Old Bolingbroke is located 3 miles south west of the market town of Spilsby.*

♥ *Short breaks available Oct–Apr.*

Pets 🐕 🐾 Unit 🏠 📺🎦📧📠🖥🍴🔥🍳💡⚙
General 🛋P♻Ⓢ Leisure ∪🚵 Shop 3 miles Pub < 0.5 miles

PEAK DISTRICT

See under Ashbourne, Buxton

RUTLAND WATER

See under Oakham

SOUTH COCKERINGTON, Lincolnshire Map ref 4D2 — **SELF CATERING**

★★★★
SELF CATERING

Units 2
Sleeps 4–5

Low season per wk
£275.00–£325.00
High season per wk
£325.00–£460.00

Grasswells Farm Holiday Cottages, Louth

contact Ms Janice Foster, Grasswells Holiday Cottages (Saddleback Leisure Ltd), Saddleback Road, Howdales, South Cockerington, Louth LN11 7DJ
t (01507) 338508 **e** thefosters2002@talk-email.com

Single barn conversions, spacious, comfortable
and well equipped. Set in three acres of grounds
with private fishing lake.

open All year
payment Cash/cheques

Pets 🐕 🐾 Unit 🏠 📺🖥🍴🍳💡⚙
General 🛋🎱P♻Ⓢ Leisure ⚓

Using map references

Map references refer to the colour maps at the front of this guide.

★★★★
SELF CATERING

Units **6**
Sleeps **2–6**

Low season per wk
£210.00–£350.00
High season per wk
£335.00–£550.00

Rural Roosts, Wragby
t (01526) 398492 & 07712 771102   e katie@ruralroots.co.uk   w ruralroosts.co.uk

open All year
payment Credit/debit cards, cash/cheques

Peaceful, rural retreats. Each lodge offers high-quality accommodation in an idyllic setting on part of our farm with plenty of wildlife, fishing and farm walks available for your enjoyment. An ideal base for relaxing and exploring all the wonderful attractions and countryside Lincolnshire has to offer.

⊕ *From A158 take turning just outside Langworth to Stainfield. In Stainfield take turning on right next to phone box. Go up 'Manor Farm' lane and follow signs.*

Pets ⛓ ♨   Unit ▥ 📺 📠 ▣ 🍴 🍷 🗑 🍽 🧷 ❄   General 🛏 🚪 ♿ P ✄ Ⓢ   Leisure ∪ 🚲   Shop 5 miles   Pub 5 miles

★★
BED & BREAKFAST

B&B per room per night
s Min £25.00
d Min £40.00

Wellbeck Farmhouse B&B
Well, Alford LN13 9LT   t (01507) 462453   f (01507) 462453

open All year
bedrooms 1 single, 2 family
bathrooms 3 private
payment Cash/cheques

Traditional farmhouse B&B at the foot of the Lincolnshire Wolds. Near the market town of Alford. Short drive to the coast. Large lock-up shed.

⊕ *Directions given at time of booking.*

Pets ⛓ ♨ 🐴 🐕 🐾 🐾   Room 📺 ☕ 🍷   General 🛏 🚪 ♿ P ✄ 🛎 ❄   Leisure ∪ 🚲 🚣

Gold and Silver Awards

Enjoy England's unique Gold and Silver Awards recognise exceptional quality in serviced accommodation.

Our assessors make recommendations for Gold and Silver Awards during assessments in recognition of levels of quality over and above that expected of a particular rating.

Look for the Gold and Silver Awards in the regional sections, or you can find an index to accommodation with a Gold or Silver Award at the back of this guide.

enjoyEngland.com   enjoyEngland.com
Gold AWARD   *Silver* AWARD

Country ways

The Countryside Rights of Way Act gives people new rights to walk on areas of open countryside and registered common land.

To find out where you can go and what you can do, as well as information about taking your dog to the countryside, go online at countrysideaccess.gov.uk.

And when you're out and about...

Always follow the Country Code
- Be safe – plan ahead and follow any signs
- Leave gates and property as you find them
- Protect plants and animals, and take your litter home
- Keep dogs under close control
- Consider other people

East of England

Bedfordshire, Cambridgeshire, Essex,
Hertfordshire, Norfolk, Suffolk

Simple pleasures in a fascinating setting

There's more to the East of
England than the Broads
and teeming wildlife;
explore this fascinating
region and you'll discover
fairytale castles, ancient
cathedrals and exquisite
gardens. (Oh, and dinosaurs
and ghosts.)

East of England Tourism
visiteastofengland.com
(01284) 727470

Tring, Hertfordshire

Ely Cathedral, Cambridgeshire

Shuttleworth Collection, Bedfordshire

Southwold, Suffolk

The East of England is crammed full of secrets. Wander around the stupendous Ely Cathedral (star of the movie 'The Golden Age') that towers like a ship over the fens. Take a chariot-ride over to historic Colchester with its chilling links with Boudica. Journey to deepest Bedfordshire and feel like royalty at Wrest Park, a French- inspired Chateau with Versailles-like gardens. Explore the Swiss Garden at Old Warden, a charming Victorian folly garden complete with grotto, Monet bridges and peacocks. And discover the gigantic Dinosaur Adventure Park near Norwich for a monster day of family thrills and fact-finding. Finally, delight the ghostbuster in you and enter Castle Rising Castle, a 12th century Norman hall-keep near King's Lynn where the cries of Queen Isabella can still be heard on dark winter afternoons.

This region holds one of the nation's greatest relics – the astonishing treasure of the mystery Saxon King in his burial ship at Sutton Hoo. If contemporary treasures are more you, check out the landmark Firstsite visual arts centre in the heart of Colchester. And be sure to catch some of the colourful local events such as the World Snail Racing Championship in Congham where 300 snails battle for the silver tankard stuffed with lettuce. Time to up the tempo? Tune-in to the high-octane drag racing at Santa Pod, back a winner at Newmarket Races or head back to the coast for a lively fun-filled day at Great Yarmouth. And for a real echo of the past, gallop over to Royston Cave in Hertfordshire where you can see a bell-shaped chamber containing medieval carvings by the Knights Templar.

Whatever your interest, you'll find something to fascinate you in this unspoilt and very special corner of England.

Destinations

Cambridge

The name Cambridge instantly summons breathtaking images – the Backs carpeted with spring flowers, King's College Chapel, punting on the river Cam and, of course, the calm of the historic college buildings. Cambridge still has the atmosphere of a bustling market town, notwithstanding its international reputation. Explore its winding streets and splendid architecture, and choose from a range of attractions, museums, hotels, restaurants and pubs. Situated in the heart of East Anglia but less than an hour from London by high-speed rail link.

Colchester

If variety's the spice of life, Colchester's the place to savour it! Two thousand years of history and everything you need for a day trip, short break or longer stay. Art lovers will find cutting-edge contemporary galleries and there's a shopper's heaven of little specialist shops and big name stores. The range of cuisine makes Colchester a magnet for food lovers – don't miss the annual Colchester Oyster Feast. Find internationally important treasures located in award-winning museums and view lush landscapes in Victorian Castle Park. At night, discover clubs, theatres, music and open-air vibes.

Great Yarmouth

One of the UK's most popular seaside resorts, with an enviable mix of sandy beaches, attractions, entertainment, heritage and quality accommodation. And beyond the seaside fun is a charming town that is steeped in history. Visit the medieval town walls, stroll the historic South Quay and discover Nelson's 'other' column. When the sun goes down, Great Yarmouth becomes a wonderland of colour as the illuminations light your way to a night on the town. Full of holiday contrasts, the area also boasts 21 villages set in beautiful coastal and rural settings alongside the famous Norfolk Broads.

0		50 miles
0		75 kms

☐ National Park & The Broads

☐ Area of Outstanding Natural Beauty

▬ Heritage Coast

⚑ National Trails
nationaltrail.co.uk

3 Sections of the
National Cycle Network
nationalcyclenetwork.org.uk

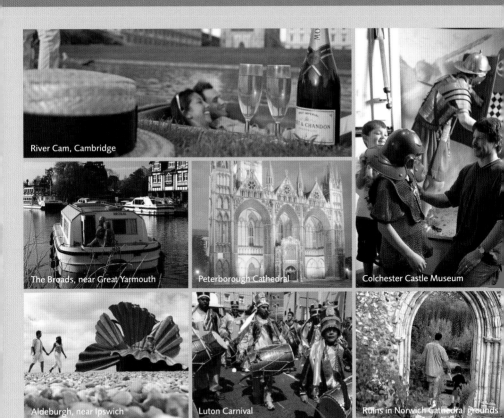

River Cam, Cambridge

The Broads, near Great Yarmouth

Peterborough Cathedral

Colchester Castle Museum

Aldeburgh, near Ipswich

Luton Carnival

Ruins in Norwich Cathedral grounds

Ipswich

In England's oldest continuously settled Anglo-Saxon town, you'll find numerous architectural gems, including twelve medieval churches. Browse important collections of work by Constable and Gainsborough and enjoy the beautifully landscaped gardens and fine Tudor mansion at Christchurch Park. You'll be able to 'shop 'til you drop' in one of the region's best retail centres, and explore the historic waterfront where the Victorian wet dock is currently undergoing an exciting renaissance. Stay longer, and explore the beautiful, unspoilt Suffolk coastline.

Luton

Discover a friendly and cosmopolitan town. Luton is surprisingly 'green' with over 7% of its area made up of open space, with more than ten sites of importance for wildlife. Shoppers will be spoilt for choice with over 100 shops in the Arndale Centre and a large, thriving market. You'll find a lively and exciting night scene with bars and nightclubs playing music from the UK dance, house and garage scenes. Visit in the spring and catch Luton International Carnival.

Norwich

Norwich, county town of Norfolk, is an enchanting cathedral city and a thriving modern metropolis. See some of the finest medieval architecture in Britain in the cathedral and castle, and wander an intricate network of winding streets. The city's newest centrepiece, The Forum, represents contemporary architecture at its best. You'll find excellent shopping as well as a vibrant mix of theatres, cinemas, arts festivals, exhibitions, museums, and a vast array of restaurants.

Peterborough

With 3,000 years of heritage, Peterborough will exceed your expectations. Its magnificent Norman cathedral sits amid peaceful precincts just a few metres from the city's superb shopping and leisure facilities. You'll find a great range of outdoor activities in picturesque countryside – including 2,000 acres of riverside parkland. And there are plenty of attractions, events and festivals to thrill all ages and interests – just 45 minutes from central London by high-speed rail link.

Places to visit

Anglesey Abbey, Gardens and Lode Mill
near Cambridge
(01223) 810080
nationaltrust.org.uk
Abbey, Jacobean-style house and Fairfax collection

Audley End House and Gardens
Saffron Walden, Essex
(01799) 522399
english-heritage.org.uk
Sumptuous splendour of a grand stately home
🐾 *(parkland only)* 🐕

Blickling Hall
near Norwich, Norfolk
(01263) 738030
nationaltrust.org.uk
Jacobean mansion with parkland and orangery
🐾 *(grounds only)* 🐕

Bressingham Steam Experience and Gardens
near Diss, Norfolk
(01379) 686900
bressingham.co.uk
Fun-packed family day out
🐕

Colchester Castle
Essex
(01206) 282939
colchestermuseums.org.uk
Spectacular displays of Colchester's early history
🐕

Colchester Zoo
Essex
(01206) 331292
colchester-zoo.com
Over 250 species with superb cat and primate collections
🐕

Ely Cathedral
Cambridgeshire
(01353) 667735
cathedral.ely.anglican.org
One of England's finest cathedrals
🐕

Go Ape!
High Wire Forest Adventure
Thetford Forest, Suffolk
0870 444 5562
goape.co.uk
Rope bridges, swings and zip slides
🐾 *(walkways only)* 🐕

Hatfield House
Hertfordshire
(01707) 287010
hatfield-house.co.uk
Magnificent Jacobean house with exquisite gardens
🐾 *(park only)* 🐕

Holkham Hall
near Wells-next-the-Sea, Norfolk
(01328) 710227
holkham.co.uk
Classic 18th-century Palladian-style mansion
🐾 *(park only)* 🐕

Imperial War Museum Duxford
near Cambridge
(01223) 835000
duxford.iwm.org.uk
The sights, sound and power of aircraft
🐕

Knebworth House, Gardens and Park
near Stevenage, Hertfordshire
(01438) 812661
knebworthhouse.com
Re-fashioned Tudor manor house in 250-acre grounds
🐾 *(grounds only)* 🐕

National Stud
Newmarket, Cambridgeshire
(01638) 663464
nationalstud.co.uk
Conducted tour of thoroughbreds
🐕

Norfolk Lavender Limited
near King's Lynn
(01485) 570384
norfolk-lavender.co.uk
Lavender farm and fragrant gardens
🐾 🐕

Norwich Cathedral
Norfolk
(01603) 218300
cathedral.org.uk
Imposing Norman cathedral with 14th-century roof bosses
🐕

The Royal Air Force Air Defence Radar Museum
Small Visitor Attraction of the Year – Gold Winner
Norwich, Norfolk
(01692) 631485
radarmuseum.co.uk
History of radar featuring Cold War Operations Room
🐕

RSPB Minsmere Nature Reserve
Saxmundham, Suffolk
(01728) 648281
rspb.org.uk
Bird-watching hides and trails plus year-round events
🐕

🐾 Pets Welcome
🐕 Assistance dogs only

Diary dates 2008

Sandringham House
Norfolk
(01553) 612908
sandringhamestate.co.uk
*The country retreat of HM The
Queen*

Whittlesea Straw Bear Festival
strawbear.org.uk
11 – 13 Jan

Shuttleworth Collection
Biggleswade, Bedfordshire
(01767) 627927
shuttleworth.org
*Unique collection of aircraft – see
a Spitfire in flying condition*

St George's Day Festival
Wrest Park, Bedfordshire
english-heritage.org.uk
19 – 20 Apr

**Somerleyton Hall
& Gardens**
near Lowestoft, Suffolk
(01502) 734901
somerleyton.co.uk
Lavish early Victorian mansion

Stilton Cheese Rolling Competition
Main Street, Stilton
stilton.org/about_rolling.html
5 May

Southend Air Show
The seafront
southendairshow.com
25 – 26 May

Luton International Carnival
Various locations, Luton
luton.gov.uk/carnival
26 May

Sutton Hoo Burial Site
Woodbridge, Suffolk
(01394) 389700
nationaltrust.org.uk
*Burial mounds overlooking River
Deben*

Aldeburgh Festival
Snape, Suffolk
aldeburgh.co.uk
13 – 29 Jun

Royal Norfolk Show
Norwich
royalnorfolkshow.co.uk
25 – 26 Jun

Thursford Collection
Norfolk
(01328) 878477
thursford.com
Organ collection with daily show

Bedford River Festival
River Great Ouse
bedford.gov.uk
12 – 13 Jul

World Snail Racing Championships
The Cricket Field, Congham
snailracing.net
19 Jul

Verulamium Museum
St Albans, Hertfordshire
(01727) 751810
stalbansmuseums.org.uk
Re-creation of life in Roman Britain

Annual British Crabbing Championship
The seafront, Walberswick
explorewalberswick.co.uk
10 Aug

Tourist Information Centres

When you arrive at your destination, visit an Official Partner Tourist Information Centre for quality assured help with accommodation and information about local attractions and events, or email your request before you go. To search for attractions and Tourist Information Centres on the move just text INFO to 62233, and a web link will be sent to your mobile phone.

Bishop's Stortford	The Old Monastery	(01279) 655831	tic@bishopsstortford.org
Bury St Edmunds	6 Angel Hill	(01284) 764667	tic@stedsbc.gov.uk
Flatford	Flatford Lane	(01206) 299460	flatfordvic@babergh.gov.uk
Harwich	Iconfield Park	(01255) 506139	harwichtic@btconnect.com
Hunstanton	The Green	(01485) 532610	hunstanton.tic@west-norfolk.gov.uk
Ipswich	St Stephens Lane	(01473) 258070	tourist@ipswich.gov.uk
King's Lynn	Purfleet Quay	(01553) 763044	kings-lynn.tic@west-norfolk.gov.uk
Lavenham*	Lady Street	(01787) 248207	lavenhamtic@babergh.gov.uk
Lowestoft	East Point Pavilion	(01502) 533600	touristinfo@waveney.gov.uk
Maldon	Coach Lane	(01621) 856503	tic@maldon.gov.uk
Saffron Waldon	1 Market Place	(01799) 510444	tourism@uttlesford.gov.uk
Southwold	69 High Street	(01502) 724729	southwold.tic@waveney.gov.uk
Stowmarket	The Museum of East Anglian Life	(01449) 676800	tic@midsuffolk.gov.uk
Sudbury	Market Hill	(01787) 881320	sudburytic@babergh.gov.uk

* seasonal opening

Knebworth House, Hertfordshire

Find out more

East of England Tourism has a comprehensive website, updated daily. Log on to visiteastofengland.com

Online brochures and information sheets can be downloaded including Major Events; Lights, Camera, Action! (film and television locations); Stars and Stripes (connections with the USA) and a range of Discovery Tours around the region.

For more information, please call (01284) 727470 or email info@eet.org.uk

Travel info

By road:
The region is easily accessible: from London and the South via the A1(M), M11, M25, A10, M1 and A12; from the North via the A1(M), A17, A15, A5, M1 and A6; from the West via the A14, A47, A421, A428, A418, A41, A422 and A427.

By rail:
Regular fast and frequent trains run to all major cities and towns. London stations which serve the region are Liverpool Street, King's Cross, Fenchurch Street, Marylebone, St Pancras and Euston. Bedford, Luton and St Albans are on the Thameslink line which runs to King's Cross and on to London Gatwick Airport. There is also a direct link between London Stansted Airport and Liverpool Street. Through the Channel Tunnel, there are trains direct from Paris and Brussels to Waterloo Station, London. A short journey on the Underground will bring passengers to those stations operating services into the East of England. Further information on rail journeys in the East of England can be obtained on 0845 748 4950.

By air:
Fly into London Luton, London Stansted or Norwich International.

Holkham Hall Estate, Norfolk

where to stay in
East of England

All place names in the blue bands are shown on the maps at the front of this guide.

Accommodation symbols
Symbols give useful information about services and facilities. Inside the back-cover flap you can find a key to these symbols. Keep it open for easy reference.

ALDEBURGH, Suffolk Map ref 3C2   **HOTEL**

★★★
HOTEL
SILVER AWARD

B&B per room per night
s £62.00–£108.00
d £100.00–£224.00
HB per person per night
£55.00–£130.00

Brudenell Hotel

The Parade, Aldeburgh IP15 5BU t (01728) 452071 f (01728) 454082 e info@brudenellhotel.co.uk
w brudenellhotel.co.uk

open All year
bedrooms 16 double, 5 twin, 6 single, 11 family, 4 suites
bathrooms All en suite
payment Credit/debit cards, cash/cheques

Modern and contemporary hotel with a stunning location right on the beach. Bedrooms enjoy unrivalled views over the sea, river and surrounding marshland. Superior and de luxe rooms (which include a king-size bed) available, panoramic bar and restaurant specialising in local seafood and grills.

⊕ From A12 take A1094 to Aldeburgh. Turn right at crossroads in Aldeburgh (past church). Brudenell is on seafront, south end of town.

Pets ⛄ ⛄ ⛄   Room ⛄ 📺 ⛄ ⛄ ⛄   General ⛄ ⛄ ⛄ P ⛄ ⛄ ⛄ ⛄ ⛄   Leisure ∪ ⛄

ALRESFORD, Essex Map ref 3B2   **SELF CATERING**

★★★
SELF CATERING

Units   **1**
Sleeps   **1–2**
Low season per wk
Min £150.00
High season per wk
Min £230.00

Creek Lodge, Colchester

contact Mrs Patricia Mountney, Creek Lodge, Ford Lane, Colchester CO7 8BE
t (01206) 825411

Tranquil riverside cottage set in extensive landscaped gardens, perfectly situated for sailing, walking and bird-watching. Only five miles from historic Colchester.

open All year
payment Cash/cheques

Pets ⛄   Unit 🏠 📺 📺 ⛄ ⛄ ⛄ ⛄ ⛄
General P ⛄   Shop 0.75 miles   Pub 0.75 miles

Place index

If you know where you want to stay, the index at the back of the guide will give you the page number listing accommodation in your chosen town, city or village. Check out the other useful indexes too.

CRATFIELD, Suffolk Map ref 3C2 · **SELF CATERING**

Holly Tree Farm Barns, Halesworth

★★★★
SELF CATERING

contact Ms Rachel Boddy, Holly Tree Farm, Bell Green, Cratfield, Halesworth IP19 0DN
t (01986) 798062 **e** hollytreebarns@lycos.co.uk **w** hollytreebarns.co.uk

Units **3**
Sleeps **2–10**
Low season per wk
£230.00–£395.00
High season per wk
£305.00–£565.00

open All year
payment Cash/cheques

Unrivalled tranquillity in recently converted barns. Private gardens offer unbroken farmland views. Heritage Coast and unspoiled delights of Suffolk nearby. Short walk to village pub. Eleven acres of meadowland. Dogs welcome. Ample parking. Sky TV. Each cottage has a sofa bed sleeping two.

⊕ *Leave centre of Cratfield village with The Poacher (pub) on your right-hand side – we are one of the last places on the left.*

♥ *Short breaks available by arrangement.*

Pets 🐕 🐾 Unit 🛏 📺 🖥 💻 ⬛🎱 🔲 🍴 🔲 💡☀ General 🛋 🍳 🔥 P ⚡ 🅾 🆂 Leisure U 🚴 ⛳ Shop 3 miles Pub 0.5 miles

DISS, Norfolk Map ref 3B2 · **GUEST ACCOMMODATION**

Old Rectory Hopton

★★★★★
BED & BREAKFAST
GOLD AWARD

High Street, Hopton, Diss IP22 2QX **t** (01953) 688135 **e** llewellyn.hopton@btinternet.com
w theoldrectoryhopton.com

B&B per room per night
s £47.50–£62.50
d £95.00
Evening meal per person
£27.50–£35.00

open All year except Christmas and New Year
bedrooms 2 double, 1 twin
bathrooms 2 en suite, 1 private
payment Cash/cheques

The Old Rectory is a listed building, dating from the 16th century, standing in walled grounds. The house is well situated to explore East Anglia, being on the Norfolk/Suffolk border. The house is beautifully furnished, and many period features add to the charm of this lovely home. A non-smoking house.

⊕ *From Bury take the A143. In Stanton take the B1111 signed to Garboldisham. The Old Rectory is immediately after the church in Hopton.*

♥ *10% discount on B&B rate for 3 nights or more, 1 Nov to 31 Mar.*

Pets 🐕 🐈 🎿🛏 🐾 Room 💧 🍵 General 🛋8 P ⚡ ⚓ ✕ 🍴 🎱 ☀ Leisure ⛳

FAKENHAM, Norfolk Map ref 3B1 · **GUEST ACCOMMODATION**

Abbott Farm

★★★
FARMHOUSE

Walsingham Road, Binham NR21 0AW **t** (01328) 830519 **f** (01328) 830519
e abbot.farm@btinternet.com **w** abbottfarm.co.uk

B&B per room per night
s £26.00–£30.00
d £52.00–£60.00

A 190-acre arable farm. Rural views of North Norfolk including the historic Binham Priory. Liz and Alan offer a warm welcome to their guesthouse.

open All year except Christmas
bedrooms 1 double, 2 twin
bathrooms All en suite
payment Cash/cheques, euros

Pets 🐕 🎿🛏 🐾 Room 🪑 📺 💧 🍵 General 🛋 🍳 ⚓ P ⚡ ✕ 🍴 🎱 ☀ Leisure U 🚴 ⛳

It's all quality-assessed accommodation

Our commitment to quality involves wide-ranging accommodation assessment. Rating and awards were correct at the time of going to press but may change following a new assessment. Please check at time of booking.

FOXLEY, Norfolk Map ref 3B1 — SELF CATERING

★★–★★★★★
SELF CATERING

Moor Farm Stable Cottages, Dereham

contact Mr Paul Davis, Moor Farm, Foxley, Dereham NR20 4QP
t (01362) 688523 f (01362) 688523 e mail@moorfarmstablecottages.co.uk
w moorfarmstablecottages.co.uk

Units **12**
Sleeps **3–10**

Low season per wk
£200.00–£550.00
High season per wk
£350.00–£860.00

open All year
payment Cash/cheques

Located on working farm, a courtyard of two- and three-bedroomed self-catering cottages, all fully equipped and centrally heated, two specially adapted for disabled. Ideally situated for coast, Broads, Norwich, Sandringham. 365 acres of mature woodland adjoining owners' farm in which to walk. Fishing available in owners' lake close by. Pets welcome. Indoor heated swimming pool and spa.

⊕ From King's Lynn take A148 to Fakenham, then A1067 to Norwich. Moor Farm is situated at the bottom of Foxley Street which is signposted off the A1067.

♥ 2/3-night breaks available (midweek or weekend) Oct–May, 5 nights Christmas/New Year.

Pets 🐾 £🐕 🐾. Unit 🏚 TV 🖃 📠 📺 🕸 ✻
General ♿ 🏘 🛝 P 🄾 🅂 Leisure 🎣 ∪ 🏊 Shop 1 mile Pub 0.5 miles

FRESSINGFIELD, Suffolk Map ref 3C2 — SELF CATERING

★★★
SELF CATERING

Watsons Farm, Fressingfield

contact Mrs Mary Hinde, Cratfield Road, Fressingfield IP21 5SH
t (01379) 586295 e mary@marywebb.co.uk w tiscover.co.uk

Units **1**
Sleeps **1–4**

Low season per wk
£220.00–£250.00
High season per wk
£300.00–£450.00

One end of a 17thC Grade II Listed farmhouse providing peaceful and secluded accommodation, surrounded by fields, 0.3 miles from a country road. Log fire. French doors onto garden.

open All year
payment Cash/cheques

Pets 🐾 Unit 🏚 TV 🖃 📠 📺 🕸 🕸 ✻
General ♿ 🏘 ✂ 🄾 🅂 Leisure 🎣 🏊 Shop 2 miles Pub 2 miles

FRETTENHAM, Norfolk Map ref 3C1 — SELF CATERING

★★★
SELF CATERING

Glebe Farm, Norwich

contact Mrs Rona Norton, Beck Farm, Off Pound Hill, Frettenham, Norwich NR12 7NF
t (01603) 897641 e rona.norton@btinternet.com w glebefarm-cottages.co.uk

Units **2**
Sleeps **1–4**

Low season per wk
£210.00–£360.00

We offer two cottages on our farm. Both are set in large gardens and offer well-equipped, comfortable, modern facilities in a picturesque rural setting with views over open countryside.

open All year
payment Cash/cheques

Pets 🐾 Unit TV 🖃 📺 📠 📺 🕸 ✻
General ♿ 🏘 🛝 P 🅂 Shop 2 miles Pub 1 mile

FRINTON-ON-SEA, Essex Map ref 3C2 — GUEST ACCOMMODATION

★★★
BED & BREAKFAST

Russell Lodge

47 Hadleigh Road, Frinton-on-Sea CO13 9HQ t (01255) 675935 & 07891 899824
e stay@russell-lodge.fsnet.co.uk w russell-lodge.fsnet.co.uk

B&B per room per night
s £25.00
d £50.00

A friendly, homely bed and breakfast in a quiet seaside town. Situated close to beaches, shops and train station. Approximately 300yds to the Greensward, town centre and Crescent Gardens.

open All year
bedrooms 1 double, 1 single, 1 family
bathrooms 2 en suite
payment Cash/cheques

Pets 🐾 🕊 Room TV 🕯 🍵 General ♿ 🏘 🛝 P ✂ 🍴 ✻ Leisure 🚴 🏊

Key to symbols
Open the back flap for a key to symbols.

HADLEIGH, Suffolk Map ref 3B2 — SELF CATERING

★★★★
SELF CATERING

Units **3**
Sleeps **1–8**

Low season per wk
£350.00–£470.00
High season per wk
£580.00–£1,000.00

Wattisham Hall Holiday Cottages, Wattisham, Ipswich

contact Jeremy and Jo Squirrell, Wattisham Hall, Wattisham, Ipswich IP7 7JX
t (01449) 740240 f (01449) 744535 e enquiries@wattishamhall.co.uk w wattishamhall.co.uk

open All year
payment Cash/cheques

Our charming barn conversion has beautifully furnished cottages, with exposed beams, oak floors, wood-burning stoves and plenty of character. All are well equipped with Freeview and access to Wi-Fi Internet. Enclosed patio gardens, shared games room and outdoor play area, as well as outdoor hot tub for Tithe Barn.

⊕ For full travel directions please visit our website or contact us.

♥ Short breaks available all year excl May and Oct half-terms, school summer holidays, Christmas and New Year.

Pets 🐾 Unit 🖼️ 📺 ⬛ 🖥️ ◻️ 🔲 General 🔲 📿 ⚲ P ✂ Ⓞ Ⓢ Leisure 🔍 Shop 2 miles Pub 2 miles

HUNSTANTON, Norfolk Map ref 3B1 — HOTEL

★★★
HOTEL

B&B per room per night
s £49.00–£100.00
d £70.00–£140.00
HB per person per night
£55.00–£120.00

Caley Hall Hotel

Old Hunstanton Road, Old Hunstanton, Hunstanton PE36 6HH t (01485) 533486 f (01485) 533348
e mail@caleyhallhotel.co.uk w caleyhallhotel.co.uk

open All year except Christmas and New Year
bedrooms 15 double, 15 twin, 4 single, 5 family, 1 suite
bathrooms All en suite
payment Credit/debit cards, cash/cheques

Caley Hall Hotel and Restaurant is set around a manor house dating back to 1648. More recently, the old farm outbuildings have been converted to provide the spacious en suite bedrooms, restaurant and bar. Most of the rooms are on the ground floor, and some feature a four-poster bed or whirlpool bath.

⊕ In Old Hunstanton, on the left-hand side of the A149, just before the turning to the golf course.

Pets 🐾 Room 📺 General 🔲 📿 ⚲ P ♞ Leisure 🏊

HUNSTANTON, Norfolk Map ref 3B1 — GUEST ACCOMMODATION

★★★★
INN
SILVER AWARD

B&B per room per night
s £50.00–£60.00
d £85.00–£90.00
Evening meal per person
£8.00–£25.00

The King William IV Country Inn & Restaurant

Heacham Road, Sedgeford, Hunstanton PE36 5LU t (01485) 571765 f (01485) 571743
e info@thekingwilliamsedgeford.co.uk w thekingwilliamsedgeford.co.uk

open All year
bedrooms 4 double
bathrooms All en suite
payment Credit/debit cards, cash/cheques

Popular and busy traditional country inn, amid Norfolk countryside. Close to North Norfolk's beautiful coastline, Peddars Way, RSPB bird reserves and golf. High-standard, comfortable en suite accommodation with king-size beds. Extensive menu and daily specials served in two non-smoking restaurants, bar and garden. A delightful escape – whatever the season.

⊕ From King's Lynn, follow A149 Hunstanton, turn right at Norfolk Lavender onto B1454 (signposted Sedgeford) into village. From Fakenham follow B1454 through Docking into Sedgeford.

♥ Midweek offer: third night half price (Sun-Thu).

Pets 🐾 Room 📺 General 🔲 📿 ⚲ P ♞ ✗ Leisure U 🚲

KETTLEBURGH, Suffolk Map ref 3C2 — SELF CATERING

★★★★
SELF CATERING

Units **1**
Sleeps **4–6**
Low season per wk
£230.00–£350.00
High season per wk
£420.00–£600.00

Church Farm, Woodbridge

contact Mrs Anne Bater, Church Farm, Kettleburgh, Woodbridge IP13 7LF
t (01728) 723532 **e** jbater@suffolkonline.net **w** tiscover.co.uk

A 400-year-old farmhouse overlooking the Deben Valley. Lovely gardens and ponds with ducks and geese. Bright, comfortable bedrooms with tea/coffee facilities. Breakfast and evening meals available. Within easy reach of the coast.

open All year
payment Cash/cheques

Pets 🐾 £🐾 🐾. Unit 🛏 📺 🍽 💻 🔌 🔥 🍳 🧺 🧷 ✳
General 🛁 🍳 🅿 ✂ S Leisure 🚲 🏛 Shop 4 miles Pub 1 mile

LITTLE BENTLEY, Essex Map ref 3B2 — SELF CATERING

★★★★
SELF CATERING

Units **1**
Sleeps **4**
Low season per wk
£250.00–£350.00
High season per wk
£400.00–£475.00

Spring Hall Cottage, Colchester

contact Mrs Tricia Maestrani, Spring Hall, Little Bentley CO7 8SR
t (01206) 251619 & 07779 264679 **f** (01206) 251619 **e** triciamaestrani@hotmail.co.uk

open All year
payment Cash/cheques, euros

Grade II Listed, 17thC thatched cottage with a wealth of character and original features including exposed beams and inglenook fireplace. Two double bedrooms, double cart lodge, 0.33-acre enclosed garden, patio area and barbecue. Ideal location for Constable Country, Manningtree, historical Harwich/Colchester and Essex coast. Excellent selection of pubs/restaurants nearby.

⊕ From Colchester, take A120 to Harwich. After approx 6 miles, take 2nd turning (signposted Little Bentley), then 1st right into Harwich Road. Property is 400yds on right.

♥ Short breaks available (min 3 nights). Welcome pack and complimentary bottle of wine for your enjoyment.

Pets 🐾 🐾. Unit 🛏 📺 🍽 💻 🔌 🍳 🧺 🧷 ✳
General 🛁5 🅿 ✂ S Leisure ∪ 🚲 🏛 Shop 2 miles Pub 0.5 miles

MILEHAM, Norfolk Map ref 3B1 — SELF CATERING

★★★
SELF CATERING

Units **5**
Sleeps **1–5**
Low season per wk
£200.00–£350.00
High season per wk
£200.00–£630.00

Mallards, Mileham

contact Mr & Mrs Jon & Joscelin Colborne, Mallards Cottages, Mileham, Kings Lynn PE32 2RA
t (01328) 700843 & 07917 390511 **f** (01328) 700061 **e** enquiries@mallards.co.uk

open All year
payment Credit/debit cards, cash/cheques, euros

A group of cottages in a tranquil setting away from the road. Each cottage is tastefully decorated and furnished with pretty fabrics, and some have exposed flint and beams. Walking and cycling in the area is superb. The North Norfolk coast, Sandringham, Norfolk Broads and Norwich all within easy reach.

⊕ Situated at the eastern end of Mileham on the north side of the B1145 opposite the church.

♥ Bed and breakfast, short breaks. Please contact for details. Wine tastings throughout the year.

Pets 🐾 £🐾 🐾. Unit 📺 💻 🍽 💻 🔌 🍳 🧺 🧷 ✳
General 🛁 🍳 🅿 ⊙ S Leisure 🎣 🚲 🏛 Shop 0.5 miles Pub 1.5 miles

To your credit

If you book by phone you may be asked for your credit card number. If so, it is advisable to check the proprietor's policy in case you have to cancel your reservation at a later date.

NAYLAND, Suffolk Map ref 3B2 — SELF CATERING

★★★★–★★★★★★
SELF CATERING

Units **9**
Sleeps **2–8**

Low season per wk
£260.00–£875.00
High season per wk
£570.00–£1,800.00

Gladwins Farm, Nayland

contact Mr R Dossor, Gladwins Farm, Harpers Hill, Colchester CO6 4NU
t (01206) 262261 **f** (01206) 263001 **e** gladwinsfarm@aol.com **w** gladwinsfarm.co.uk

open All year
payment Credit/debit cards, cash/cheques

Extensive wooded grounds in Suffolk's rolling Constable Country with marvellous views make ours a wonderful location. Charming villages and gardens to explore – not far from the sea. Heated indoor pool, sauna, hot tub, tennis, fishing, animals and playground. Pets welcome. Chelsworth and Melford cottages have private hot tubs.

⊕ *From A12 take A133 to Colchester. Follow signs to A134 Sudbury. Nayland is 6 miles out. Entrance to farm approximately 800m past village.*

♥ *Short breaks Oct-Easter. 3-night weekends or 4-night midweek breaks at 70% full-week rate.*

Pets ♉ ⌂♉ Unit ▥ TV ◨▨▨ ◻ ▯ ▯ ▯ ◻✿
General ♨ ▥ ♠ P ◻ S Leisure ⚲ ⚲ ∪ ♿ Shop 0.5 miles Pub < 0.5 miles

NORFOLK BROADS

See under Norwich, Wroxham

NORWICH, Norfolk Map ref 3C1 — GUEST ACCOMMODATION

★★★
GUEST ACCOMMODATION

B&B per room per night
s £35.00–£40.00
d £40.00–£48.00

Edmar Lodge

64 Earlham Road, Norwich NR2 3DF **t** (01603) 615599 **f** (01603) 495599 **e** mail@edmarlodge.co.uk
w edmarlodge.co.uk

open All year
bedrooms 3 double, 1 twin, 1 family
bathrooms All en suite
payment Credit/debit cards, cash/cheques, euros

Edmar Lodge is a family-run guesthouse where you will receive a warm welcome from Ray and Sue. We are situated only ten minutes' walk from the city centre. All rooms have en suite facilities and digital TV. We are well known for our excellent breakfasts that set you up for the day.

⊕ *On the B1108. Off the Norwich ring road.*

Pets ♉ ⌂♉ Room ⌂ TV ♦ ▯ General ♨ ▥ ♠ P ✄ ▦ ♿✿

SEDGEFORD, Norfolk Map ref 3B1 — SELF CATERING

★★★★
SELF CATERING

Units **1**
Sleeps **8**

Low season per wk
£452.00–£531.00
High season per wk
£578.00–£699.00

Cobble Cottage, Sedgeford

Norfolk Country Cottages, Carlton House, Market Place, Reepham, Norwich NR10 4JJ
t (01603) 871872 **f** (01603) 870304 **e** info@norfolkcottages.co.uk
w norfolkcottages.co.uk/properties/841

open All year
payment Credit/debit cards, cash/cheques, euros

Sedgeford is close to both the sandy beaches of the North Norfolk Heritage Coast and the west-facing coastline of the Wash, and the RSPB reserves of Titchwell Marsh and Snettisham. Recently refurbished with two car-parking bays, parts of the cottage are thought to date from the late 1700s.

⊕ *Take A149 from King's Lynn, then B1454 towards Docking. Left onto gravel track 100yds past 30mph sign. Access to cottage at the rear.*

♥ *3- to 6-night stays available Oct-Apr (excl Bank Holidays and school half-terms) and sometimes from Apr-Oct.*

Pets ♉ ⌂♉ Unit ▥ TV ◨▨▨ ◻ ▯ ▯ ▯ ✿
General ♨ ▥ ♠ P ✄ ◻ S Leisure ∪ Shop 2 miles Pub < 0.5 miles

SIBTON, Suffolk Map ref 3C2 — SELF CATERING

★★★★
SELF CATERING

Units **1**
Sleeps **1–5**

Low season per wk
£230.00–£390.00
High season per wk
£390.00–£565.00

Cardinal Cottage, Sibton, Saxmundham

contact Mr & Mrs Eric Belton, Cardinal Cottage, Pouy Street, Sibton, Saxmundham IP17 2JH
t (01728) 660111   **e** jan.belton@btinternet.com   **w** cardinalcottageholidays.co.uk

open All year
payment Cash/cheques

Delightfully cosy, period, timber-framed cottage with spectacular beams. Three bedrooms, sitting room, dining room, kitchen and bathroom, all fully equipped to high standard. Enclosed private garden with car park. Close Heritage Coast, Minsmere, Aldeburgh and Southwold. Ideal base for walkers and bird-watchers, or those after a quiet country retreat.

⊕ From A12 at Yoxford, A1120 to Peasenhall. Through Yoxford into Sibton. At signposted nursery school turn right, over junction to right-hand bend. Cardinal Cottage on left.

♥ 3- and 4- night breaks available Nov-Mar (excl Christmas, New Year and Easter).

Pets 🐕 🐾   Unit 🛏 📺 🍽 ▦ 🖥 🍴🍷 ⏛ 🔲 ✿
General 🗺 ▦ ⚲ P ✂ Ⓢ   Leisure ∪ 🚲   Shop 0.75 miles   Pub < 0.5 miles

SOUTHWOLD, Suffolk Map ref 3C2 — SELF CATERING

Rating Applied For
SELF CATERING

Units **1**
Sleeps **1–6**

Low season per wk
Min £400.00
High season per wk
Max £800.00

15 Stradbroke Road, Southwold

contact H A Adnams, 89 High Street, Southwold IP18 6DP
t (01502) 723292   **f** (01502) 724794   **w** haadnams.com

A delightful family house, sympathetically modernised to a high standard. Situated close to the sea and within easy reach of the shops and town centre. Strictly non-smoking.

open All year
payment Credit/debit cards

Pets 🐕   Unit 🛏 📺 🍽 ▦ 🖥 🍴🍷 ✿
General 🗺 P ✂   Leisure ✎ ∪   Shop < 0.5 miles   Pub < 0.5 miles

STOKE-BY-NAYLAND, Suffolk Map ref 3B2 — GUEST ACCOMMODATION

★★★★
INN

B&B per room per night
s £65.00–£85.00
d £65.00–£95.00
Evening meal per person
£8.00–£25.00

The Angel Inn

Polstead Street, Stoke by Nayland, Colchester CO6 4SA   **t** (01206) 263245   **e** info@theangelinn.net   **w** theangelinn.net

A 16thC inn situated in one of Constable's favourite villages. Offering quality food and a busy ambience. Five miles from the A12 and two miles from the A134.

open All year
bedrooms 5 double, 1 twin
bathrooms All en suite
payment Credit/debit cards, cash/cheques

Pets 🐕 £🐕 🐎   Room 🛁 ☎ 📺 🍵 🍷   General 🗺1 P 🍽 ✕ 🛏 🌼 🖥 ✿

TATTERSETT, Norfolk Map ref 3B1 — SELF CATERING

★★★★
SELF CATERING

Units **5**
Sleeps **4–6**

Low season per wk
£200.00–£280.00
High season per wk
£400.00–£580.00

Tatt Valley Holiday Cottages, Tattersett

contact Mr Thomas Hurn, Tatt Valley Holiday Cottages, Tattersett PE31 8RT
t (01485) 528506   **e** enquiries@norfolkholidayhomes.co.uk   **w** norfolkholidayhomes.co.uk

Luxury barn conversions. High-standard accommodation with many original features. A large games barn with facilities for all ages. Situated on a working farm near to Burnham Market and the Norfolk coast.

open All year
payment Cash/cheques

Pets 🐕 £🐕 🐾   Unit 🛏 📺 🍽 ▦ 🖥 🍴🍷 ⏛ 🔲 ✿
General 🗺 ▦ ⚲ P Ⓢ   Leisure ✎   Shop 2 miles   Pub 2 miles

Chequers Inn

★★★★
INN

B&B per room per night
s £40.00
d £60.00
Evening meal per person
£6.00–£25.00

Griston Road, Thompson IP24 1PX **t** (01953) 483360 **f** (01953) 488092
e richard@chequers-inn.wanadoo.co.uk **w** thompson-chequers.co.uk

open All year
bedrooms 2 double, 1 twin
bathrooms All en suite
payment Credit/debit cards, cash/cheques

The Chequers is a 16thC village inn with a thatched roof, still retaining all of its original character. A true country retreat, in the heart of Breckland. Local produce and fresh fish a speciality. Local real ales include Breckland Gold, Wolf, Wherry, Adnams and Greene King IPA to name a few.

✦ Twelve miles north east of Thetford, just off the A1075.

Pets 🐾 Room 📺 General P X 🍴 Leisure U

Thornham Hall and Restaurant

★★★★★
GUEST ACCOMMODATION
SILVER AWARD

B&B per room per night
s £65.00–£95.00
d £100.00
Evening meal per person
£17.50–£25.00

Thornham Hall, Thornham Magna, Eye IP23 8HA **t** (01379) 783314 **f** (01379) 788347
e hallrestaurant@aol.com **w** thornhamhallandrestaurant.com

open All year
bedrooms 2 double, 1 suite
bathrooms All en suite
payment Credit/debit cards, cash

Thornham Hall & Restaurant offer exclusive accommodation in the hall and delightful dining in the restaurant in the converted coach house. Thornham Hall is situated in its own private park at the centre of the Thornham estate, the baronial home of the Henniker family since 1750.

✦ From Stoke Ash on A140 turn left towards Thornham Magna. After 300yds turn right and go through village past road to Gislingham and past church. Turn in at drive marked Thornham Hall.

Pets 🐾 Room General P X Leisure U

Potash Farm Cottage, Lavenham

★★★★
SELF CATERING

Units 1
Sleeps 4
Low season per wk
£230.00–£387.00
High season per wk
£397.00–£518.00

t (01284) 828396 & 07812 956402 **f** (01284) 827224 **e** emmadib@aol.com

Comfortable cottage, idyllic country surroundings, excellent walks, abundant wildlife. One twin, one double and double sofa bed. Cosy woodburner. Enclosed private garden overlooking owner's large fenced pond. Lavenham three miles.

open All year
payment Cash/cheques, euros

Pets 🐾 Unit General P Leisure U Shop 2.5 miles Pub 1.5 miles

Bolding Way Holidays, Weybourne

★★★★
SELF CATERING

Units 1
Sleeps 2
Low season per wk
£250.00–£410.00
High season per wk
£320.00–£440.00

contact Mr Charlie Harrison, Bolding Way Holidays, Bolding Way, Weybourne, Holt NR25 7SW
t (01263) 588666 **e** holidays@boldingway.co.uk **w** boldingway.co.uk

Private secluded garden and summerhouse. Plenty to see and do for all ages. Use of games room: pool table, table tennis, darts, selection of board games. On heritage coastline. Ten minutes' walk to the sea.

open All year
payment Cash/cheques

Pets 🐾 Unit General P S Leisure U Shop < 0.5 miles Pub < 0.5 miles

WICKHAM SKEITH, Suffolk Map ref 3B2 — SELF CATERING

★★★
SELF CATERING

Units **1**
Sleeps **1–4**
Low season per wk
£195.00–£235.00
High season per wk
£255.00–£275.00

Netus Barn, Wickham Skeith, Eye

contact Mrs Joy Homan, Street Farm, Eye IP23 8LP
t (01449) 766275 e joygeoff@homansf.freeserve.co.uk w netusbarn.co.uk

Single-storey period barn, well-equipped kitchen-cum-living room, bathroom (shower), two twin bedrooms, disabled-friendly, parking, patio garden. Rural views. Dogs welcome.

open All year
payment Cash/cheques

Pets 🐕 🐾 Unit 🏠 📺 🔲 📼 💷 🍳 ✳
General 🛏 🍴 P ✂ S Leisure ∪ Shop 2 miles Pub 2 miles

WINGFIELD, Suffolk Map ref 3B2 — GUEST ACCOMMODATION

★★★★
BED & BREAKFAST
SILVER AWARD

Gables Farm

Earsham Street, Wingfield, Diss IP21 5RH t (01379) 586355 & 07824 445464
e enquiries@gablesfarm.co.uk w gablesfarm.co.uk

B&B per room per night
s £38.00–£42.00
d £58.00–£62.00

open All year except Christmas and New Year
bedrooms 2 double, 1 twin
bathrooms All en suite
payment Cash/cheques

A 16thC timbered farmhouse in moated gardens. Wingfield is a quiet village in the centre of East Anglia, central to everywhere and in the middle of nowhere!

⊕ See website for details of how to find us.

Pets 🐕 🐿 Room 📺 🛁 🍵 General 🛏 🍴 P ✂ 🥘 ✳ Leisure ∪

WORTHAM, Suffolk Map ref 3B2 — SELF CATERING

★★★★
SELF CATERING

Units **5**
Sleeps **4–10**
Low season per wk
£275.00–£760.00
High season per wk
£570.00–£1,660.00

Ivy House Farm, Wortham, Diss

contact Mr Paul Bradley, Ivy House Farm, Wortham, Diss IP22 1RD
t (01379) 898395 f (01379) 898395 e prjsdrad@aol.com w ivyhousefarmcottages.co.uk

open All year
payment Cash/cheques, euros

This peaceful complex, set in spacious grounds surrounded by common land in the heart of East Anglia, consists of a 17thC farmhouse and four purpose-built cottages, one of which has facilities for the disabled. Other facilities include heated indoor swimming pool and cosy barn with table-tennis, pool, piano, snooker table and library.

⊕ A143 Bury St Edmunds into Wortham. In Wortham, 1st turn left past village sign opposite school towards church. After 60yds, left to Long Green/Redgrave. Farm 0.5 miles on left.

Pets 🐕 £🐕 Unit 🏠 📺 🔲 📼 💷 🍳 🍵 🍳 ✳
General 🛏 🍴 P 🅿 S Leisure 🎣 ⚲ ⚲ ∪ 🚲 Shop 0.5 miles Pub 0.5 miles

Best foot forward

Walkers feel at home in accommodation participating in our Walkers Welcome scheme. Look out for the symbol. Consider walking all or part of a long-distance route – go online at nationaltrail.co.uk.

WROXHAM, Norfolk Map ref 3C1

★★★★
SELF CATERING

Units **6**
Sleeps **2–6**

Low season per wk
£420.00–£530.00
High season per wk
£685.00–£920.00

Old Farm Cottages, Tunstead, Norwich

contact Mrs Kay Paterson, Old Farm Cottages, Tunstead, Norwich NR12 8HS
t (01692) 536612 **e** mail@oldfarmcottages.fsnet.co.uk **w** oldfarmcottages.com

payment Credit/debit cards, cash/cheques

Beautifully furnished cottage barn conversions, providing outstandingly comfortable and well-appointed accommodation. Indoor swimming pool, spa, fitness room, play area and games room. Perfectly situated for coast, countryside, riverside pubs, boat/canoe hire, stately homes and Norwich. Closed 18 November to 22 December, open Christmas and New Year. Closed 6 January to 10 February.

⊕ A1151 through Wroxham. After 4 miles branch left, signposted Dilham. Left at crossroad and follow this road until you come to Old Farm Cottages.

♥ See website.

Pets 🐾 🐕 Unit 🏠 📺 ⊟ 🎮 ■ 🔊 🔌 🍴 💻 ⚙
General 🛋 🏠 🅿 ⓢ Leisure 🎣 ⚲ 🚲 🏊 Shop 1.5 miles Pub 1.5 miles

London

A city of secrets and surprises

So you think you know London? Take a closer look and you'll discover a treasure house of secret attractions just crying out to be explored. Just remember to leave yourself with enough time (a year should do).

Visit London
visitlondon.com
0870 156 6366

The Globe Theatre, Bankside

Hampton Court

South Bank

Marvel (and cringe) at how operations were performed in The Old Operating Theatre Museum in Southwark. This fascinating theatre along with its Herb Garret were built in the roof space of the English Baroque Church of St Thomas's. Get even more surreal and visit Dali Universe on the South Bank, where you can enter the psyche of the genius artist and see mind-bending furniture, film sets and original Dali sculptures. But if there's only one thing you see, make it the Tutankhamun and the Golden Age of the Pharaohs exhibition at The O2 (formerly the Dome). This is the first time in almost 30 years that artefacts of the boy-king's burial chamber have left their home in Egypt. See the fabulous golden canopic cofinette and get a glimpse of the golden age of the Pharaohs.

One of the joys of London is the shopping. From the 83 colourful street markets such as Brick Lane to the most exclusive designer stores on Bond Street, there's retail therapy enough to keep anyone sane. Check out the Mall Antiques Arcade in Islington. Set in a former tram station and packed with over 35 specialist dealers, it's a magnet for interior designers.

And did you know there's a viewing area inside Wellington Arch in Hyde Park Corner where you can see into the gardens of Buckingham Palace? Or that Britain's first botanical garden was at the enigmatic Chelsea Physic Garden? Or that at Firepower – the Royal Artillery Museum in Woolwich – you can trace the story of the Royal Arsenal from Henry VIII and the battle of Crecy to peacekeeping mission in Bosnia?

Another fascinating trip out is to HMS Belfast, the historic World War II battleship that's now a floating naval museum. Explore all nine decks from the Captain's Bridge to the boiler room.

Destinations

Greenwich

Stand with one foot in the East and one foot in the West astride the Greenwich Meridian, and set your watch by the red 'Time Ball' that drops each day at 1300hrs precisely and has done so for 170 years. There's a laid-back feel to Greenwich. Take time to browse the market stalls – crafts, antiques, records, bric-a-brac and, most famously, vintage clothing. Then pop into a riverside pub for lunch and some mellow jazz.

Kew

Stroll the finest botanic gardens in the country – 400 acres and 40,000 plant varieties. The Palm House hosts a tropical jungle of plants including bananas, pawpaws and mangoes. Marvel at the giant Amazonian water lily, aloe vera and several carnivorous plants in the Princess of Wales Conservatory where ten climatic zones are recreated. You'll find activities for children and a full calendar of special events.

Notting Hill

A colourful district filled with clubs, bars and dance venues, and now trendier than ever. Wander the celebrated Portobello Road market where over 1,500 traders compete for your custom at the Saturday antiques market. Find jewellery, silverware, paintings and more. Summertime is carnival time and the Caribbean influence has ensured the phenomenal growth of the world-famous, multi-cultural Notting Hill Carnival. Join the throng of millions – exotic costume recommended. On a quieter day, visit beautiful Holland Park, a haven of greenery with its own theatre.

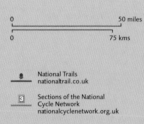

National Trails
nationaltrail.co.uk

Sections of the National
Cycle Network
nationalcyclenetwork.org.uk

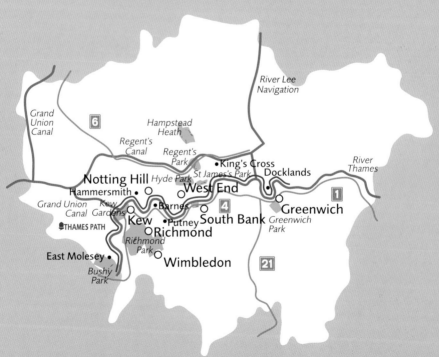

Notting Hill Carnival

Greenwich Park

West End

Tate Modern, South Bank

Wimbledon

Richmond Park

Palm House, Kew

Richmond

The River Thames runs through the heart of the beautiful borough of Richmond. Arrive by summer riverboat from Westminster Pier and explore the delightful village with its riverside pubs, specialist boutiques, galleries and museums. Glimpse herds of deer in the Royal parks and step into history in Henry VIII's magnificent Hampton Court Palace, the oldest Tudor palace in England. Round off your visit with a world-class rugby match at England's Twickenham Stadium.

South Bank

One of London's coolest quarters, the South Bank positively teems with must-see attractions and cultural highlights. Tate Modern has gained a reputation as one of the greatest modern art galleries in the world boasting works by Moore, Picasso, Dali, Warhol and Hepworth. Take in a play at the National Theatre or Shakespeare's magnificently restored Globe, and hit the heights on British Airways London Eye, the world's highest observation wheel.

West End

Shop in the best department stores and international designer boutiques in Oxford Street, Regent Street and Bond Street. Take lunch in a stylish eatery, and then see a major exhibition at the Royal Academy of Arts. At the heart of the West End are the landmarks of Trafalgar Square and Piccadilly Circus, and just a few minutes' stroll will take you into legendary Soho, the entertainment heart of the city, crammed with bars, pubs, clubs and restaurants.

Wimbledon

Wimbledon village is only ten miles from the centre of London but you could be in the heart of the countryside. Enjoy the open spaces of Wimbledon Common then wander along the charming high street with its unique medieval buildings, boutiques and pavement cafes. Visit the legendary All England Club where the Lawn Tennis Museum is a must-see for fans of the sport, not to mention the chance to tour the legendary Centre Court.

Places to visit

BBC Television Centre Tours
Shepherd's Bush, W12
0870 603 0304
bbc.co.uk/tours
Behind the scenes of world-famous television studios

British Airways London Eye
South Bank, SE1
0870 990 8883
ba-londoneye.com
The world's largest observation wheel

British Museum
WC1
(020) 7323 8299
thebritishmuseum.ac.uk
One of the great museums of the world

Buckingham Palace
SW1
(020) 7766 7300
royalcollection.org.uk
HM The Queen's official London residence

Churchill Museum and Cabinet War Rooms
SW1
(020) 7930 6961
iwm.org.uk/cabinet
Churchill's wartime headquarters

Hampton Court Palace
East Molesey, KT8
0870 752 7777
hrp.org.uk
Outstanding Tudor palace with famous maze

HMS Belfast
Southwark, SE1
(020) 7940 6300
iwm.org.uk
World War II cruiser, now a naval time capsule

Imperial War Museum
Lambeth, SE1
(020) 7416 5320
iwm.org.uk
History of Britain at war since 1914

Kensington Palace State Apartments
W8
0870 751 5170
hrp.org.uk
Home to the Royal Ceremonial Dress Collection

Kew Gardens (Royal Botanic Gardens)
Richmond, TW9
(020) 8332 5655
kew.org
Stunning plant collections and magnificent glasshouses

London Aquarium
South Bank, SE1
(020) 7967 8000
londonaquarium.co.uk
Come face-to-face with two-metre long sharks

The London Dungeon
Southwark, SE1
(020) 7403 7221
thedungeons.com
So much fun it's frightening!

London Wetland Centre
Barnes, SW16
(020) 8409 4400
wwt.org.uk
Observe wildlife in recreated wetland habitats

Madame Tussauds and the London Planetarium
Marylebone, NW1
0870 999 0046
madame-tussauds.com
Meet the stars then enter the Chamber of Horrors

National Gallery
Trafalgar Square, WC2
(020) 7747 2885
nationalgallery.org.uk
One of the great collections of European art

National Maritime Museum
Outstanding
Customer Service
– Silver Winner
Greenwich, SE10
(020) 8858 4422
nmm.ac.uk
Over 2 million exhibits of seafaring history

Natural History Museum
Kensington, SW7
(020) 7942 5000
nhm.ac.uk
World-class collections bringing the natural world to life

Science Museum
Kensington, SW7
0870 870 4868
sciencemuseum.org.uk
State-of-the-art simulators, IMAX cinema and more

Somerset House
Strand, WC2
(020) 7845 4600

somerset-house.org.uk
Magnificent art collections in grand 18th century house

Tate Modern
Bankside, SE1
(020) 7887 8008
tate.org.uk
Britain's flagship museum of modern art

Tower Bridge Exhibition
SE1
(020) 7403 3761
towerbridge.org.uk
Learn all about the world's most famous bridge

Tower of London
EC3

0870 756 6060
hrp.org.uk
The Crown Jewels and 900 years of history

Victoria and Albert Museum
Kensington, SW7
(020) 7942 2000
vam.ac.uk
3,000 years of art and design

Diary dates 2008

New Year's Day Parade
Parliament Square, SW1 to Berkeley Street, W1
londonparade.co.uk
1 Jan

London Boat Show
ExCeL London, E16
londonboatshow.com
11 – 20 Jan

Oxford and Cambridge Boat Race
River Thames from Putney, SW15 to Mortlake, SW14
theboatrace.org
29 Mar

Chelsea Flower Show
rhs.org.uk
20 – 24 May*

Trooping the Colour
Horseguards Parade, SW1
royal.gov.uk
14 Jun

Wimbledon Lawn Tennis Championships
wimbledon.org
23 Jun – 6 Jul

The Proms
Royal Albert Hall, SW7
bbc.co.uk/proms
18 Jul – 13 Sep

Notting Hill Carnival
Streets around Ladbroke Grove, W10 and W11
visitlondon.com
24 – 25 Aug

The Mayor's Thames Festival
Westminster Bridge, SW1 to Tower Bridge, SE1,
thamesfestival.org
13 – 14 Sep

Lord Mayor's Show
From the Guildhall, EC2 to the Royal Courts of Justice, WC2 and back
lordmayorsshow.org
8 Nov

* provisional date at time of going to press

Tourist Information Centres

When you arrive at your destination, visit an Official Partner Tourist Information Centre for quality assured help with accommodation and information about local attractions and events, or email your request before you go. To search for attractions and Tourist Information Centres on the move just text INFO to 62233, and a web link will be sent to your mobile phone.

Britain & London Visitor Centre	1 Regent Street	0870 156636	blvcenquiries@visitlondon.com
Croydon	Katharine Street	(020) 8253 1009	tic@croydon.gov.uk
Greenwich	2 Cutty Sark Gardens	0870 608 2000	tic@greenwich.gov.uk
Lewisham	199-201 Lewisham High Street	(020) 8297 8317	tic@lewisham.gov.uk
Swanley	London Road	(01322) 614660	touristinfo@swanley.org.uk

The London Eye

Travel info

By road:
Major trunk roads into London include: A1, M1, A5, A10, A11, M11, A13, A2, M2, A23, A3, M3, A4, M4, A40, M40, A41, M25 (London orbital).
Transport for London is responsible for running London's bus services, the underground rail network and the DLR (Docklands Light Railway), and river and tram services.
(020) 7222 1234 (24-hour telephone service; calls answered in rotation).

By rail:
Main rail terminals: Victoria/Waterloo/ Charing Cross – serving the South/South East; King's Cross – serving the North East; Euston – serving the North West/Midlands; Liverpool Street – serving the East; Paddington – serving the Thames Valley/West.

By air:
Fly into London City, London Gatwick, London Heathrow, London Luton and London Stansted.

For more information, go to visitlondon.com/travel or tfl.gov.uk/journeyplanner

Horse Guards Parade

Find out more

By logging on to visitlondon.com
or calling 0870 1 LONDON for the following:

- **A London tourist information pack**

- **Tourist information on London**
  Speak to an expert for information and advice on
  museums, galleries, attractions, riverboat trips,
  sightseeing tours, theatre, shopping, eating out and
  much more! Or simply go to visitlondon.com.

- **Accommodation reservations**

Or visit one of London's tourist information centres
listed opposite.

Which part of London?
The majority of tourist accommodation is situated in the
central parts of London and is therefore very convenient
for most of the city's attractions and nightlife.

However, there are many establishments in Outer
London which provide other advantages, such as easier
parking. In the accommodation pages which follow, you
will find establishments listed under INNER LONDON
(covering the E1 to W14 London Postal Area) and
OUTER LONDON (covering the remainder of Greater
London). Colour maps 6 and 7 at the front of the guide
show place names and London postal area codes and will
help you to locate accommodation in your chosen area.

where to stay in
London

All place names in the blue bands are shown on the maps at the front of this guide.

Accommodation symbols
Symbols give useful information about services and facilities. Inside the back-cover flap you can find a key to these symbols. Keep it open for easy reference.

INNER LONDON

LONDON W5 — GUEST ACCOMMODATION

★★
GUEST HOUSE

B&B per room per night
s £37.00–£49.00
d £49.00–£61.00

Grange Lodge

48-50 Grange Road, London W5 5BX t (020) 8567 1049 f (020) 8579 5350
e enquiries@londonlodgehotels.com w londonlodgehotels.com

Quiet, comfortable hotel, close to three Underground stations. Midway central London and Heathrow. Colour TV, tea-/coffee-making facilities, radio/alarm, most rooms en suite.

open All year
bedrooms 2 double, 2 twin, 8 single, 2 family
bathrooms 9 en suite
payment Credit/debit cards, cash/cheques, euros

Pets 🐕 🐾 Room 📺 🛁 General 🚭 🛏 P 🅿 ♿ ☀

OUTER LONDON

RICHMOND — GUEST ACCOMMODATION

★★★
GUEST ACCOMMODATION

B&B per room per night
s £32.50–£39.50
d £55.00–£69.00

Ivy Cottage

Upper Ham Road, Ham Common, Richmond TW10 5LA t (020) 8940 8601 & 07742 278247
e taylor@dbta.freeserve.co.uk w dbta.freeserve.co.uk

Charming, wisteria-clad Georgian home offering exceptional views over Ham Common. Period features dating from 1760. Large garden. Self-catering an option. Good bus route and parking.

open All year
bedrooms 1 double, 1 twin, 1 single, 1 family
bathrooms 2 en suite, 2 private
payment Cash/cheques, euros

Pets 🐕 🐾 Room 📺 🛁 General 🚭 8 ✂ ✕ ☀ Leisure ⛵

Tales of the city

Allow the London Explorer to guide you through the streets of the capital leaving no stone unturned. All you need for the perfect day out is in this handy package – featuring an easy-to-use fold out map and illustrated guide. You can purchase the Explorer series from good bookshops and online at visitbritaindirect.com.

Quality
visitor attractions

VisitBritain operates a Visitor Attraction Quality Assurance Service.

Participating attractions are visited annually by trained, impartial assessors who look at all aspects of the visit, from initial telephone enquiries to departure, customer service to catering, as well as all facilities and activities.

Only those attractions which have been assessed by Enjoy England and meet the standard receive the quality marque, your sign of a Quality Assured Visitor Attraction.

Look out for the quality marque and visit with confidence.

South East England

Berkshire, Buckinghamshire, East Sussex, Hampshire, Isle of Wight, Kent, Oxfordshire, Surrey, West Sussex

Family fun in classic England

The South East is your quintessential slice of England. And whilst there's plenty for singles and couples to enjoy, this region is bursting with great family days out that the kids will treasure forever.

Tourism South East
visitsoutheastengland.com
(023) 8062 5400

Deal Beach, Kent Coast

Sheffield Park Garden, East Sussex   Winchester Cathedral, Hampshire

Uffington, Oxfordshire

With 400 miles of glorious coastline including the towering chalk cliff of Beachy Head and kid-friendly beaches galore, the South East has always been a family favourite. Add the gorgeous countryside of the South Downs, evocative castles like Leeds and a wealth of colourful venues such as Woburn Safari Park, and this region has it all. As you'd expect, sailing is big in these parts, and you can simply stroll around one of the many marinas or set sail for a course at Calshot Activities Centre near Southampton. And if you're really brave, try one of the extreme watersports like wakeboarding. Finally, head off to a rural inn where you can unwind, enjoy a pint of real ale and savour a superb bistro-like meal.

Experience life in the Dickens era at Dickens World Kent with its Victorian shopping mall, music hall and an exciting time travel ride. With a new Viking Land and two top-secret new rides, Legoland Windsor is even more of a draw for all the family (time your visit right and catch their flagship firework bonanza). And if you're in battle mood, charge over to the interactive visitor centre at Battle Abbey in East Sussex and experience the Battle of Hastings brought to terrifying life.

Check out the atmospheric Winchester Cathedral where the foundations were laid in 1079 in stone brought from the Isle of Wight. Drop anchor at the Portsmouth Historic Dockyard, too, and marvel at HMS Victory and the Mary Rose. And don't miss Oxford Castle, where boutique stalls, pulsating bars and a feast of visual arts are set against the prison backdrop.

South East England is a region rich in experiences. It has something to offer every age group and every traveller. Whether you are looking at visiting for a weekend or a month this region has everything you could want.

Destinations

Brighton

England's favourite seaside city, Brighton is historic, elegant and offbeat. Wander a beachfront packed with cafes and bars, then step into town for fine antiques and designer boutiques. Don't miss the Royal Pavilion, surely the most extravagant royal palace in Europe, and come in springtime for an arts festival second to none. Find the world's cuisine in over 400 restaurants, and then relax with dance, comedy or music in the thriving pub and club culture. Brighton has it all – and just 49 minutes from central London.

Canterbury

Marvel with fellow 'pilgrims' from the four corners of the world as Canterbury Cathedral dominates your approach to this World Heritage Site. Let Canterbury Tales 'Medieval Misadventures' take you on a journey back to Chaucer's England. Wander traffic-free daytime streets to enjoy historic buildings and modern attractions, and then head further afield to explore the valleys, woods and coastline of this beautiful region of Kent.

Dover

Discover the rich history of Dover – 'the lock and key of England' - and its celebrated White Cliffs. Tour Dover Castle and relive the epic sieges of 1216-17. Delve into the secrets contained in the Wartime Tunnels, nerve centre for the evacuation of Dunkirk and Command Centre from whose depths Churchill witnessed the Battle of Britain. Enjoy the pier and stroll the stylish marina before heading out of town to tour the scenic beaches of White Cliffs Country.

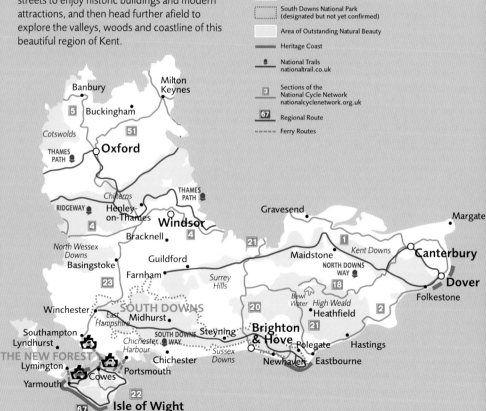

0	50 miles
0	75 kms

National Park

South Downs National Park (designated but not yet confirmed)

Area of Outstanding Natural Beauty

Heritage Coast

National Trails nationaltrail.co.uk

3 Sections of the National Cycle Network nationalcyclenetwork.org.uk

67 Regional Route

Ferry Routes

Windsor Castle

Canterbury Cathedral

Freshwater Bay, Isle of Wight

Dover Castle

New Forest

Oxford spires

Brighton seafront

Isle of Wight

Sixty miles of spectacular coastline, picturesque coves and safe bathing in bays of golden sand. Explore the maritime history of Cowes, the beautiful and historic town of Newport and take the family to the welcoming resorts of Shanklin and Ventnor. Follow the trail of dinosaurs, ancient tribes, Romans and monarchs in this diamond-shaped treasure trove.

New Forest

Roam a landscape little changed since William the Conqueror gave it his special protection over 900 years ago. You'll meet wild heath and dappled woodland, thatched hamlets, bustling market towns, and tiny streams meandering to the sparkling expanse of the Solent. Watch ponies eating by the roadside, pigs foraging for beechnuts, and donkeys ambling along the streets. As evening falls, hear the humming song of the nightjar, glimpse deer and watch bats flitting across the darkening sky.

Oxford

This ancient university city is both timeless and modern. Wander among its 'dreaming spires' and tranquil college quadrangles. Find national and international treasures, displayed in a family of museums whose scope and scholarship is second to none. Hire a punt and spend the afternoon drifting along the River Cherwell or seek out bustling shops and fashionable restaurants. Experience candlelit evensong in college chapels or Shakespeare in the park, and after dark enjoy the cosmopolitan buzz of countless cafés, pubs and theatres.

Windsor

Explore Windsor and the Royal Borough, to the west of London. Gaze at the priceless treasures in the Royal Collection at Windsor Castle, royal home and fortress for over 900 years. Henry VI founded Eton College in 1440. Lose yourself in the history of the cloisters and the chapel. Sail the churning rapids at Legoland's incredible Vikings' River Splash, and find peace and quiet in the rural landscape of Royal Berkshire, traversed by the timeless flow of the Thames.

Places to visit

Bedgebury National Pinetum & Forest
Goudhurst, Kent
(01580) 879820
forestry.gov.uk/bedgebury
World's finest conifer collection

Blenheim Palace
Woodstock, Oxfordshire
(01993) 811091
blenheimpalace.com
Baroque palace and beautiful parkland
(parkland only)

Canterbury Cathedral
Kent
(01227) 762862
canterbury-cathedral.org
Seat of the Archbishop of Canterbury

Carisbrooke Castle
Newport, Isle Of Wight
(01983) 522107
english-heritage.org.uk
Splendid Norman castle

Dickens World
Chatham, Kent
(01634) 890421
dickensworld.co.uk
Fascinating journey through Dickens' lifetime

Dinosaur Isle
Sandown, Isle Of Wight
(01983) 404344
dinosaurisle.com
Britain's first purpose-built dinosaur attraction

Dover Castle and Secret Wartime Tunnels
Kent
(01304) 211067
english-heritage.org.uk
Historic nerve centre for Battle of Britain
(outdoors only)

Exbury Gardens and Steam Railway
Hampshire
(023) 8089 1203
exbury.co.uk.
Over 200 acres of woodland garden

Explosion! Museum of Naval Firepower
Gosport, Hampshire
(023) 9250 5600
explosion.org.uk
Naval firepower from gunpowder to the Exocet

Groombridge Place Gardens and Enchanted Forest
Tunbridge Wells, Kent
(01892) 861444
groombridge.co.uk
Peaceful gardens and ancient woodland

Hever Castle and Gardens
near Edenbridge, Kent
(01732) 865224
hevercastle.co.uk
Beautiful childhood home of Anne Boleyn
(gardens only)

Highclere Castle and Gardens
Newbury, Hampshire
(01635) 253210
highclerecastle.co.uk
Imposing Victorian castle and parkland
(parkland only)

The Historic Dockyard Chatham
Kent
(01634) 823800
thedockyard.co.uk
Maritime heritage site with stunning architecture
(except galleries)

INTECH Science Centre
Winchester, Hampshire
(01962) 863791
intech-uk.com
Hands-on science and technology exhibits

LEGOLAND Windsor
Berkshire
0870 504 0404
legoland.co.uk
More Lego bricks than you ever dreamed possible

Loseley Park
Guildford, Surrey
(01483) 304440
loseley-park.com
Beautiful Elizabethan mansion and gardens

National Motor Museum Beaulieu
Brockenhurst, Hampshire
(01590) 612345
beaulieu.co.uk
Vintage cars and stately home in New Forest
(gardens only)

Osborne House
East Cowes, Isle of Wight
(01983) 200022
english-heritage.org.uk
Queen Victoria's seaside retreat

Paultons Park
Romsey, Hampshire
(023) 8081 4442
paultonspark.co.uk
Over 50 rides for all the family

🐕 Pets Welcome
Assistance dogs only

Diary dates 2008

Polesden Lacey
near Dorking, Surrey
(01372) 452048
nationaltrust.org.uk
Opulent Edwardian interiors in downland setting
 (grounds only)

RHS Garden Wisley
Woking, Surrey
0845 260 9000
rhs.org.uk
A working encyclopedia of British gardening

Royal Botanic Gardens, Wakehurst Place
near Haywards Heath, West Sussex
(01444) 894000
rbgkew.org.uk
Beautiful gardens throughout the seasons

Spinnaker Tower
Portsmouth, Hampshire
(023) 9285 7520
spinnakertower.co.uk
Breathtaking views from 170-metre landmark

Thorpe Park
Chertsey, Surrey
0870 444 4466
thorpepark.com
An adrenaline-charged day out for all the family

Windsor Castle
Berkshire
(020) 7766 7304
royalcollection.org.uk
Official residence of HM The Queen

New Year Steamday
Didcot Railway
didcotrailwaycentre.org.uk
1 Jan

Brighton Festival
Various locations, Brighton
brightonfestival.org
3 – 25 May*

Royal Windsor Horse Show
Windsor Castle
royal-windsor-horse-show.co.uk
8 – 11 May

Royal Ascot
ascot.co.uk
17 – 21 Jun

Henley Royal Regatta
River Thames
hrr.co.uk
2 – 6 Jul

Parham Garden Weekend
Pulborough, West Sussex
parhaminsussex.co.uk
5 – 6 Jul*

Farnborough International Air Show
farnborough.com
14 – 20 Jul

New Forest Show
Brockenhurst, Hampshire
newforestshow.co.uk
29 – 31 Jul

Cowes Week
The Solent, Isle of Wight
skandiacowesweek.co.uk
2 – 9 Aug

Ringwood Carnival
ringwoodcarnival.org
20 Sep

* provisional date at time of going to press

Tourist Information Centres

When you arrive at your destination, visit an Official Partner Tourist Information Centre for quality assured help with accommodation and information about local attractions and events, or email your request before you go. To search for attractions and Tourist Information Centres on the move just text INFO to 62233, and a web link will be sent to your mobile phone.

Bicester	Unit 86a, Bicester Village	(01869) 369055	bicester.vc@cherwell-dc.gov.uk
Brighton	Pavilion Buildings	0906 711 2255**	brighton-tourism@brighton-hove.gov.uk
Canterbury	12/13 Sun Street	(01227) 378100	canterburyinformation@canterbury.gov.uk
Chichester	29a South Street	(01243) 775888	chitic@chichester.gov.uk
Cowes	9 The Arcade	(01983) 813818	info@islandbreaks.co.uk
Dover	The Old Town Gaol	(01304) 205108	tic@doveruk.com
Hastings	Queens Square	0845 274 1001	hic@hastings.gov.uk
Lyndhurst & New Forest	Main Car Park	(023) 8028 2269	information@nfdc.gov.uk
Newport	High Street	(01983) 813818	info@islandbreaks.co.uk
Oxford	15/16 Broad Street	(01865) 726871	tic@oxford.gov.uk
Portsmouth	The Hard	(023) 9282 6722	vis@portsmouthcc.gov.uk
Rochester	95 High Street	(01634) 843666	visitor.centre@medway.gov.uk
Royal Tunbridge Wells	The Pantiles	(01892) 515675	touristinformationcentre@ tunbridgewells.gov.uk
Ryde	81-83 Union Street	(01983) 813818	info@islandbreaks.co.uk
Sandown	8 High Street	(01983) 813818	info@islandbreaks.co.uk
Shanklin	67 High Street	(01983) 813818	info@islandbreaks.co.uk
Southampton	9 Civic Centre Road	(023) 8083 3333	tourist.information@southampton.gov.uk
Winchester	High Street	(01962) 840500	tourism@winchester.gov.uk
Windsor	Windsor Royal Shopping	(01753) 743900	windsor.tic@rbwm.gov.uk
Yarmouth	The Quay	(01983) 813818	info@islandbreaks.co.uk

** *calls to this number are charged at premium rate*

The Lee, Buckinghamshire

Chatham, Kent

Find out more

The following publications are available from Tourism South East by logging on to visitsoutheastengland.com or calling (023) 8062 5400:

Publications

- **Escape into the Countryside**
- **Great Days Out in Berkshire, Buckinghamshire and Oxfordshire**
- **Distinctive Country Inns**
- **We Know Just the Place**

E-Brochures

- **Family Fun**
- **Fine Tradition**
- **Just the Two of Us**
- **Great Days Out**
- **Go Golf**
- **Countryside**
- **Cities**

Travel info

By road:
From the North East – M1 & M25;
the North West – M6, M40 & M25;
the West and Wales – M4 & M25;
the East – M25;
the South West – M5, M4 & M25;
London – M25, M2, M20, M23, M3, M4 or M40.

By rail:
Regular services from London's Charing Cross, Victoria, Waterloo and Waterloo East stations to all parts of the South East. Further information on rail journeys in the South East can be obtained on 0845 748 4950.

By air:
Fly into London City, London Heathrow, London Gatwick, London Southend, Luton, Southampton, Shoreham (Brighton City) or Stanstead.

where to stay in
South East England

All place names in the blue bands are shown on the maps at the front of this guide.

Accommodation symbols
Symbols give useful information about services and facilities. Inside the back-cover flap you can find a key to these symbols. Keep it open for easy reference.

ADDERBURY, Oxfordshire Map ref 2C1   GUEST ACCOMMODATION

★ ★ ★
INN

B&B per room per night
s £45.00–£65.00
d £55.00–£85.00
Evening meal per person
£6.00–£15.00

The Bell Inn
High Street, Adderbury, Banbury OX17 3LS t (01295) 810338 e info@the-bell.com w the-bell.com

open All year
bedrooms 1 double, 1 twin
bathrooms 1 en suite, 1 private
payment Credit/debit cards, cash/cheques

Traditional English inn serving award-winning ales and home-cooked food. With its striking inglenook fireplace, the Bell offers a warm and friendly welcome to customers old and new. Quiet location, pretty village on the edge of the Cotswolds. Regular folk and quiz nights. Traditional pub games including 'Aunt Sally'!

⊕ *M40 jct 11 straight through Banbury (A4260). Once in Twyford, turn right after traffic lights, signposted West Adderbury. Bell situated on left down by church.*

Pets 🐕 ⌂ 🐾 🍽   Room 📺 🌢 ⌨   General 🛏 🌣 ♨ ⌇ ✕ 🕮 🔥 ✿   Leisure ∪ ⚲

BIDDENDEN, Kent Map ref 3B4   GUEST ACCOMMODATION

★ ★ ★ ★
GUEST ACCOMMODATION

B&B per room per night
s £40.00–£50.00
d £50.00–£65.00
Evening meal per person
£17.50

Heron Cottage
Biddenden, Ashford TN27 8HH t (01580) 291358 w heroncottage.info

bedrooms 3 double, 2 twin, 2 family
bathrooms 6 en suite
payment Cash/cheques

Situated between historic Biddenden and Sissinghurst Castle, this delightful cottage is set in five acres surrounded completely by farmland. The carefully furnished bedrooms are thoughtfully equipped and have co-ordinated soft furnishings. Breakfast is served in the smart dining room and there is a cosy lounge with an open fire. Open February to December.

⊕ *From Biddenden A262 west. 1st right after 0.25m, sharp left bend, cross bend, through stone pillars opposite, then left along unmade road.*

Pets 🐕 🐾   Room 🛏 📺 🌢 ⌨   General 🛏 🚿 ♨ P ✕ 🔥 ⌷ ✿   Leisure 🚲

BRADING, Isle of Wight Map ref 2C3 | SELF CATERING

★★★★★
SELF CATERING

Units **1**
Sleeps **6**

Low season per wk
£750.00–£950.00
High season per wk
£1,200.00–£1,875.00

Hill Farm Barn, Brading

contact Mrs Sheila Lovegrove, Hill Farm, Carpenters Road, Brading PO36 0BB
t (01983) 875184 f (01983) 874816 e enquiries@hillfarmbrading.co.uk w hillfarmbrading.co.uk

open All year
payment Cash/cheques, euros

18thC threshing barn on 1,000-acre family farm. Sleeps six in three en suite bedrooms. Additional bedroom with separate bathroom for two children. Carefully restored, retaining original features. Extensive grounds with beautiful views. Beach, sailing, pubs and restaurants at St Helens (one mile) and Bembridge (two miles). Bookings Fri-Fri, weekends, short breaks. Low-occupancy discounts available.

⊕ *Ryde A3055 to Sandown/Shanklin. Follow this road until left turn at B3330 Carpenters Road to St Helens and Bembridge for 0.4 miles. Hill Farm on left.*

♥ *Weekend breaks (min 3 nights) from £450. Valid 4 Jan to 17 May, 19 Sep to 12 Dec, excl school holidays.*

Pets ♉ Unit ▥ 📺 ▨▢▤ ▣ ▤▦▣▣▨◐ ✿
General ♨ ▥ ♣ P ⚲ ◎ S Leisure ∪ ⚲ ♨ Shop 1.25 miles Pub 1.25 miles

BRIGHTON & HOVE, East Sussex Map ref 2D3 | SELF CATERING

★★★★★
SELF CATERING

Units **1**
Sleeps **2–6**

Low season per wk
£550.00–£680.00
High season per wk
£750.00–£900.00

Kilcolgan Bungalow, Rottingdean, Brighton

contact Mr J C St George, 22 Baches Street, London N1 6DL
t (020) 7250 3678 f (020) 7250 1955 e jc.stgeorge@virgin.net w holidaybungalowsbrightonuk.com

open All year
payment Cash/cheques, euros

Welcome to excellence in self-catering accommodation. Exceptional, detached, three-bedroomed bungalow comprehensively equipped, with emphasis on comfort. Secluded, landscaped garden overlooking farmland. Accessible to the disabled. Rottingdean is a delightful seaside village with seafront and promenade, four miles Brighton. Ideal, quiet retreat. Pets by arrangement (small charge). Something special – just come and relax.

⊕ *Left at Brighton Pier onto A259 towards Newhaven. At Rottingdean traffic lights, left onto High Street. Bear right around Kipling gardens, then left into Dean Court Road.*

♥ *Short breaks (min 3 nights) possible during low season (excl Christmas and New Year). Terms on request.*

Pets ♉ ♙♈ ♉. Unit ▥ 📺 ▨▢▤ ▣ ▤▦▣ ▧ ▣ ▨◐✿
General ♨ ▥ ♣ P ⚲ S Leisure ∪ Shop 0.75 miles Pub 0.75 miles

BROCKENHURST, Hampshire Map ref 2C3 | GUEST ACCOMMODATION

★★
BED & BREAKFAST

B&B per room per night
s £20.00–£25.00
d £40.00–£50.00

Goldenhayes

9 Chestnut Road, Brockenhurst SO42 7RF t (01590) 623743

Single-storey, owner-occupied home, in central but quiet situation. Close to village, station and open forest. Large garden.

open All year
bedrooms 1 twin, 1 family
payment Cash/cheques, euros

Pets ♉ ♘♙ ♉. Room ⬚ 📺 ♜ General ♨ ▥ ♣ P ⚲ ▨ ✿ Leisure ∪ ⚲ ♨

Place index

If you know where you want to stay, the index at the back of the guide will give you the page number listing accommodation in your chosen town, city or village. Check out the other useful indexes too.

CANTERBURY, Kent Map ref 3B3 GUEST ACCOMMODATION

★★★★
**BED & BREAKFAST
SILVER AWARD**

Bower Farm House

Bossingham Road, Stelling Minnis, Canterbury CT4 6BB **t** (01227) 709430
e anne@bowerbb.freeserve.co.uk **w** bowerfarmhouse.co.uk

B&B per room per night
s £42.00
d £60.00

open All year except Christmas
bedrooms 1 double, 1 twin
bathrooms All en suite
payment Cash/cheques, euros

Delightful, heavily beamed, 17thC farmhouse between the villages of Stelling Minnis and Bossingham. Canterbury and Hythe are approximately seven miles away. Home-laid eggs, home-made bread … a peaceful countryside experience.

⊕ *From B2086 turn to Stelling Minnis. Into Curtis Lane, 1st left past Rose and Crown. Turn left at T-junction towards Bossingham. Down track on right signed B&B.*

Pets 🐕 🐾 🐈. Room 💧 🍴 General 📺 ⊞ 🔥 P ⅍ 🍳 🗟 ✳ Leisure ∪ 🚲 🏛

CANTERBURY, Kent Map ref 3B3 GUEST ACCOMMODATION

★★★★
**GUEST HOUSE
SILVER AWARD**

Yorke Lodge

50 London Road, Canterbury CT2 8LF **t** (01227) 451243 **f** (01227) 462006
e enquiries@yorkelodge.com **w** yorkelodge.com

B&B per room per night
s £50.00–£60.00
d £90.00–£115.00

open All year
bedrooms 5 double, 1 twin, 1 single, 1 family
bathrooms All en suite
payment Credit/debit cards, cash/cheques

Yorke Lodge is the ideal retreat after a long day sightseeing or a busy day at the office. Built in 1887 and fully refurbished over the last two years, this quintessential Victorian town house offers a warm home-from-home atmosphere, with all the modern conveniences now expected by the discerning traveller.

⊕ *From London via M2 and A2, take 1st exit signposted Canterbury. At 1st roundabout turn left into London Road, we are 100m on the left.*

♥ *Special low season deals. See website or ring for details.*

Pets 🐕 🐾 Room 📺 💧 🍴 General 📺 🔥 P 🍳 🗟 ✦ ✳ Leisure ∪ 🚲

CANTERBURY, Kent Map ref 3B3 SELF CATERING

★★★★
SELF CATERING

The Smithy, Chilham, Canterbury

contact Ms Anna Vitiello, The Smithy, Tudor Cottage, The Square, Chilham, Canterbury CT4 8BY
t (01227) 731303 **f** (01227) 731303 **e** info@smithy-cottage.com **w** smithy-cottage.com

Units **1**
Sleeps **2**
Low season per wk
£230.00–£280.00
High season per wk
£290.00–£350.00

open All year except Christmas and New Year
payment Credit/debit cards, cash/cheques

The Smithy is a charming Grade II Listed cottage in immaculate condition situated in the square of the picturesque village of Chilham on the North Downs National Trail close to Canterbury. Fully furnished to a very high standard with charming open fireplace and oak beams. Walking distance to village shop and pubs.

⊕ *From A28 (Canterbury to Ashford) follow signs to Chilham village. The Smithy is situated in the village square, left-hand side of the gift shop.*

♥ *Short breaks available Oct-Apr, 3 nights stay (excl Easter). Discounts available for two or more consecutive weeks booked.*

Pets 🐕 🐈 Unit 🏠 📺 🗄 🖥 📠 🍴 📻 🍽 ✳
General 📺 ⊞ 🔥 P ⅍ S Leisure ∪ Shop 1 mile Pub 0.5 miles

DEAL, Kent Map ref 3C4   **GUEST ACCOMMODATION**

★★★★
GUEST ACCOMMODATION

B&B per room per night
s £45.00–£50.00
d £60.00–£70.00

Ilex Cottage

Temple Way, Worth, Deal CT14 0DA   **t** (01304) 617026   **f** (01304) 620890   **e** info@ilexcottage.com
w ilexcottage.com

Renovated 1736 house with lovely conservatory and country views. Secluded yet convenient village location north of Deal. Sandwich five minutes, Canterbury, Dover and Ramsgate 25 minutes.

open All year
bedrooms 1 double, 2 twin
bathrooms All en suite
payment Credit/debit cards, cash/cheques

Pets ♦   Room   General   Leisure

DOVER, Kent Map ref 3C4   **GUEST ACCOMMODATION**

★★★★
BED & BREAKFAST

B&B per room per night
s £35.00–£40.00
d £60.00–£65.00

Colret House

The Green, Coldred, Dover CT15 5AP   **t** (01304) 830388   **f** (01304) 830348   **e** jackiecolret@aol.com
w colrethouse.co.uk

open All year
bedrooms 1 double, 1 twin
bathrooms All en suite
payment Cash/cheques, euros

An early-Edwardian property with modern, purpose-built, en suite garden rooms, standing in extensive, well-maintained grounds. Situated beside the village green in a conservation area on downs above Dover. Ideally situated for overnight stays when travelling by ferries or shuttle. Close to Canterbury and Sandwich. Ample, secure parking.

⊕ *Leave A2 at the junction signposted Coldred. Colret House is a large house facing the village green, painted pale yellow, and only 0.25 miles from the A2.*

Pets ♦   Room   General   Leisure

EAST PRESTON, West Sussex Map ref 2D3   **SELF CATERING**

★★★★
SELF CATERING

Units   **1**
Sleeps   **2**
Low season per wk
£325.00–£450.00
High season per wk
£450.00–£625.00

Mariners House, East Preston, Littlehampton

t (01293) 871937   **f** (020) 8542 1647   **e** derekedwards@sovereignprinters.co.uk   **w** marinershouse.net

Mariners House, situated on a private estate 100yds from beach, is a quiet, pretty seaside home with two bedrooms – one double, one twin. The bright rooms are centrally heated and a sunny lounge leads to a private south-facing garden.

open All year
payment Cash/cheques, euros

Pets ♦   Unit   General   Leisure   Shop < 0.5 miles   Pub < 0.5 miles

---

EASTBOURNE, East Sussex Map ref 3B4   **GUEST ACCOMMODATION**

★★★★
GUEST HOUSE

B&B per room per night
s £30.00–£35.00
d £65.00–£70.00

The Gladwyn

16 Blackwater Road, Eastbourne BN21 4JD   **t** (01323) 733142   **e** gladwynhotel@aol.com
w gladwynhotel.com

Family-run hotel overlooking Devonshire Park. Close to sea, shops and theatres. Residential licence. TV and tea-/coffee-making facilities in recently redecorated and refurbished en suite bedrooms.

open All year
bedrooms 4 double, 3 twin, 2 single, 1 family
bathrooms 8 en suite
payment Credit/debit cards, cash/cheques, euros

Pets ♦   Room   General

Key to symbols
Open the back flap for a key to symbols.

EASTLEIGH, Hampshire Map ref 2C3   **HOTEL**

★★★
HOTEL

B&B per room per night
s £70.00–£100.00
d £85.00–£125.00

Ellington Lodge Hotel

Concorde Club, Stoneham Lane, Eastleigh SO50 9HQ t (023) 8065 1478 f (023) 8065 1479
e reservations@theconcordeclub.com w theconcordeclub.com

open All year
bedrooms 29 double, 6 twin
bathrooms All en suite
payment Credit/debit cards

Comfortable air-conditioned bedrooms, just two minutes from Southampton International Airport/ Parkway railway station. In quiet woodland setting with ample free parking. The atmospheric Moldy Fig wine bar is open all day and offers excellent food and fine wines.

⊕ Exit M27 jct 5, follow signs for Concorde Club and hotel.

Pets 🐈 £🐕 🐕 🐾. Room 🛗 📞 📺 ☕ 🍴 ♿ General P 🍽 🧺 🎱 🖥 ✿

FARNBOROUGH, Hampshire Map ref 2C2   **GUEST ACCOMMODATION**

★★★
BED & BREAKFAST

B&B per room per night
s £25.00–£35.00
d £50.00–£70.00
Evening meal per person
£7.00–£20.00

Langfords Bed & Breakfast

165 Cheyne Way, Farnborough GU14 8SD t (01252) 547311 e bookings@langfordsbandb.co.uk
w langfordsbandb.co.uk

open All year except Christmas
bedrooms 2 twin, 1 single
payment Cash/cheques

Twin- and single-bedded rooms. Quiet estate approximately two miles from the town centre, buses and trains. Near junction 4 of the M3. Children and domesticated pets accepted, evening meal on request.

Pets 🐈 Room 📺 ☕ General 🛋 🍳 🚻 P 🍴 ✕ 🧺 🖥 ✿ Leisure ∪ ⛵

FINDON, West Sussex Map ref 2D3   **GUEST ACCOMMODATION**

★★★★
INN

B&B per room per night
s £65.00
d £80.00–£90.00
Evening meal per person
Min £13.00

John Henry's Inn

The Forge, Nepcote Lane, Findon, Worthing BN14 0SE t (01903) 877277 f (01903) 877178
e enquiries@john-henrys.com w john-henrys.com

open All year
bedrooms 3 double, 2 family, 1 suite
bathrooms All en suite
payment Credit/debit cards, cash/cheques, euros

In the heart of the village, John Henry's Inn has luxury en suite rooms, most with vaulted ceilings, including a suite with washer/dryer, satellite TV/ DVD and air-conditioning. Fully licensed bar and restaurant. Open to non-residents. Ideally situated for Goodwood, Arundel, Chichester and Brighton. WiFi Internet.

⊕ Signposted at roundabout on A24 and A280. Take Findon direction. Downhill to crossroads. Straight for 350yds. Establishment is on left and ahead.

Pets 🐈 🦮 Room 🛗 📺 ☕ 🍴 General 🛋 🍳 🚻 P 🍽 ♿ ✿ Leisure ♦ ∪ 🚴 ⛵

Using map references

Map references refer to the colour maps at the front of this guide.

FRESHWATER, Isle of Wight Map ref 2C3 — GUEST ACCOMMODATION

Seahorses

★★★★
GUEST ACCOMMODATION

B&B per room per night
s £27.00–£31.00
d £54.00–£62.00

Victoria Road, Freshwater PO40 9PP t (01983) 752574 f (01983) 752574
e seahorses-iow@tiscali.co.uk w seahorsesisleofwight.com

A charming early-19thC rectory, standing in 2.5 acres of lovely gardens with direct footpath access to Yarmouth and Freshwater Bay. Art courses available in our studio. Pets welcome.

open All year
bedrooms 1 double, 1 twin, 2 family
bathrooms All en suite
payment Cash/cheques

Pets ♘ ♞ ♗ ♘. Room ☑ ⬙ ⬙ General ⬙ P ⬙ ⬙ ⬙ ⬙ ⬙ Leisure ∪ ⬙ ⬙

GILLINGHAM, Kent Map ref 3B3 — GUEST ACCOMMODATION

King Charles Hotel

★★★
GUEST ACCOMMODATION

B&B per room per night
s £44.00
d £54.00
Evening meal per person
£5.00–£25.00

Brompton Road, Gillingham ME7 5QT t (01634) 830303 f (01634) 829430
e enquiries@kingcharleshotel.co.uk w kingcharleshotel.co.uk

open All year
bedrooms 30 double, 30 twin, 10 single, 26 family, 2 suites
bathrooms All en suite
payment Credit/debit cards, cash/cheques, euros

A privately owned, modern hotel with a cosy restaurant and first-class conference and banqueting facilities. All bedrooms have en suite bathroom, tea-/coffee-making facilities, hairdryer, telephone and TV. We are ideal as a base for exploring South East England and London, and we offer extremely competitive group rates.

⊕ M2 jct 4 to Gillingham/Medway Tunnel. Turn left to Brompton before tunnel. We are on left.

Pets ♘ ♞ ♗ Room ⬙ ⬙ ☑ ⬙ ⬙ General ⬙ ⬙ ⬙ P ⬙ X ⬙ ⬙ ⬙ ⬙ Leisure ⬙ ⬙ ⬙

GUILDFORD, Surrey Map ref 2D2 — HOTEL

The Hurtwood Inn Hotel

★★★
HOTEL

B&B per room per night
s £51.95–£73.95
d £63.90–£117.90

Walking Bottom, Peaslake, Guildford GU5 9RR t (01306) 730851 f (01306) 731390
e sales@hurtwoodinnhotel.com w hurtwoodinnhotel.com

bedrooms 9 double, 3 twin, 3 single, 6 family
bathrooms All en suite
payment Credit/debit cards, cash/cheques

Situated in the heart of the outstandingly beautiful Surrey Hills. Privately run and recently refurbished, the Hurtwood has a superb restaurant, real country bar and conference, banqueting and wedding facilities, offering a genuine warmth rarely found in the modern hotel business. Once discovered you will need very little excuse to return. Closed New Year.

⊕ Approx halfway between Guildford and Dorking, Peaslake can be accessed by turning off the A25 at Gomshall. Hotel is located in the centre of the village.

♥ Please see website for up-to-date promotions.

Pets ♘ ♞ ♗ Room ⬙ ⬙ ☑ ⬙ ⬙ ⬙ General ⬙ ⬙ ⬙ P ⬙ ⬙ ⬙ ⬙ Leisure ⬙

It's all quality-assessed accommodation

Our commitment to quality involves wide-ranging accommodation assessment. Rating and awards were correct at the time of going to press but may change following a new assessment. Please check at time of booking.

HAILSHAM, East Sussex Map ref 2D3 — SELF CATERING

★★★–★★★★★
SELF CATERING

Units **5**
Sleeps **4–11**

Low season per wk
Min £396.00
High season per wk
Max £1,112.00

Pekes, Chiddingly

contact Ms Eva Morris, 124 Elm Park Mansions, Park Walk, London SW10 0AR
t (020) 7352 8088   **f** (020) 7352 8125   **e** pekes.afa@virgin.net   **w** pekesmanor.com

open All year
payment Cash/cheques

Spacious oast house, cottages and wing of Tudor manor in extensive grounds. Hard tennis court, indoor heated pool, sauna, jacuzzi, badminton. Children and pets welcome. Prices shown are for the cottages; oast house is £1,290.00-£1,940.00, excluding Christmas and New Year.

⊕ Directions given at time of booking.

♥ Off-peak and short breaks available (excl school holidays). Cottages £248-£690, oast house £855-£1,120.

Pets ♥   Unit ▥ ⊡ ▥ ▣ ▤ ▣ ▤ ▣ ▤ ▣ ▣ ❋
General ▧ ▥ ▵ P Ⓢ   Leisure ▨ ▨ ∪   Shop 1.25 miles   Pub 1.25 miles

HOVE

See under Brighton & Hove

ISLE OF WIGHT

See under Brading, Freshwater, Shanklin, Totland Bay, Ventnor, Wroxall

IVINGHOE, Buckinghamshire Map ref 2D1 — SELF CATERING

★★★
SELF CATERING

Units **3**
Sleeps **4–6**

Low season per wk
£450.00–£500.00
High season per wk
£500.00–£550.00

Town Farm Holiday Cottages, Ivinghoe, Leighton Buzzard

contact Mrs Angie Leach, Town Farm Holiday Cottages, Icknield Way, Ivinghoe, Leighton Buzzard LU7 9EL
t (01296) 668455   **f** (01296) 662836   **e** angie@letsunlimited.com   **w** letsunlimited.com

open All year
payment Credit/debit cards, cash/cheques

We have seven attractive, three-bedroom cottages with views overlooking the Chiltern Hills, which are comfortably furnished for up to six guests. The cottages are on a working farm with sheep, a pick-your-own and arable. Communal tennis court, trampoline and play area.

⊕ Town Farm is located on the B489 between Ivinghoe Village and Dunstable. Easy access to stately homes, Oxford, M1, M25 and London.

♥ Stays of four weeks or more can attract a 10% discount on website prices.

Pets ♥ £♥   Unit ▥ ⊡ ▥ ▣ ▤ ▣ ▣ ▣ ▥ ❋
General ▧ ▥ ▵ P   Leisure ▨ ∪   Shop 1 mile   Pub 0.5 miles

MIDHURST, West Sussex Map ref 2C3 — HOTEL

★★★
HOTEL
SILVER AWARD

B&B per room per night
s £80.00–£375.00
d £120.00–£475.00
HB per person per night
£80.00–£475.00

Spread Eagle Hotel & Health Spa

South Street, Midhurst GU29 9NH   **t** (01730) 816911   **f** (01730) 815668
e reservations-se@hshotels.co.uk   **w** hshotels.co.uk

Dating back to c1430 and steeped in history, the hotel has been sympathetically renovated and extended whilst retaining a wealth of period features such as open log fires and Flemish stained-glass windows.

open All year
bedrooms 23 double, 13 twin, 3 suites
bathrooms 35 en suite, 4 private
payment Credit/debit cards

Pets ♥ £♥ ♥♥ ♥   Room ☎ ⊡ ♥ ▨ ⌀   General ▧ ▥ ▵ P ▼ ▥ ⋈ ❋   Leisure ▨ ∪ ☖

NEW FOREST

See under Brockenhurst

If you have access needs...

Look for the National Accessible Scheme symbols if you have special hearing, visual or mobility needs.

NEWBURY, Berkshire Map ref 2C2 — GUEST ACCOMMODATION

★★★★
BED & BREAKFAST

B&B per room per night
s £40.00–£45.00
d £65.00–£70.00

Highclere Farm

Highclere, Newbury RG20 9PY t (01635) 255013 e walshhighclere@newburyweb.net

An extremely comfortable and peaceful converted coach house close to Highclere Castle in an Area of Outstanding Natural Beauty. Within reach of Stonehenge, Winchester, Salisbury and Oxford.

open All year except Christmas
bedrooms 1 double, 1 twin
bathrooms All en suite
payment Cash/cheques

Pets 🐕 ⛄ 🐾 ⛄ 🐾. Room 📺 ♨ General ♨ P 🏠 Leisure ∪ ⚲

NEWHAVEN, East Sussex Map ref 2D3 — GUEST ACCOMMODATION

★★★
GUEST HOUSE

B&B per room per night
s £22.50–£30.00
d £45.00–£60.00

Newhaven Lodge Guest House

12 Brighton Road, Newhaven BN9 9NB t (01273) 513736 f (01273) 734619
e newhavenlodge@aol.com w newhavenlodge.co.uk

A comfortable, bright, family-run establishment located close to the Newhaven/Dieppe ferry terminal. Brighton, Lewes and South Downs nearby. The establishment motto is 'Arrive as a guest and leave as a friend'.

open All year
bedrooms 1 double, 2 single, 3 family
bathrooms 4 en suite
payment Credit/debit cards, cash/cheques, euros

Pets 🐕 ⛄ 🐾 Room ♨ 📺 ♨ 🍽 General ♨ 🏠 🍴 P ❄ Leisure ∪ 🚲

PULBOROUGH, West Sussex Map ref 2D3 — GUEST ACCOMMODATION

★★★★
INN

B&B per room per night
s £50.00–£60.00
d £90.00–£120.00
Evening meal per person
£6.95–£16.95

The Labouring Man

Old London Road, Pulborough RH20 1LF t (01798) 872215 e philip.beckett@btconnect.com
w thelabouringman.co.uk

Pub/restaurant with five luxury bed and breakfast rooms. Walkers, car park, home-cooked food, real ales, log fire.

open All year
bedrooms 4 double, 1 twin
bathrooms All en suite
payment Credit/debit cards, cash/cheques

Pets 🐕 ⛄ 🐾 🐾. Room ♨ 📺 ♨ General ♨ 🍴 P ⚲ ⛄ X 🍽 🔔 ❄ Leisure 🎣

ROCHESTER, Kent Map ref 3B3 — SELF CATERING

★★★★
SELF CATERING

Units **6**
Sleeps **5–8**

Low season per wk
£300.00–£500.00
High season per wk
£550.00–£800.00

Stable Cottages, Rochester

contact Mrs Debbie Symonds, Stable Cottages, Fenn Croft, Newland Farm Road, St Mary Hoo, Rochester ME3 8QS
t (01634) 272439 & 07802 662702 f (01634) 272205 e stablecottages@btinternet.com
w stable-cottages.com

open All year
payment Cash/cheques

These luxury, oak-beamed cottages are set in 20 acres of secluded farmland close to RSPB reserve with panoramic views of the Thames. Access to motorways and ports. London/Canterbury 45 minutes. Perfect base for walking, bird-watching, sightseeing or just getting away from it all. Warm welcome. Family run. Indoor pool.

⊕ *From M2 jct 1, follow A228 towards Grain, turn off towards Allhallows. 1st left, follow lane to end, bear right at pond and follow track to end.*

♥ *Short breaks and split weeks available.*

Pets 🐕 ⛄ 🐾. Unit 🏠 📺 🖥 ▣ 🗄 🔔 🍴 📱 ❄
General ♨ 🍴 P 🔲 🅂 Leisure ⚲ 🐾 Shop 3 miles Pub 1 mile

Check it out

Please check prices, quality ratings and other details when you book.

RODMELL, East Sussex Map ref 2D3 — GUEST ACCOMMODATION

★★★★
GUEST ACCOMMODATION

Garden Studio

Robin Hill, Mill Lane, Rodmell, Lewes BN7 3HS t (01273) 476715 & 07775 624235

B&B per room per night
s £30.00
d £60.00

Self-contained studio flat on South Downs Way. Twin beds, bed-settee, own kitchen, breakfast supplied. Close to Glyndebourne, Brighton, port of Newhaven. Use of garden. Popular village inn.

open All year
bedrooms 1 family
bathrooms En suite
payment Cash/cheques

Pets 🐾 🐕 Room 📺 ♿ General P ✦ 🅿 ◻ ✿

RUCKINGE, Kent Map ref 3B4 — SELF CATERING

★★★
SELF CATERING

Units 1
Sleeps 1–7

Low season per wk
£330.00–£415.00
High season per wk
£415.00–£600.00

The Old Post Office, Ruckinge, Ashford

contact Mr Chris Cook, 241 Lower Addiscombe Road, Croydon CR0 6RD
t (020) 8655 4466 f (020) 8656 7755 e c.cook@btinternet.com w ruckinge.info

open All year
payment Credit/debit cards, cash/cheques

A comprehensively equipped large house, very suitable for two families holidaying together. Four bedrooms, two kitchens, two bathrooms, a huge garden from which public footpaths lead off, canal walks 100yds. Full central heating, digital TV and many books and guides. Website has pictures of all the rooms.

⊕ From M20 jct 10, go south on A2070 (signposted Hastings). After 4 miles turn right onto B2067 for 2 miles through Ham Street to Ruckinge.

♥ Short and weekend breaks throughout the year.

Pets 🐾 🐕. Unit 🏠 📺 ◻ 🖥 🖨 ◻ 🔔 ✿
General 🅿 P S Leisure 🏊 Shop 1.5 miles Pub < 0.5 miles

RYE, East Sussex Map ref 3B4 — HOTEL

★★★
SMALL HOTEL

B&B per room per night
s £65.00–£85.00
d £65.00–£95.00
HB per person per night
£55.00–£60.00

The Hope Anchor Hotel

Watchbell Street, Rye TN31 7HA t (01797) 222216 f (01897) 223796 e info@thehopeanchor.co.uk
w thehopeanchor.co.uk

18thC hotel situated at the end of a cobbled street with magnificent views of surrounding countryside. Attractive restaurant open to non-residents.

open All year
bedrooms 9 double, 2 twin, 1 family, 3 suites
bathrooms All en suite
payment Credit/debit cards, cash/cheques

Pets 🐾 🐕 Room 📺 ♿ General P ✦ 🅿 ♥ 🅿 ◻ ✿ Leisure U 🚲 🏊

RYE, East Sussex Map ref 3B4 — HOTEL

★★★
SMALL HOTEL
GOLD AWARD

B&B per room per night
s £75.00–£125.00
d £100.00–£200.00
HB per person per night
£79.50–£129.50

Rye Lodge Hotel

Hilders Cliff, Rye TN31 7LD t (01797) 223838 f (01797) 223585 e info@ryelodge.co.uk
w ryelodge.co.uk

open All year
bedrooms 12 double, 6 twin
bathrooms All en suite
payment Credit/debit cards, cash/cheques, euros

Stunning estuary views yet adjacent to town centre. Luxurious rooms. Dine by candlelight in the elegant, marble-floored Terrace Restaurant serving delicious food and fine wines. Full room service – enjoy breakfast in bed. Heated indoor swimming pool and sauna, private car park, plus all the delights of the medieval Cinque Port town of Rye.

⊕ Enter town, follow town centre signs. After passing through Landgate Arch, hotel is 100yds on right.

♥ Wine and food breaks: gourmet meals, wine tastings, talks, visits to vineyards. Historic interludes include special visits to historic stately homes etc.

Pets 🐾 🐕 🐕 Room 📺 ♿ General P ✦ 🅿 ♥ 🅿 ◻ ✿ Leisure 🏊 🚲

RYE, East Sussex Map ref 3B4 — SELF CATERING

Brandy's Cottage, Rye

★★★★
SELF CATERING

Units **1**
Sleeps **2**

Low season per wk
£295.00–£325.00
High season per wk
£350.00–£395.00

contact Mrs Jane Apperly, Brandy's Cottage, Udimore Road, Rye TN31 6AA
t (01797) 225426 **e** apperly@cadborough.co.uk **w** cadborough.co.uk

Brandy's Cottage offers spacious luxury accommodation for two people. Situated one mile from Rye in a quiet location. Surrounded by delightful countryside yet only 15 minutes' walk from town centre.

open All year
payment Cash/cheques

Pets 🐕 Unit 🏠 📺 🖥 💻 🖥 🍽 🔥 ♨ 🧺 🧼 ❄
General **P** ✂ **S** Leisure 🚲 Shop 1 mile Pub 1 mile

SEAFORD, East Sussex Map ref 2D3 — GUEST ACCOMMODATION

The Silverdale

★★★★
GUEST HOUSE

B&B per room per night
s £40.00–£45.00
d £40.00–£70.00
Evening meal per person
£15.00–£20.00

21 Sutton Park Road, Seaford BN25 1RH **t** (01323) 491849 **f** (01323) 890854
e silverdale@mistral.co.uk **w** silverdaleseaford.co.uk

open All year
bedrooms 3 double, 2 family, 2 suites
bathrooms All en suite
payment Credit/debit cards, cash/cheques, euros

Small, expertly run house-hotel in the centre of peaceful Edwardian town. Beautiful food, a host of English wines and over 120 single malts. Only a few minutes' walk to the beach, antique shops and the friendly pubs. National dog-friendly prize winner. Green Tourism Business Scheme gold-award winner.

⊕ *On A259 in centre of Seaford.*

♥ *Special winter deals – contact us for more details.*

Pets 🐕 🐾 👣 Room 🛏 📞 📺 💧 ♨ General 🍽 🖥 🔥 **P** 🍽 ✕ 🍴 Leisure ∪ 🚲 🏊

SELSEY, West Sussex Map ref 2C3 — SELF CATERING

BeachFront House, Chichester

★★★★
SELF CATERING

Units **1**
Sleeps **4–8**

Low season per wk
£600.00–£850.00
High season per wk
£900.00–£1,250.00

contact Angela Kelly, BeachFront House, 85 Bounces Road, London N9 8LD
t 07976 957004 **f** (020) 8141 1579 **e** angela@phoenixcommunity.co.uk **w** selseyretreat.co.uk

open All year
payment Credit/debit cards, cash/cheques

This spacious four-bedroomed house is ideal for family gatherings and special occasions. Accommodation comprising two double bedrooms and two twin bedrooms (two of the rooms are en suite). Family bathroom, study, kitchen/diner, dining room, living room, downstairs cloakroom, games room, hot tub and landscaped front and rear gardens.

⊕ *Take B2145 from the A27 Chichester bypass, towards Selsey. From Selsey High Street take left onto Latham Road, then right onto Grafton Road. Left is Lifeboat Way, right is Barnes Close.*

♥ *New this season. Please check our website or telephone for unbelievable introductory prices.*

Pets 🐕 Unit 🏠 📺 🖥 💻 🖥 🍽 🔥 ♨ 🧺 🧼 ❄
General 🖥 🔥 **P** 🖥 **S** Leisure 🎣 Shop 0.5 miles Pub 0.5 miles

Ancient and modern

Experience timeless favourites or discover the latest must-sees. Whatever your choice, be inspired by the places of interest and events highlighted for each region.

SHANKLIN, Isle of Wight Map ref 2C3   **HOTEL**

★★
HOTEL

B&B per room per night
s £30.00–£50.00
d £60.00–£100.00
HB per person per night
£40.00–£60.00

Orchardcroft Hotel

Victoria Avenue, Shanklin PO37 6LT   t (01983) 862133   f (01983) 862133

open All year
bedrooms 7 double, 4 twin, 2 single, 3 family
bathrooms All en suite
payment Credit/debit cards, cash/cheques, euros

This elegant but friendly hotel has a private leisure complex, secluded gardens, and a reputation for good food and service. 'A very family-friendly hotel who do all they can to ensure a pleasant stay. Friendly staff, good food and wonderful pool and games facilities' – Hazel and Darren, London.

⊕ Situated on Victoria Avenue, the main road into Shanklin from Godshill.

❤ Excellent-value, ferry-inclusive breaks available Oct-May. Christmas and New Year packages. Discounts on ferry prices all year.

Pets 🐕 ⛓🐓🐖🐎   Room 🛏 📺 💧🍵 🦽   General 🧺🍴🎱 ♿ P 🍽 🎮 🍴 ✿   Leisure 🎣 🔍 ∪ 🚴 🏊

SHANKLIN, Isle of Wight Map ref 2C3   **GUEST ACCOMMODATION**

★★★
GUEST ACCOMMODATION

B&B per room per night
s £25.00–£32.50
d £50.00–£65.00

The Palmerston

16 Palmerston Road, Shanklin PO37 6AS   t (01983) 865547   f (01983) 868008
e info@palmerston-hotel.co.uk   w palmerston-hotel.co.uk

Located in an ideal position in Shanklin just a few minutes' walk to the beach, town centre and Old Village. A family-run hotel offering a friendly and attentive service.

open All year
bedrooms 3 double, 1 twin, 1 single, 2 family, 1 suite
bathrooms All en suite
payment Credit/debit cards, cash/cheques

Pets 🐕 🐓🐖   Room 📺 💧🍵   General 🧺 P 🍽 🦽 ✿   Leisure ∪ 🚴

THURNHAM, Kent Map ref 3B3   **GUEST ACCOMMODATION**

★★★★
INN

B&B per room per night
s £60.00–£70.00
d £80.00–£100.00
Evening meal per person
£7.50–£18.00

Black Horse Inn

Pilgrims Way, Thurnham, Maidstone ME14 3LD   t (01622) 737185   f (01622) 739170
e info@wellieboot.net   w wellieboot.net

Kentish country pub with award-winning restaurant in the heart of the North Downs. Beautiful gardens with fountains and ponds. Alfresco terrace dining. Fantastic walking area.

open All year
bedrooms 8 double, 4 twin, 4 family
bathrooms All en suite
payment Credit/debit cards, cash/cheques

Pets 🐕 ⛓🐓🐖🐎   Room 🛏 📺 💧🍵   General 🧺🍴🎱 P 🍽 ✕ 🎮 ✿   Leisure ∪ 🚴 🏊

TOTLAND BAY, Isle of Wight Map ref 2C3   **HOTEL**

★★★
SMALL HOTEL

B&B per room per night
s £57.00–£78.00
d £114.00–£152.00
HB per person per night
£78.00–£91.00

Country Garden Hotel

Church Hill, Totland Bay PO39 0ET   t (01983) 754521   f (01983) 754521
e countrygardeniow@aol.com   w thecountrygardenhotel.co.uk

Our delightful adults-only intimate hotel in tranquil West Wight is set in lovely gardens that are a riot of colour most of the year. A five-minute stroll to the Solent; easy access to lovely walks/ hikes including Tennyson Down and the Needles.

open All year
bedrooms 10 double, 5 twin, 1 suite
bathrooms All en suite
payment Credit/debit cards, cash/cheques

Pets 🐕 ⛓🐓🐓   Room 🛏 📞 📺 💧🍵   General 🍽 🎮 ✿   Leisure ∪

Mention our name
Please mention this guide when making your booking.

TOTLAND BAY, Isle of Wight Map ref 2C3   **HOTEL**

★★★
HOTEL
SILVER AWARD

Sentry Mead Hotel

Madeira Road, Totland Bay PO39 0BJ **t** (01983) 753212 **f** (01983) 754710 **e** info@sentrymead.co.uk
w sentrymead.co.uk

B&B per room per night
s £45.00–£65.00
d £90.00–£130.00
HB per person per night
£65.00–£85.00

open All year
bedrooms 8 double, 3 twin, 1 single, 1 family
bathrooms All en suite
payment Credit/debit cards, cash/cheques

Beautifully situated in the tranquil West Wight, Sentry Mead is set in its own gardens, opposite Turf Walk and just two minutes from the beach. Excellent food, attentive staff and an informal atmosphere all combine to make this the perfect place for relaxing and unwinding. Dogs welcome. Ferry inclusive available.

⊕ *A3054 signed Freshwater and Totland. Straight on at roundabout (The Broadway, B3322). Turn right at second roundabout (Madeira Road). Sentry Mead is on the right.*

♥ *Midweek and weekend breaks plus golfing breaks available. Please see website for latest details or contact hotel direct.*

Pets 🐕 ⛫🐾🐕🦺 Room 🔌 📺 🔥 🍵 General 🛏️ ▥ 🍴 P 🍽️ 🍷 🎂 ◉ ✳ Leisure ∪ 🚴 🚣

VENTNOR, Isle of Wight Map ref 2C3   **SELF CATERING**

★★★–★★★★★
SELF CATERING

Westfield Lodges & Apartments, Bonchurch

t (01983) 852268 **f** (01983) 853992 **e** mail@westfieldlodges.co.uk **w** westfieldlodges.co.uk

Units   **30**
Sleeps **2–6**

Low season per wk
£205.00–£255.00
High season per wk
£545.00–£735.00

open All year
payment Credit/debit cards, cash/cheques

Westfield Lodges are situated in the peaceful and historic village of Bonchurch on the south west coast of the Island. Located on a quiet, private site only five minutes from the beach.

♥ *3-4 night short breaks available Oct-Mar. Open Christmas and New Year. Pets welcome.*

Pets 🐕 Unit ▥ 📺 🔲 🖥 🍵 🍷 ✳
General 🛏️ ▥ 🍴 P 🔌 ◉ S Leisure 🎣 🚴

WINCHESTER, Hampshire Map ref 2C3   **GUEST ACCOMMODATION**

★★★
BED & BREAKFAST

12 Christchurch Road

Winchester SO23 9SR **t** (01962) 854272 **e** pjspatton@yahoo.co.uk

B&B per room per night
s £35.00–£40.00
d £45.00–£50.00

Elegant Victorian house furnished with style. Easy, pleasant walk to city centre, cathedral and water meadows. Breakfast in conservatory, overlooking beautiful gardens, features home-made bread, preserves and local produce.

open All year except Christmas and New Year
bedrooms 1 double, 1 twin
payment Cash/cheques

Pets 🐕 ⛫🐾🐕🦺 Room 🔥 🍵 General 🛏️ ▥ 🍴 ✂ ▥ Leisure 🚣

Town, country or coast

The entertainment, shopping and innovative attractions of the big cities, the magnificent vistas of the countryside or the relaxing and refreshing coast – this guide will help you find what you're looking for.

WINDSOR, Berkshire Map ref 2D2
GUEST ACCOMMODATION

★★★
GUEST HOUSE

B&B per room per night
s £45.00–£67.00
d £55.00–£78.00

The Clarence

9 Clarence Road, Windsor SL4 5AE t (01753) 864436 f (01753) 857060 w clarence-hotel.co.uk

open All year except Christmas
bedrooms 4 double, 6 twin, 4 single, 6 family
bathrooms All en suite
payment Credit/debit cards, cash/cheques

Comfortable hotel with licensed bar and steam-sauna. Located near town centre and short walk from Windsor Castle, Eton College and River Thames. All rooms with en suite bathroom, TV, tea-/coffee-making facilities, hairdryer and radio-alarm. Free Wi-Fi Internet. Convenient for Legoland and Heathrow Airport.

⊕ From M4 jct 6 take the road to Windsor. Stay on dual carriageway and turn left at the roundabout onto Clarence Road.

Pets 🐾 🐕 Room 🛏 📺 📶 ☕ General ⌕ P ⚑ 🅟 ♿ ✿

WINDSOR, Berkshire Map ref 2D2
SELF CATERING

★★
SELF CATERING

Units **3**
Sleeps **1–14**

Low season per wk
£420.00–£966.00
High season per wk
£420.00–£966.00

Dorney Self-Catering Appartments, Windsor

contact Sarah Everitt, Wisteria & Gardeners Bothy, The Old Place, Lock Path Dorney, Windsor SL4 6QQ
t (01753) 827037 f (01753) 855022 e enquiries@troppo.uk.com w troppo.uk.com

open All year
payment Credit/debit cards, cash/cheques

Apartments set in rural location. Close to Windsor, Legoland, Dorney Lake, trains to London. Rowers welcome. Large secure garden with barbecue. Free Wi-Fi Internet. Pets welcome. Book by the night from £60. Look at availability on our website.

⊕ M4 jct 7, left on A4 to Maidenhead. 1 mile, left at 'Sainsbury' roundabout, 2 miles, through Dorney, right into Boveney Road, follow to end.

♥ Discount rates for rowing teams and long stays (winter).

Pets 🐾 Unit 🏠 📺 📼 🗄 ☕ 🍽 ✿
General ⌕ 🏠 P 🅢 Leisure ∪ ⛵ Shop 3 miles Pub 1 mile

WROXALL, Isle of Wight Map ref 2C3
GUEST ACCOMMODATION

★★★
FARMHOUSE

B&B per room per night
s £25.00–£50.00
d £50.00–£54.00

Little Span Farm B&B

Rew Lane, Ventnor PO38 3AU t (01983) 852419 f (01983) 852419 e info@spanfarm.co.uk
w spanfarm.co.uk

open All year
bedrooms 2 double, 1 twin, 1 family
bathrooms All en suite
payment Cash/cheques

17thC stone farmhouse on working sheep farm in Area of Outstanding Natural Beauty. Short drive to sandy beaches of Shanklin, Sandown and Ventnor. Close to footpaths, cycle route, golf course and tourist attractions. Ideal for family holidays. Kennels available for dogs. English or vegetarian breakfast.

⊕ B3327 to Wroxall. By post office turn into West Street. Drive out of village up hill around bend, ignore next turning, first farm on right.

Pets 🐾 🐈 💷 🐕 ✂ 🐾 Room 📺 📶 ☕ General ⌕ 🏠 ⚑ P ✂ 🍽 ♿ ✿ Leisure ⛵

Confirm your booking
It's always advisable to confirm your booking in writing.

WROXALL, Isle of Wight Map ref 2C3   `SELF CATERING`

★★★
SELF CATERING

Units **2**
Sleeps **4–6**

Low season per wk
£225.00–£575.00
High season per wk
£425.00–£725.00

The Brewhouse & Stable Cottage, Ventnor

contact Mrs Felicity Corry, Little Span Farm, Rew Lane, Ventnor PO38 3AU
t (01983) 852419   **f** (01983) 852419   **e** info@spanfarm.co.uk   **w** spanfarm.co.uk

open All year
payment Cash/cheques

Two sympathetically converted old stone farm buildings, Stable Cottage sleeping six and Brewhouse sleeping four, situated on a working sheep farm in an Area of Outstanding Natural Beauty close to sandy beaches, footpaths, cycle route, golf course and tourist attractions. Ideal for family holidays. Kennels available for dogs.

⊕ *B3327 to Wroxall. By post office turn into West Street. Drive out of village up hill around bend, ignore next turning, first farm on right.*

Pets 🐕 🐾 🐈   Unit ▦ 📺 📼 ▯ ▯ ▯ ▯ ▯ ✿
General ♿ 🏠 ♿ P ✂ Ⓢ   Leisure ⛲   Shop 1 mile   Pub 1 mile

Country ways

The Countryside Rights of Way Act gives people new rights to walk on areas of open countryside and registered common land.

To find out where you can go and what you can do, as well as information about taking your dog to the countryside, go online at countrysideaccess.gov.uk.

And when you're out and about…

Always follow the Country Code

- Be safe – plan ahead and follow any signs
- Leave gates and property as you find them
- Protect plants and animals, and take your litter home
- Keep dogs under close control
- Consider other people

South West England

Bath, Bristol, Cornwall, Cotswolds and the Forest of Dean, Devon, Dorset, Gloucestershire, Isles of Scilly, Somerset, Wiltshire

Sun, surf, sensational wildlife – and so much more

The South West has always been a magnet for holidaymakers. And with a great climate, masses of activities, teeming wildlife and magical landscapes, is it any wonder?

South West Tourism
visitsouthwest.co.uk
(01392) 360050

Polzeath Beach, Cornwall

Forest of Dean, Gloucestershire   Tarr Steps, Exmoor National Park

Corfe, Dorset

The coastline is one of this region's real gems, from Dorset's spectacular Lulworth Cove and the fossil-rich Jurassic Coast to the elegant English Riviera and Devon's surf-piled north Atlantic coast. Look closely and you may spot whales, dolphins, basking sharks or even a dinosaur tooth or two. And with more Blue Flag beaches than anywhere else in England, you can enjoy high adrenaline watersports or simply build sandcastles to your heart's content. Inland you'll find the romantic wilderness of Dartmoor and Exmoor National Parks along with the scenic Forest of Dean, secret wooded valleys and the Tarka Trail. It's the perfect terrain for mountain biking and horse riding. And from family theme parks to special interest holidays in yoga or glass making, this region has it all.

One of the must-see attractions is 'Breaking the Chains', a major exhibition at Bristol's British Empire and Commonwealth Museum. Marking the bicentenary of the abolition of the slave trade, it's a moving account of one of the darkest episodes in human history. Another great new attraction is the Artificial Surf Reef at Boscombe seafront, set to deliver rollers on the calmest of days. And when you need a little peace and quiet, head off to Gloucester Cathedral. This architectural marvel features massive cylindrical pillars in the Norman nave, glorious fan-vaulted cloisters and the tomb of King Edward II.

Wherever you go you will see spectacular scenery, wonderful countryside and a beautiful coastline. Discover St Nectan's Glen near Tintagel, where a 60ft waterfall cascades into a stone basin before pouring out through an arch in the rock. Another mystical place is Silbury Hill near Marlborough, Wiltshire. Dating back to 2,780 BC and covering 5 acres, it's the largest man made mound in Europe and still shrouded in mystery.

Destinations

Bath

Beautiful Bath is not to be missed. Set in rolling countryside, less than two hours from London, this exquisite Georgian spa city was founded by the Romans and is now a World Heritage Site. Explore the compact city centre on foot and discover a series of architectural gems including the Roman baths and Pump Room, the 15th-century Abbey, and stunning Royal Crescent. Follow in the footsteps of Romans and Celts and bathe in the naturally warm waters of the Thermae Bath Spa.

Bournemouth

Award-winning Bournemouth is the perfect holiday and short-break destination, renowned for its seven miles of family-friendly, golden beaches, beautiful parks and gardens and cosmopolitan ambience. Enjoy the buzz of the town then head out and savour the beauty of the New Forest, the splendour of Dorset's spectacular World Heritage Jurassic Coastline, and the rolling countryside immortalised by Thomas Hardy.

Bristol

In bygone times, explorers and merchants set off on epic journeys from its harbour. Nowadays, Bristol's spirit of boldness and creativity expresses itself in art, architecture and an enviable quality of life. One of the UK's best short-break destinations – take in Georgian terraces, waterfront arts centres, green spaces, great shopping and acclaimed restaurants. The city's treasure chest of heritage glitters with the work of historic figures such as Isambard Kingdom Brunel, and all set against a truly classic view – the River Avon and its dramatic gorge reaching almost into the heart of the city.

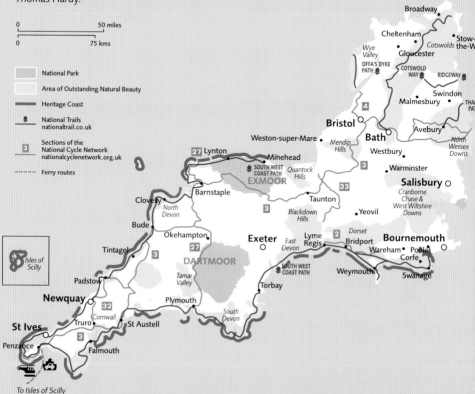

National Park

Area of Outstanding Natural Beauty

Heritage Coast

National Trails
nationaltrail.co.uk

Sections of the
National Cycle Network
nationalcyclenetwork.org.uk

Ferry routes

Pulteney Bridge, Bath

Russell-Cotes Museum, Bournemouth

SS Great Britain, Bristol

Tate St Ives

Newquay Zoo

Exeter Cathedral

Stonehenge

Exeter

Devon's regional capital for culture, leisure and shopping is a vibrant city, steeped in ancient history. Don't miss the superb Decorated Gothic cathedral. Stroll along the historic Quayside, once the setting for a thriving wool trade and now a bustling riverside resort. Choose from over 700 shops, join a free Red Coat-guided city tour and dine in any one of numerous acclaimed restaurants. You've also found the perfect base from which to explore the sweeping National Parks of Dartmoor and Exmoor.

Newquay

A beach paradise, stretching for seven miles, drawing all ages like a magnet and making this one-time fishing village Cornwall's premier resort. Soaring cliffs alternate with sheltered coves, and thundering surf with secluded rock pools, smugglers' caves and soft golden sands. Whatever the weather, make a splash at Waterworld, or visit Newquay Zoo, one of the best wildlife parks in the country. Newquay will offer you an unforgettable holiday memory.

St Ives

What was once a small, thriving fishing village is now an internationally renowned haven for artists, attracted by the unique light. Explore the narrow streets and passageways and come upon countless galleries, studios and craft shops. Don't miss the Tate Gallery and Barbara Hepworth Museum. Enjoy the natural beauty of the harbour and explore the Blue Flag beaches and coastal walks. Perfectly placed for all of West Cornwall's stunning scenery and famous attractions.

Salisbury

Nestling in the heart of southern England, Salisbury is every bit the classic English city. The majestic cathedral boasts the tallest spire in England and rises elegantly above sweeping lawns. Wander through this medieval city and you'll find first-class visitor attractions, theatre, shopping, food and drink. And, of course, no trip to Salisbury would be complete without the eight-mile pilgrimage to one of the greatest prehistoric sites in the world – Stonehenge.

Places to visit

Babbacombe Model Village
Torquay, Devon
(01803) 315315
babbacombemodelvillage.co.uk
England in miniature, in four acres of gardens

Bristol City Museum & Art Gallery
(0117) 922 3571
bristol.gov.uk
Art and archaeology in a magnificent baroque building

Buckland Abbey
Yelverton, Devon
(01822) 853607
nationaltrust.org.uk
Home of seafarer Sir Francis Drake

Cheddar Caves & Gorge
Somerset
(01934) 742343
cheddarcaves.co.uk
Britain's finest caves and deepest gorge

Eden Project
St Austell, Cornwall
(01726) 811911
edenproject.com
A global garden for the 21st century

Exmoor Falconry & Animal Farm
Allerford, Somerset
(01643) 862816
exmoorfalconry.co.uk
Unique farm with falconry centre and activities

Kingston Lacy House and Gardens
Wimborne Minster, Dorset
(01202) 883402
nationaltrust.org.uk
Elegant country mansion with important collections
(parkland only)

Living Coasts
Torquay, Devon
(01803) 202470
livingcoasts.org.uk
Fascinating coastal creatures in stunning location

Longleat
Warminster, Wiltshire
(01985) 844400
longleat.co.uk
Lions, tigers and a stately home
(except attractions)

The Lost Gardens of Heligan
near St Austell, Cornwall
(01726) 845100
heligan.com
Beautifully restored gardens
(Dec-Feb only)

Monkey World - Ape Rescue Centre
Wareham, Dorset
(01929) 462537
monkeyworld.org
Internationally acclaimed primate rescue centre

Morwellham Quay The Morwellham & Tamar Valley Trust
Tavistock, Devon
(01822) 832766
morwellham-quay.co.uk
Evocative museum and visitor centre

National Marine Aquarium
Plymouth, Devon
(01752) 600301
national-aquarium.co.uk
The ocean experience of a lifetime

National Maritime Museum Cornwall
Falmouth, Cornwall
(01326) 313388
nmmc.co.uk
Exhibitions and boat collections

Newquay Zoo
Cornwall
(01637) 873342
newquayzoo.org.uk
Exotic animals in sub-tropical lakeside gardens

Oceanarium
Bournemouth, Dorset
(01202) 311993
oceanarium.co.uk
An underwater journey

Paignton Zoo Environmental Park
Devon
(01803) 697500
paigntonzoo.org.uk
One of England's most beautiful zoos

Roman Baths
Bath, Somerset
(01225) 477785
romanbaths.co.uk
Roman temple and baths

STEAM - Museum of the Great Western Railway
Swindon, Wiltshire
(01793) 466646
swindon.gov.uk/steam
Interactive story of pioneering railway network

Diary dates 2008

Stonehenge and Avebury World Heritage Site
near Salisbury, Wiltshire
0870 333 1181
english-heritage.org.uk
World-famous prehistoric monument

Stourhead House and Garden
Wiltshire
(01747) 841152
nationaltrust.org.uk
Celebrated 18th century landscaped gardens and mansion
(grounds only)

The Tank Museum
Wareham, Dorset
(01929) 405096
tankmuseum.co.uk
The world's finest display of armoured fighting vehicles

Tate St Ives
St Ives, Cornwall
(01736) 796226
tate.org.uk/stives
A unique introduction to modern art

Wookey Hole Caves and Papermill
near Wells, Somerset
(01749) 672243
wookey.co.uk
Spectacular caves and family attractions

WWT Slimbridge Wetlands Centre
Gloucestershire
(01453) 891900
wwt.org.uk
Wetland centre with amazing array of wildlife

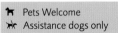

Pets Welcome
Assistance dogs only

South West England Food Festival
Various locations, Exeter
visitsouthwest.co.uk/foodfestival
4 – 6 Apr

Helston Flora Day
helstonfloraday.org.uk
8 May

Bath International Music Festival
Various locations, Bath
visitbath.co.uk
16 May – 1 Jun

Salisbury Festival
Various locations, Salisbury
salisburyfestival.co.uk
23 May – 8 Jun

Royal Bath and West Show
Bath & West Showground, Shepton Mallet
bathandwest.com
28 – 31 May

Golowan Festival Incorporating Mazey Day
Various locations, Penzance
golowan.org
22 – 29 Jun

Sidmouth Folk Week
Various locations, Sidmouth
sidmouthfolkweek.co.uk
1 – 8 Aug

Great Dorset Steam Fair
South Down Farm, Tarrant Hinton
gdsf.co.uk
27 – 31 Aug

Tar Barrels
Ottery St Mary
otterytourism.org.uk
5 Nov

Bridgwater Guy Fawkes Carnival Procession
bridgwaterguyfawkescarnival.co.uk
7 Nov

Tourist Information Centres

When you arrive at your destination, visit an Official Partner Tourist Information Centre for quality assured help with accommodation and information about local attractions and events, or email your request before you go. To search for attractions and Tourist Information Centres on the move just text INFO to 62233, and a web link will be sent to your mobile phone.

Avebury	Green Street	(01672) 539425	all.atic@kennet.gov.uk
Bath	Abbey Church Yard	0906 711 2000**	tourism@bathnes.gov.uk
Bodmin	Mount Folly Square	(01208) 76616	bodmintic@visit.org.uk
Bourton-on-the-Water	Victoria Street	(01451) 820211	bourtonvic@btconnect.com
Bridport	47 South Street	(01308) 424901	bridport.tic@westdorset-dc.gov.uk
Bristol Harbourside	Harbourside	0906 711 2191**	ticharbourside@destinationbristol.co.uk
Brixham	The Quay	(01803) 211211	holiday@torbay.gov.uk
Bude	The Crescent	(01288) 354240	budetic@visitbude.info
Burnham-on-Sea	South Esplanade	(01278) 787852	burnham.tic@sedgemoor.gov.uk
Camelford*	The Cleese	(01840) 212954	manager@camelfordtic.eclipse.co.uk
Cartgate	A303/A3088 Cartgate Picnic Site	(01935) 829333	cartgate.tic@southsomerset.gov.uk
Cheddar	The Gorge	(01934) 744071	cheddar.tic@sedgemoor.gov.uk
Cheltenham	77 Promenade	(01242) 522878	info@cheltenham.gov.uk
Chippenham	Market Place	(01249) 665970	tourism@chippenham.gov.uk
Chipping Camden	High Street	(01386) 841206	information@visitchippingcamden.com
Christchurch	49 High Street	(01202) 471780	enquiries@christchurchtourism.info
Cirencester	Market Place	(01285) 654180	cirencestervic@cotswold.gov.uk
Coleford	High Street	(01594) 812388	tourism@fdean.gov.uk
Corsham	31 High Street	(01249) 714660	enquiries@corshamheritage.org.uk
Devizes	Market Place	(01380) 729408	all.dtic@kennet.gov.uk
Dorchester	11 Antelope Walk	(01305) 267992	dorchester.tic@westdorset-dc.gov.uk
Falmouth	11 Market Strand	(01326) 312300	info@falmouth.co.uk
Gloucester	28 Southgate Street	(01452) 396572	tourism@gloucester.gov.uk
Looe*	Fore Street	(01503) 262072	looetic@btconnect.com
Lyme Regis	Church Street	(01297) 442138	lymeregis.tic@westdorset-dc.gov.uk
Malmesbury	Market Lane	(01666) 823748	malmesburyip@northwilts.gov.uk
Moreton-in-Marsh	High Street	(01608) 650881	moreton@cotswolds.gov.uk
Padstow	North Quay	(01841) 533449	padstowtic@btconnect.com
Paignton	The Esplanade	(01803) 211211	holiday@torbay.gov.uk
Plymouth Mayflower	3-5 The Barbican	(01752) 306330	barbicantic@plymouth.gov.uk
Salisbury	Fish Row	(01722) 334956	visitorinfo@salisbury.gov.uk
Somerset	Sedgemoor Services	(01934) 750833	somersetvisitorcentre@somerserset.gov.uk
Sherborne	Digby Road	(01935) 815341	sherborne.tic@westdorset-dc.gov.uk
Stow-on-the-Wold	The Square	(01451) 831082	stowvic@cotswold.gov.uk
Stroud	George Street	(01453) 760960	tic@stroud.gov.uk

Swanage	Shore Road	(01929) 422885	mail@swanage.gov.uk
Swindon	37 Regent Street	(01793) 530328	infocentre@swindon.gov.uk
Taunton	Paul Street	(01823) 336344	tauntontic@tauntondeane.gov.uk
Tewkesbury	64 Barton Street	(01684) 295027	tewkesburytic@tewkesburybc.gov.uk
Torquay	Vaughan Parade	(01803) 211211	holiday@torbay.gov.uk
Truro	Boscawen Street	(01872) 274555	tic@truro.gov.uk
Wadebridge	Eddystone Road	(01208) 813725	wadebridgetic@btconnect.com
Wareham	South Street	(01929) 552740	tic@purbeck-dc.gov.uk
Warminster	off Station Rd	(01985) 218548	visitwarminster@westwiltshire.gov.uk
Wells	Market Place	(01749) 672552	touristinfo@wells.gov.uk
Weston-super-Mare	Beach Lawns	(01934) 888800	westontouristinfo@n-somerset.gov.uk
Weymouth	The Esplanade	(01305) 785747	tic@weymouth.gov.uk
Winchcombe	High Street	(01242) 602925	winchcombetic@tewkesbury.gov.uk
Yeovil	Hendford	(01935) 845946	yeoviltic@southsomerset.gov.uk

*seasonal opening **calls to this number are charged at premium rate*

Avebury, Wiltshire

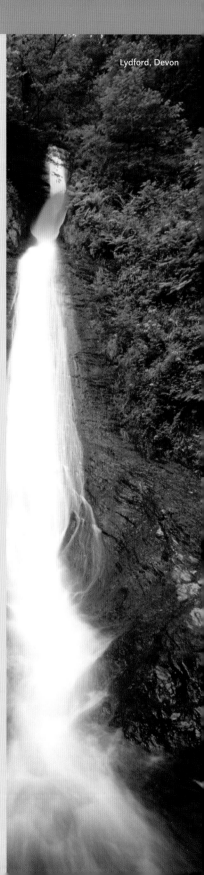

Lydford, Devon

Find out more

Visit the following websites for further information on South West England (or call 01392 360050):

* visitsouthwest.co.uk
* swcp.org.uk
* accessiblesouthwest.co.uk

Also available from South West Tourism:

* The Trencherman's Guide to Top Restaurants in South West England
* Adventure South West
  Your ultimate activity and adventure guide.
* World Heritage Map
  Discover our World Heritage.

Travel info

By road:
The region is easily accessible from London, the South East, the North and the Midlands by the M6/M5 which extends just beyond Exeter, where it links in with the dual carriageways of the A38 to Plymouth, the A380 to Torbay and the A30 into Cornwall. The North Devon Link Road A361 joins junction 27 with the coast of North Devon and the A39, which then becomes the Atlantic Highway into Cornwall.

By rail:
The main towns and cities in the South West are served throughout the year by fast, direct and frequent rail services from all over the country. Trains operate from London (Paddington) to Chippenham, Swindon, Bath, Bristol, Weston-super-Mare, Taunton, Exeter, Plymouth and Penzance. A service runs from London (Waterloo) to Exeter, via Salisbury, Yeovil and Crewkerne.

By air:
Daily flights into Bristol, Bournemouth, Exeter, Gloucester, Isles of Scilly, Newquay and Plymouth operate from airports around the UK and Europe. For schedules, log on to visitsouthwest.co.uk/flights.

enjoyEngland ™

official tourist board guides

Hotels, including country house and town house hotels, metro and budget hotels in England 2008

£10.99

Guest accommodation, B&Bs, guest houses, farmhouses, inns, restaurants with rooms, campus and hostel accommodation in England 2008

£11.99

Self-catering holiday homes, including serviced apartments and approved caravan holiday homes, boat accommodation and holiday cottage agencies in England 2008

£11.99

Touring parks, camping holidays and holiday parks and villages in Britain 2008

£8.99

informative, easy to use and great value for money

Pet-friendly hotels, B&Bs and self-catering accommodation in England 2008

£9.99

Great ideas for places to visit, eat and stay in England

£10.99

Places to stay and visit in South West England

£9.99

Places to stay and visit in Northern England

£9.99

Accessible places to stay in Britain

£9.99

Now available in good bookshops.
For special offers on VisitBritain publications,
please visit **enjoyenglanddirect.com**

where to stay in
South West England

All place names in the blue bands are shown on the maps at the front of this guide.

Accommodation symbols
Symbols give useful information about services and facilities. Inside the back-cover flap you can find a key to these symbols. Keep it open for easy reference.

ALTON PANCRAS, Dorset Map ref 2B3 | **SELF CATERING**

★★★★–★★★★★★
SELF CATERING

Units **4**
Sleeps **4–10**

Low season per wk
£330.00–£550.00
High season per wk
£500.00–£1,100.00

Bookham Court, Dorchester

contact Mr & Mrs Andrew Foot, Whiteways, Bookham, Alton Pancras, Dorchester DT2 7RP
t (01300) 345511 **f** (01300) 345511 **e** andy.foot1@btinternet.com **w** bookhamcourt.co.uk

Luxurious and tranquil cottages with disabled access. Games room, wildlife hide, private fishing, glorious walks in Hardy Country. 20 miles from sea. Sleeps two to ten people.

open All year
payment Cash/cheques

Pets 🐕 £🐕 Unit 🛏 📺 ⬚ ⬚ ⬚ ⬚ ⬚ ⬚ ⬚ ⬚ ⬚ ⬚ ✿
General 🏕 🏠 🅿 ⑤ Leisure 🎣 ∪ Shop 1 mile Pub 1 mile

ASHBURTON, Devon Map ref 1C2 | **SELF CATERING**

Parkers Farm Cottages & Caravans

The Rockery, Caton, Ashburton, Devon TQ13 7LH
Tel (01364) 653008 Fax (01364) 652915
E-mail: parkerscottages@btconnect.com • Web: www.parkersfarm.co.uk

*15 attractive holiday cottages set around a large courtyard with ample car parking areas. Each cottage is fully equipped with full size cooker, microwave, refrigerator, airing cupboard and colour TV. All bed linen is provided, with beds made up for your arrival. We also have 14 self-contained holiday caravans set in lovely open countryside, some with moorland views – see **www.parkersfarm.co.uk***

---

enjoyEngland.com

Get in the know – log on for a wealth of information and inspiration. All the latest news on places to visit, events and quality-assessed accommodation is literally at your fingertips. Explore all that England has to offer.

ASHTON, Cornwall Map ref 1B3 — SELF CATERING

★★★
SELF CATERING

Units **9**
Sleeps **1–4**

Low season per wk
£110.00–£240.00
High season per wk
£300.00–£470.00

Chycarne Farm Cottages, Helston

contact Mrs Ross, Chycarne Farm Cottages, Balwest, Ashton TR13 9TE
t (01736) 762473 **f** (01736) 762473 **e** chycarnefarmcottages@hotmail.com
w chycarne-farm-cottages.co.uk

payment Credit/debit cards, cash/cheques

Nestling in the tranquil countryside of Tregonning Hill, 17thC granite farm buildings converted into cosy self-contained cottages, set in five acres with parking. Stunning views over Mounts Bay. Located in historic World Heritage Site. Many places of interest within easy reach. Coastal and country walks. Pub/restaurant one mile. Colour brochure. Closed February, March and November.

⊕ *Take A394 Penzance to Helston road. At Ashton post office turn left into Higher Lane. Chycarne Farm entrance exactly 1 mile on right-hand side.*

♥ *3-and 4-night breaks available in off-peak periods. Call for details.*

Pets 🐕 £🐕 🐾. Unit 📺 ☐ 🖥 ■ 🖵 ✿
General 🛏 ♿ P ✂ ☐   Shop 1 mile   Pub 1 mile

BATHEASTON, Somerset Map ref 2B2 — SELF CATERING

★★★★★
SELF CATERING

Units **2**
Sleeps **1–8**

Low season per wk
£375.00–£482.00
High season per wk
£518.00–£971.00

Avondale Riverside, Batheaston, Bath

contact Mr & Mrs Sheila Pecchia, Avondale Riverside Apartments, 104 Lower Northend, North End, Batheaston, Bath BA1 7HA
t (01225) 852226 & 07929 842504 **f** (01225) 852226 **e** sheilapex@questmusic.co.uk
w riversapart.co.uk

Balconied apartments overlooking river and nature reserve. Garden, secure parking, widescreen TV, whirlpool bath, en suite bedrooms, hot tub. Short breaks and hen parties. Ten to fifteen minutes' city centre.

open All year
payment Cash/cheques

Pets 🐕 £🐕 🐾. Unit 🖳 📺 ☐ 🖥 📷 ■ 🖶 🖵 🖫 🖳 ✿
General 🛏 🏠 ♿ P ✂ ☐ S   Leisure ∪ 🚲   Shop < 0.5 miles   Pub < 0.5 miles

BERRYNARBOR, Devon Map ref 1C1 — SELF CATERING

★★★
SELF CATERING

Units **4**
Sleeps **2–7**

Low season per wk
£95.00–£301.00
High season per wk
£320.00–£894.00

Smythen Farm Coastal Holiday Cottages, Ilfracombe

contact Mr & Ms Thompson & Elstone, Smythen Farm Coastal Holiday Cottages, Symthen, Sterridge Valley, Berrynarbor, Ilfracombe EX34 9TB
t (01271) 882875 **f** (01271) 882875 **e** jayne@smythenfarmholidaycottages.co.uk
w smythenfarmholidaycottages.co.uk

payment Cash/cheques

Near golden sands with sea and coastal views. Heated, covered swimming pool in a suntrap enclosure, gardens and games room with pool table, table tennis, football machine. Tree-house on two levels. Free pony rides, ball pond and bouncy castle, 14-acre recreation field and dog walk. For colour brochure phone Jayne. Open March to January.

⊕ *A361 to Barnstaple then A39 for 1 mile towards Lynton. Left onto B3230, through Muddiford and Milltown. Right by garage onto A3123, next left to Sterridge Valley.*

Pets 🐕 £🐕 🐾. Unit 🖳 📺 🖤 ☐ 🖥 ■ 🖶 🖵 🖫 ✿
General 🛏 🏠 ♿ P ☐ S   Leisure ♐ 🎣 ● ∪ 🚲 ⚓   Shop 1.5 miles   Pub 1.5 miles

Place index

If you know where you want to stay, the index at the back of the guide will give you the page number listing accommodation in your chosen town, city or village. Check out the other useful indexes too.

BIDEFORD, Devon Map ref 1C1 — SELF CATERING

★★★
SELF CATERING

Units 1
Sleeps 2

Low season per wk
£150.00–£200.00
High season per wk
£200.00–£275.00

Coachmans Cottage, Monkleigh, Bideford

contact Mr & Mrs Tom & Sue Downie, Cream Tea Cottages, Staddon House, Monkleigh, Bideford EX39 5JR
t (01805) 623670 f (01805) 624549 e tom.downie@ukonline.co.uk w creamteacottages.co.uk

Charming character cottage set in traditional courtyard surroundings. Our price includes all linen, logs for the wood-burner and a cream tea to help you settle in after your journey.

open All year
payment Credit/debit cards, cash/cheques

Pets 🐕 £🐈 🐾. Unit 📺 📺 💻 🍽 🔌 📶 🎛 🍳 ♨
General 🛏 🍴 ♿ P ⓞ Ⓢ Leisure 🚲 ⛵ Shop < 0.5 miles Pub < 0.5 miles

BIDEFORD, Devon Map ref 1C1 — SELF CATERING

★★★★
SELF CATERING

Units 3
Sleeps 4–14

Low season per wk
£180.00–£250.00
High season per wk
£250.00–£575.00

Cream Tea Cottages, Little Torrington, Torrington

contact Mr & Mrs Tom & Sue Downie, Staddon House, Monkleigh, Bideford EX39 5JR
t (01805) 623670 f (01805) 624559 e tom.downie@ukonline.co.uk w creamteacottages.co.uk

open All year
payment Credit/debit cards, cash/cheques

Set in a lovely location, these cottages are converted barns dating back to the 1700s. They retain many original features but are renovated to modern standards. The properties all have french windows opening onto their own patios. There is also a play and picnic area for children.

⊕ Approx 2 miles outside Great Torrington at Little Torrington, turn right just after caravan park; after approx 150yds, right again. Cottages about 50yds on left.

♥ Special prices for out-of-season 3-night or weekend breaks. Please ring for details.

Pets 🐕 £🐈 🐾. Unit 🛏 📺 💻 🖥 📶 🍳 ♨ General 🛏 🍴 ♿ P ⓞ Ⓢ Leisure 🚲 ⛵ Shop 2 miles Pub 2 miles

BIGBURY-ON-SEA, Devon Map ref 1C3 — SELF CATERING

★★★★★
SELF CATERING &
SERVICED APARTMENTS

Units 1
Sleeps 1–4

Low season per wk
£450.00–£1,024.00
High season per wk
£1,148.00–£1,580.00

Apartment 5, Burgh Island Causeway, Bigbury-on-Sea

Helpful Holidays, Mill Street, Chagford, Newton Abbot TQ13 8AW
t (01647) 433593 f (01647) 433694 e help@helpfulholidays.com w helpfulholidays.com

open All year
payment Credit/debit cards, cash/cheques

Luxury, modern, ground-floor apartment set into cliff with panoramic southerly views from large patio. Facilities include pool, gym, sauna, cafe/bar, grassy cliff-top grounds and direct access to beautiful large sandy beach and coastal path. Popular for surfing and near golf course and village shop/post office. View www.burghislandcauseway.com

⊕ From A38 at Ivybridge, take the 'B' road to Modbury then the A379 towards Kingsbridge. Very soon leave on B3392 for Bigbury-on-Sea.

♥ Bargain weekend and short-stay breaks available in autumn and winter months.

Pets 🐕 £🐈 🐾. Unit 🛏 📺 💻 🖥 📷 🔌 🍳 ♨ General 🛏 🍴 ♿ P Ⓢ Leisure 🎾 Shop < 0.5 miles Pub < 0.5 miles

It's all quality-assessed accommodation

Our commitment to quality involves wide-ranging accommodation assessment. Rating and awards were correct at the time of going to press but may change following a new assessment. Please check at time of booking.

BRIXHAM, Devon Map ref 1D2 · **HOTEL**

★★★
HOTEL

B&B per room per night
s £48.00–£78.00
d £96.00–£168.00
HB per person per night
£58.00–£94.00

The Berry Head Hotel

Berry Head, Brixham TQ5 9AJ **t** (01803) 853225 **f** (01803) 882084 **e** stay@berryheadhotel.com
w berryheadhotel.com

open All year
bedrooms 12 double, 10 twin, 3 single, 7 family
bathrooms All en suite
payment Credit/debit cards, cash/cheques, euros

Steeped in history, nestling on water's edge in acres of outstanding natural beauty. Traditional hospitality, excellent, friendly and personal service with attention to detail. Comfortable accommodation, thoughtfully equipped. Imaginative menus, varied dining options, featuring quality local produce and fresh fish. Lounge, bars and terrace, equally popular with locals and residents.

⊕ *Enter Brixham, continue to harbour and around up King Street for 1 mile to Berry Head.*

♥ *Special-event packages. Extensive range of conference and business facilities. Weddings and special occasions. Christmas and New Year celebrations.*

Pets 🐾 Room 📞 📺 👜 🍴 & General 🛏 🍽 🎄 P ♟ ♨ 🎱 ◉ ✻ Leisure ⚓ ∪ 🚲 ⛵

BRIXHAM, Devon Map ref 1D2 · **SELF CATERING**

★★★
SELF CATERING

Units   **7**
Sleeps **1–4**

Low season per wk
£120.00–£210.00
High season per wk
£250.00–£480.00

Brixham Harbourside Holiday Flats, Brixham

contact Mrs Helgard Stone, 13 Cambridge Road, Brixham TQ5 8JW
t (01803) 851919 **e** david.f.stone@btinternet.com **w** brixham-harbourside-holiday-flats.com

open All year
payment Cash/cheques

Four one-bedroom, and three two-bedroom, self-contained flats. Clean, well-furnished and comfortable. Sea and harbour views of fishing boats, yachts and pleasure craft. Hot water, central heating, electricity, all bed linen, towels and parking are inclusive. We do our best to make your stay a pleasant one.

⊕ *Last property on the left of Brixham harbour.*

♥ *Short breaks available Nov-Feb.*

Pets 🐾 Unit 🛏 📺 📺 🍴 📻 🍽 📱 General 🛏 🍽 🎄 ✂ Shop < 0.5 miles Pub < 0.5 miles

Discover Britain's heritage

Discover the history and beauty of over 250 of Britain's best-known historic houses, castles, gardens and small manor houses. You can purchase Britain's Historic Houses and Gardens – Guide and Map from good bookshops and online at visitbritaindirect.com.

BUDE, Cornwall Map ref 1C2 — GUEST ACCOMMODATION

★★★★
GUEST HOUSE
SILVER AWARD

B&B per room per night
s Min £40.00
d Min £54.00
Evening meal per person
Min £20.00

Harefield Cottage

Upton, Bude EX23 0LY t (01288) 352350 f (01288) 352712 e sales@coast-countryside.co.uk
w coast-countryside.co.uk

open All year
bedrooms 2 double, 1 twin
bathrooms All en suite
payment Credit/debit cards, cash/cheques

Stone-built cottage with outstanding views. Luxurious and spacious en suite bedrooms, king-size beds and four-poster available. Home cooking our speciality. All diets catered for. Personal attention assured at all times. Only 250yds from the coastal footpath. One mile downhill to the National Cycle network. Hot tub available.

⊕ From A39 follow signs to Bude town centre, turn left at mini-roundabout, over Canal bridge, uphill for 1 mile. Red telephone box on right-hand side, past this there is a left-hand turn to Upton. Harefield Cottage on left.

♥ Special 3-night breaks including DB&B and packed lunch – £130. With walking – £150.

Pets 🐕 🐎 Room 📺 ⬩ 🍴 General ⬩ ▥ ⬩ P ⬩ ✕ ⬩ ▥ ✿ Leisure 🚲 🛞

BUDE, Cornwall Map ref 1C2 — GUEST ACCOMMODATION

★★★★
GUEST HOUSE

B&B per room per night
s £28.00–£40.00
d £48.00–£60.00
Evening meal per person
£12.00–£15.00

Surf Haven

31 Downs View, Bude EX23 8RG t (01288) 353923 e info@surfhaven.co.uk w surfhaven.co.uk

open All year
bedrooms 4 double, 2 twin, 3 family
bathrooms 7 en suite, 2 private
payment Credit/debit cards, cash/cheques

Surf Haven is a warm and friendly guest house. Ideally situated, overlooking the golf course and 200yds from the beach. It is just a short walk to the town with its shops and restaurants. Fresh, locally sourced and organic produce used wherever possible.

⊕ From A3072 follow signs to Bude town centre, bear left at the top of the hill and follow signs for Crooklets Beach.

♥ Special breaks – stay for 3 nights Oct-Apr and get an extra night free (excl Bank Holidays).

Pets 🐕 £🐈 🐎 🐾 Room 🛏 📺 ⬩ 🍴 General ⬩ ▥ ⬩ P ⬩ ✕ ⬩ ▥ ⬩ ✿ Leisure U 🚲 🛞

BUDE, Cornwall Map ref 1C2 — SELF CATERING

★★★★
SELF CATERING

Units **18**
Sleeps **1–6**

Low season per wk
£340.00–£595.00
High season per wk
£785.00–£1,415.00

Broomhill Manor Country Estate, Bude

contact Mr A Biggs & Ms L Winstanley, Broomhill Manor Country Estate, Broomhill Manor, Bude EX23 9HA
t (01288) 352940 f (01288) 356526 e info@broomhillmanor.co.uk w broomhillmanor.co.uk

BROOMHILL MANOR
country holidays by the sea

open All year
payment Credit/debit cards, cash/cheques

Quality cottages in extensive grounds of old manor house. Own riding stables. Indoor swimming pool with jacuzzi, gymnasium, sauna and treatment room. Outdoor pool (seasonal), tennis court. Play areas. Hot tubs. Close to beaches. Easy access to all attractions.

⊕ From the A39 in Stratton turn west up Stamford Hill, then turn left again almost immediately by a white cottage. We are on the right.

♥ Short breaks (Mon-Fri/Fri-Mon) available Oct–Easter.

Pets 🐕 £🐈 Unit ▥ 📺 ⬩ ⬩ ⬩ ⬩ ⬩ ⬩ ✿
General ⬩ ▥ ⬩ ✂ ◎ S Leisure ⬩ ⬩ ⬩ ⬩ U 🚲 Shop 1 mile Pub 1 mile

CAMELFORD, Cornwall Map ref 1B2 — SELF CATERING

Helsbury Park, Camelford

★★★★★
SELF CATERING

Units **4**
Sleeps **2–7**

Low season per wk
£550.00–£850.00
High season per wk
£850.00–£1,400.00

contact Mrs Leza Wilson, 42 Easthorpe Street, Ruddington, Nottingham NG11 6LA
t (0115) 914 7212 **e** info@helsburypark.co.uk **w** helsburypark.co.uk

open All year
payment Credit/debit cards, cash/cheques

Award-winning, dog-friendly, luxury accommodation set in 100 acres of parkland with woods and river frontage. The cottages mix traditional character with modern comfort, including well-equipped kitchens, en suite bathrooms, log fires and four-poster beds. Situated in beautiful north Cornwall.

⊕ Helsbury is located on the B3266 between Camelford and St Breward. It is marked with granite stones at the entrance.

Pets 🐕 🐈 🐾 Unit ▦ 📺 📱 … General … Leisure ∪ 🚲 … Shop 2 miles Pub 2 miles

CHAPEL AMBLE, Cornwall Map ref 1B2 — SELF CATERING

Carclaze Cottages, Wadebridge

★★★★
SELF CATERING

Units **4**
Sleeps **2–6**

Low season per wk
£280.00–£440.00
High season per wk
£605.00–£1,285.00

contact Mrs Nicholls, Carclaze Cottages, Chapel Amble, Wadebridge PL27 6EP
t (01208) 813886 **e** carclazecottages@btinternet.com **w** carclaze.co.uk

Peaceful countryside setting with superb views, yet only ten minutes from spectacular coast. Ideal location to explore North Cornwall. Cottages furnished to high standards. For those who seek something special.

open All year
payment Cash/cheques

Pets 🐕 🐈 🐾 Unit ▦ 📺 … General … Leisure ∪ 🚲 … Shop 0.5 miles Pub 0.5 miles

CHAPEL AMBLE, Cornwall Map ref 1B2 — SELF CATERING

Homeleigh Farm Holiday Cottages, Chapel Amble, Wadebridge

★★★★
SELF CATERING

Units **2**
Sleeps **2–7**

Low season per wk
Min £200.00
High season per wk
Min £450.00

contact Mrs Ann Rees, Homeleigh Farm, Chapel Amble, Wadebridge PL27 6EU
t (01208) 812411 **f** (01208) 815025 **e** homeleigh@eclipse.co.uk **w** eclipse.co.uk/homeleigh

Two- and three-bedroom cottages in traditional Cornish stone, on edge of village. Pub and shop 150m. Individual gardens plus six acres to play in. Pets welcome.

open All year
payment Cash/cheques

Pets 🐕 🐈 🐾 Unit ▦ 📺 … General … Leisure ∪ 🚲 … Shop < 0.5 miles Pub < 0.5 miles

CHEDDAR, Somerset Map ref 1D1 — GUEST ACCOMMODATION

Waterside

★★
BED & BREAKFAST

B&B per room per night
s £25.00–£30.00
d £50.00–£60.00

Cheddar Road, Axbridge BS26 2DP **t** (01934) 743182 **e** gillianaldridge@hotmail.com
w watersidecheddar.co.uk

A warm and friendly welcome awaits you. Surrounded by the Mendip hills, ideal for discovering Glastonbury, Wells, Bream, Weston, Wookey Hole, or Cheddar Gorge and show caves. Children and dogs welcome.

open All year
bedrooms 1 double, 1 twin, 1 family
bathrooms All en suite
payment Cash/cheques, euros

Pets 🐕 🐈 🐴 🐾 Room … General … Leisure ∪ …

Key to symbols
Open the back flap for a key to symbols.

COMBE MARTIN, Devon Map ref 1C1   **SELF CATERING**

★★★★
SELF CATERING

Units **5**
Sleeps **2–9**

Low season per wk
£310.00–£660.00
High season per wk
£530.00–£2,200.00

Coulscott House, Combe Martin, Ilfracombe

contact Dr Sue Jay, Coulscott House, Nutcombe Hill, Combe Martin, Ilfracombe EX34 0PQ
t (01271) 883339   **e** stay@coulscott.co.uk   **w** coulscott.co.uk

open All year
payment Cash/cheques

Just five properties set in private valley with streams, meadows, woods. Sleeping two to nine. Indoor heated pool. Close to Exmoor, coastal footpaths, massive surfing beaches, hidden coves, pubs, restaurants. Immaculate, well behaved dogs welcome in selected cottages. Hot tub. Wood-burning stoves. History, nature, beauty, fun, activity, relaxation.

⊕ *One mile out of Combe Martin. Fringes of Exmoor. Nutcombe Hill. Close to sea. 45 minutes from M5 Tiverton.*

♥ *Short breaks out of season. Three nights minimum. Last-minute bargains – phone to enquire.*

Pets 🐕 🐈 🐾   Unit 🖼️ 📺 🎛️ 🍽️ 📶 🧺 🔥 🔌 🍴 💺
General 🛏️ 🏛️ ♿ P ✂️ ⊘ S   Leisure 🎣 ∪ 🚴 ⛵   Shop 1 mile   Pub 1 mile

---

CONSTANTINE, Cornwall Map ref 1B3   **SELF CATERING**

★★★★
SELF CATERING

Units **1**
Sleeps **2–6**

Low season per wk
£285.00–£345.00
High season per wk
£585.00–£785.00

Green Bank Cottage, Seworgan, Falmouth

contact Mrs Carole Scobie-Allin, Selective Cornish Retreats, Green Valley, Seworgan, Constantine, Falmouth. Cornwall TR11 5QN
t (01326) 340147 & 07767 896359   **f** (01326) 340147   **e** caroleselectiveretreats@yahoo.com
w connexions.co.uk/schr

A traditional cottage in a peaceful hamlet, close to the Helford River. Well-equipped with log fire. One double, two twin bedrooms. Private use of spa, sauna and gym. Dogs welcome.

open All year
payment Cash/cheques

Pets 🐕 🐈 🐾   Unit 🖼️ 📺 🎛️ 🍽️ 📶 🧺 🔥 🔌 🍴 💺
General 🛏️ 🏛️ ♿ P S   Leisure ∪ ⛵   Shop 2 miles   Pub 4 miles

---

CORSE LAWN, Gloucestershire Map ref 2B1   **HOTEL**

★★★
HOTEL
SILVER AWARD

B&B per room per night
s £90.00
d £145.00
HB per person per night
£115.00

Corse Lawn House Hotel

Corse Lawn, Gloucester GL19 4LZ   **t** (01452) 780771   **f** (01452) 780840   **e** enquiries@corselawn.com
w corselawn.com

open All year except Christmas
bedrooms 8 double, 8 twin, 1 single, 2 suites
bathrooms All en suite
payment Credit/debit cards, cash/cheques, euros

Delightful family-owned Queen Anne country house famed for food, wine, service and lovely warm atmosphere and welcome. Set in tranquil gardens and grounds in the beautiful Severn Valley between the Cotswolds, the Malverns and the Forest of Dean. Wonderfully friendly and relaxing.

⊕ *5 miles south west of Tewkesbury on B4211.*

Pets 🐕 🐾 🐈 🐾   Room 🛁 ☎ 📺 🍴 🔌 💺   General 🛏️ 🏛️ ♿ P ✂️ 🍽️ 🎱 🔌 💺   Leisure 🎣 ♿ ∪

Friendly help and advice

Tourist Information Centres offer friendly help with accommodation and holiday ideas as well as suggestions of places to visit and things to do. You'll find contact details at the beginning of each regional section.

COSSINGTON, Somerset Map ref 1D1   **SELF CATERING**

★★★★★
SELF CATERING

Units **1**
Sleeps **8–13**

Low season per wk
£1,415.00–£2,055.00
High season per wk
£2,195.00–£3,325.00

Cossington Park, Cossington, Bridgwater

contact Ms Lesley Pinnell, Middle Road, Cossington, Bridgwater TA7 8LH
t (01278) 429852 & 07977 040579 **e** info@cossingtonpark.com **w** cossingtonpark.com

open All year
payment Credit/debit cards, cash/cheques

Cossington Park is a superb period home with extensive, superbly-maintained gardens in one of England's finest tourist locations; owned for 300 years by the same family whose pictures, antiques and 5,000 books are there for your enjoyment; loved by all ages for family reunions, dinners and celebrations.

⊕ *In a tranquil Somerset village only 3 miles from the M5 jct 23 – easy to reach from the Midlands, South East and London/Bristol airports.*

♥ *For special occasions/celebrations, we offer a choice of two superb cordon bleu cooks and wonderful aromatherapy and beauty treatments.*

Pets 🐾   Unit 🛏 TV ⬚⬚⬚⬚⬚⬚⬚⬚⬚⬚⬚⬚⬚ ✿
General ⬚⬚⬚P ⬚ S   Leisure ◕ ∪   Shop 1 mile   Pub 0.5 miles

COTSWOLDS

See under Owlpen, Stow-on-the-Wold

CRANTOCK, Cornwall Map ref 1B2   **SELF CATERING**

★★★–★★★★★
SELF CATERING

Units **6**
Sleeps **4–8**

Low season per wk
£220.00–£480.00
High season per wk
£700.00–£1,850.00

Seaspray Holiday Cottages, Crantock

Cornwall Holiday Cottages, PO Box 24, Truro TR1 9AG
t 0845 226 5507 **e** rentals@cornwall-cottages.biz **w** cornwall-cottages.biz

open All year
payment Cash/cheques

Comfortable cottages, some with spectacular sea views at West Pentire; others are period properties with conservation listing located in the village; all have gardens; some have log burners; some welcome dogs; all are within easy reach of popular Crantock village and beach. Sleeping from two to eight people, all are equipped to a high standard.

⊕ *Take A392 from A30 to Newquay, follow signs to Crantock.*

♥ *Short breaks Nov-Mar. Christmas and New Year packages.*

Pets 🐾 £🐾   Unit 🛏 TV ⬚⬚⬚ ⬚⬚⬚⬚ ✿
General ⬚⬚⬚P ⬚ S   Shop 1 mile   Pub 1 mile

DARTMOUTH, Devon Map ref 1D3   **HOTEL**

★★★
HOTEL
SILVER AWARD

B&B per room per night
s £90.00–£105.00
d £130.00–£219.00

Royal Castle Hotel

11 The Quay, Dartmouth TQ6 9PS **t** (01803) 833033 **f** (01803) 835445 **e** enquiry@royalcastle.co.uk
w royalcastle.co.uk

Historic 17thC quayside coaching inn set in the heart of Dartmouth. Two busy bars, a restaurant overlooking the river and 25 luxurious bedrooms.

open All year
bedrooms 14 double, 6 twin, 2 single, 3 family
bathrooms All en suite
payment Credit/debit cards, cash/cheques

Pets 🐾 £🐾 ⬚⬚   Room ◕ TV ⬚⬚⬚   General ⬚⬚⬚P ⬚⬚⬚⬚ ⬚   Leisure ∪ ⬚

Check it out

Information on accommodation listed in this guide has been supplied by proprietors.
As changes may occur you should remember to check all relevant details at the time of booking.

DARTMOUTH, Devon Map ref 1D3 — SELF CATERING

★★★
SELF CATERING

Units **4**
Sleeps **2–6**
Low season per wk
£255.00–£385.00
High season per wk
£395.00–£685.00

The Old Bakehouse, Dartmouth

contact Mrs Sylvia Ridalls, The Old Bakehouse, 7 Broadstone, Dartmouth TQ6 9NR
t (01803) 834585 **f** (01803) 834585 **e** gparker@pioneerps.co.uk **w** oldbakehousedartmouth.co.uk

Three character cottages, with beams and old stone fireplaces. In a conservation area, two minutes from historic town centre and river. Free parking. Beach 15 minutes' drive. Dogs free. Non-smoking.

open All year
payment Credit/debit cards, cash/cheques

Pets 🐾 Unit 🏠 📺 Ⓥ 🖥 🗄 🎱
General 🖑 🛏 🚶 ✂ Ⓢ Shop < 0.5 miles Pub < 0.5 miles

DULVERTON, Somerset Map ref 1D1 — GUEST ACCOMMODATION

★★★★★
BED & BREAKFAST

B&B per room per night
s £50.00–£70.00
d £60.00–£85.00

Hawkwell Farm House

Dulverton, Somerset TA22 9RU **t** (01398) 341708 **f** (01398) 341708
e jan@hawkwellfarmhouse.co.uk **w** hawkwellfarmhouse.co.uk

open All year
bedrooms 1 double, 1 twin, 1 family
bathrooms All en suite
payment Credit/debit cards, cash/cheques

South-facing, 16thC traditional Devonshire longhouse, on the edge of Exmoor National Park, full of charm and character, dating back to the Domesday era. Secluded, yet easily accessible, standing in 14 acres of mature gardens, paddocks, and woodland. Inglenook fireplaces, exposed beams, four-poster beds, providing luxurious, spacious en suite accommodation. Heated swimming pool. Warm welcome and hearty breakfasts.

⊕ *Easily accessible from jct 27 of M5. Just a few minutes from Dulverton.*

♥ *Discounts on stays of 4 or more days (excl Saturdays) – see website for details.*

Pets 🐾 🐈 🐾 🐕 Room 📺 👜 🍴 General 🖑 12 P ✂ 🍳 🍽 ❄ Leisure ⚓ ∪ 🏊

DULVERTON, Somerset Map ref 1D1 — SELF CATERING

★★★★
SELF CATERING

Units **3**
Sleeps **4–20**
Low season per wk
£305.00–£1,550.00
High season per wk
£575.00–£2,700.00

Deer's Leap Country Cottages, Yeo Mill, Nr Dulverton

contact Mrs Heather Fuidge, Deer's Leap Country Cottages, West Anstey EX36 3NZ
t (01398) 341407 **f** (01398) 341407 **e** deersleapcottages@lineone.net **w** deersleap.com

open All year
payment Credit/debit cards, cash/cheques

Deer's Leap is the perfect place to get together with friends or family for a special occasion or just to spend some quality time together. The main house sleeps up to 20 and with a games room, sauna, hot tub and gym, there's something here for everyone.

⊕ *Detailed directions on application.*

Pets 🐾 🐈 🐾 Unit 🏠 📺 👜 Ⓥ 🖥 🗄 🎱 📺 ❄
General 🖑 🛏 🚶 P ✂ ◎ Ⓢ Leisure ⚓ ∪ 🚲 Shop 0.75 miles Pub 2.5 miles

Ancient and modern

Experience timeless favourites or discover the latest must-sees. Whatever your choice, be inspired by the places of interest and events highlighted for each region.

DUNSTER, Somerset Map ref 1D1 | HOTEL

★★★
SMALL HOTEL

B&B per room per night
s £50.00–£70.00
d £80.00–£120.00
HB per person per night
£60.00–£90.00

Yarn Market Hotel (Exmoor)

25 High Street, Dunster, Minehead TA24 6SF t (01643) 821425 f (01643) 821475
e yarnmarket.hotel@virgin.net w yarnmarkethotel.co.uk

open All year
bedrooms 10 double, 2 twin, 1 single, 2 family
bathrooms All en suite
payment Credit/debit cards, cash/cheques

Within Exmoor National Park, our hotel is ideal for walking, riding and fishing. Family-run with a friendly, relaxed atmosphere. All rooms en suite with colour TV. Four-poster and superior rooms available. Totally non-smoking. Home-cooked dishes to cater for all tastes. Group bookings welcomed. Conference facilities. Special Christmas and New Year breaks.

⊕ From M5 jct 25 follow signs for Exmoor/Minehead A358/A39. Dunster signed approx 0.5 miles from A39 on left. Hotel in centre of village beside Yarn Market.

♥ Discounted rates for longer stays and midweek bookings. Ring for newsletter with information on special events. Group bookings welcome.

Pets 🐕 🏠 Room 🔌 📺 🍽 General 🖼 🎿 🍷 Leisure ♻ 🚲

EAST BUDLEIGH, Devon Map ref 1D2 | SELF CATERING

★★★★
SELF CATERING

Units **1**
Sleeps **6–8**
Low season per wk
£330.00–£435.00
High season per wk
£535.00–£875.00

Brook Cottage, Budleigh Salterton

contact Mrs Jo Simons, Foxcote, Noverton Lane, Prestbury, Cheltenham GL52 5BB
t (01242) 574031 e josimons@tesco.net w brookcottagebudleigh.co.uk

open All year
payment Cash/cheques

Spacious thatched cottage. Two showers and bathroom. Beaches, walking, golf, karting, bird-watching, riding nearby – but the cottage is so comfortable it's a pleasure to be indoors. Two living rooms with TVs, one for the adults, and a snug, with sofa bed, for the children! Visit our website for more photos.

⊕ From A376 take B3179 signed for Woodbury and Budleigh Salterton; proceed through Woodbury and Yettington; right after Bicton gates and again on entering East Budleigh.

♥ Reduced-rate winter breaks for 3-night stays with or without linen (excl Christmas and New Year).

Pets 🐕 Unit 📺 General 🖼 🅿 🇸 Leisure ♻ Shop 2 miles Pub < 0.5 miles

EXETER, Devon Map ref 1D2 | GUEST ACCOMMODATION

★★
INN

B&B per room per night
s £40.00–£50.00
d £65.00–£80.00
Evening meal per person
£10.00–£20.00

Thorverton Arms

Thorverton, Exeter EX5 5NS t (01392) 860205 e info@thethorvertonarms.co.uk
w thethorvertonarms.co.uk

open All year
bedrooms 3 double, 1 twin, 1 single, 1 family
bathrooms All en suite
payment Credit/debit cards, cash/cheques

Traditional English country inn set in the heart of the beautiful village of Thorverton. Situated in the Exe Valley, yet only seven miles from Exeter. Comfortable en suite rooms, bar, award-winning restaurant, large south facing garden and car park. Ideal touring base for Exmoor, Dartmoor and the Devon coasts.

⊕ Just off the A396, seven miles north of Exeter. 11 miles from jct 27 of the M5. Eight miles from Exeter Airport.

♥ DB&B – £50 per person (min 2 people).

Pets 🐕 Room 📺 General 🖼 🅿 🍷 ✕ Leisure ♻

EXETER, Devon Map ref 1D2 | SELF CATERING

★★★★
SELF CATERING

Units **7**
Sleeps **6–7**

Low season per wk
£280.00–£480.00
High season per wk
£400.00–£875.00

Bussells Farm Cottages, Exeter

contact Andy and Lucy Hines, Bussells Farm, Huxham, Nr Stoke Canon, Exeter EX5 4EN
t (01392) 841238 **f** (01392) 841345 **e** bussellsfarm@aol.com **w** bussellsfarm.co.uk

open All year
payment Credit/debit cards, cash/cheques

Lovely barn-conversion cottages, heated outdoor swimming pool from May to September, adventure playground, well-equipped games room and excellent coarse fishing in the private lakes. We offer a wonderful base from which to explore the beautiful Exe Valley, Dartmoor, the South Devon beaches and the ancient city of Exeter.

⊕ At Stoke Canon, take road next to church signposted Huxham and Poltimore; just after Barton Cross Hotel (0.5 miles) turn left. Bussells Farm is 0.5 miles on left.

♥ 3-night stays available. Low season discounts for 1 or 2 people. Pets welcome.

Pets 🐕 🐾. Unit ▥ TV ▣ 🍴🗄 🖳 🖥 🖨✿
General ⛱ 🏢 🏃 P ✂ 🅾 Ⓢ Leisure ⚲ ♣ ⚲ Ü 🚵 🚣 Shop 1 mile Pub 1 mile

---

EXMOOR

See under Combe Martin, Dulverton, Dunster, Lynton, Porlock

FALMOUTH, Cornwall Map ref 1B3 | HOTEL

★★★★
HOTEL
SILVER AWARD

B&B per room per night
s £62.00–£110.00
d £124.00–£220.00
HB per person per night
£74.00–£124.00

Budock Vean Hotel on the River

Helford Passage, Mawnan Smith, Falmouth TR11 5LG **t** (01326) 252100 **f** (01326) 250892
e relax@budockvean.co.uk **w** budockvean.co.uk

bedrooms 24 double, 23 twin, 7 single, 2 family, 1 suite
bathrooms All en suite
payment Credit/debit cards, cash/cheques

Budock Vean is a family-owned hotel nestled in 65 acres of organic subtropical gardens and parkland with private foreshore on the tranquil Helford river. Outstanding leisure facilities include golf, indoor swimming, sauna, outdoor hot tub, health spa, and award-winning restaurant. Closed 2 – 25 January.

Pets 🐕 £🐕 🐕 🐾. Room 📞 TV 🛁 🖳 🗜 General ⛱1 ▥ 🏃 P ♟ 🍴 🎱 🎬◉✿ Leisure ⚲ ♣ ⚲ Ü 🚵

FALMOUTH, Cornwall Map ref 1B3 | SELF CATERING

★★★
SELF CATERING

Units **6**
Sleeps **2–5**

Low season per wk
£220.00–£395.00
High season per wk
£415.00–£475.00

Good-Winds Holiday Apartments, Falmouth

contact Mrs Goodwin, Good-Winds Holiday Apartments, 13 Stratton Terracce, Falmouth TR11 2SY
t (01326) 313200 **f** (01326) 313200 **e** goodwinds13@aol.com

open All year
payment Cash/cheques, euros

Modern, two-bedroom apartments with balconies having marvellous views over the harbour, River Pen and the quaint fishing village of Flushing. Undercover parking for two cars. Walking distance to town. One double bed, two singles and extra single in three units.

⊕ Follow signs into Falmouth. When you see 'Park and Float' signs, left at next roundabout. 1 mile. Right into Symons Hill. Right into Penwerris Lane.

♥ Three-day plus short breaks available out of season.

Pets 🐕 £🐕 Unit ▥ TV ▣ 🖳 🖥
General ⛱ ▥ 🏃 P Ⓢ Shop 0.5 miles Pub 0.75 miles

FOREST OF DEAN

See under Littledean

FOWEY, Cornwall Map ref 1B3 — HOTEL

Fowey Hotel

★★★
HOTEL

B&B per room per night
s £67.00–£220.00
d £90.00–£220.00
HB per person per night
£65.00–£130.00

The Esplanade, Fowey PL23 1HX t (01726) 832551 f (01726) 832125
e reception@thefoweyhotel.co.uk w thefoweyhotel.co.uk

open All year
bedrooms 29 double, 6 twin, 1 family, 1 suite
bathrooms All en suite
payment Credit/debit cards, cash/cheques

Majestically positioned on the bank of the Fowey
Estuary, the Fowey Hotel, built in 1882, offers
friendly service, comfortable rooms and rosette
award-winning food. Located only 20 minutes from
the Eden Project, the hotel is in the ideal location for
exploring many of the gardens and attractions in
Cornwall. DB&B rates available on request.

⊕ On entering Fowey, take Daglands Road (on right),
continue for 200yds. The Fowey Hotel drive is on the left
before the bend in the road.

♥ Special midweek and 3-day Eden breaks available
throughout the year.

Pets 🐕 £🐾 🐎 Room 📞 📺 ⛴ 🍵 ⚲ General 🛎 🏛 🏃 P 🍽 🎱 🎪 ✿

HELSTON, Cornwall Map ref 1B3 — SELF CATERING

Carminowe View, Helston

★★★★
SELF CATERING

Units   1
Sleeps   4

Low season per wk
£230.00–£325.00
High season per wk
£400.00–£540.00

contact Mr Huddleston, Carminowe View, 3 Northfield Road, Portishead BS20 8LE
t (01275) 848899 e jhuddl2144@aol.com

open All year
payment Cash/cheques

Overlooking Carminowe Valley and close to Loe
Pool. An inverted, two-storey barn conversion with
two en suite bedrooms, separate fitted kitchen and
lounge and dining area. Washing/drying facilities.
Central heating and wood-burning stove. Linen and
towels supplied. Walled, secluded garden with
seating and barbecue.

Pets 🐕 🐾 Unit 🛏 📺 📷 📟 🖥 💻 🗄 🍴 🔥 🔌 🗑 📼 ✿
General 🛎 🏛 🏃 P 🅿 🆂 Leisure 🚲 Shop 2.5 miles Pub 3 miles

LAUNCESTON, Cornwall Map ref 1C2 — SELF CATERING

Frankaborough Farm Cottages, Lifton

★★★★
SELF CATERING

Units   3
Sleeps   4–6

Low season per wk
£150.00–£300.00
High season per wk
£250.00–£600.00

contact Mrs Linda Banbury, Frankaborough Farm Cottages, Lifton PL16 0JS
t (01409) 211308 f (01409) 211308 e banbury960@aol.com w devonfarmcottage.co.uk

Close to Devon/Cornwall border, 260-acre mixed
dairy farm offering imaginative barn conversions
decorated to a high standard, set in a rural
location but easily accessible to the A30.

open All year
payment Cash/cheques, euros

Pets 🐕 Unit 🛏 📺 📟 🖥 💻 🗄 🍴 🔥 🗑 🔌 ✿
General 🛎 🏛 🏃 P 🅿 🆂 Leisure 🎣 Shop 4 miles Pub 4 miles

It's all quality-assessed accommodation

Our commitment to quality involves wide-ranging accommodation assessment. Rating
and awards were correct at the time of going to press but may change following a
new assessment. Please check at time of booking.

LAUNCESTON, Cornwall Map ref 1C2 — SELF CATERING

★★★–★★★★★
SELF CATERING

Units **4**
Sleeps **2–4**

Low season per wk
£140.00–£260.00
High season per wk
£260.00–£450.00

Langdon Farm Holiday Cottages, Launceston

contact Mrs Fleur Rawlinson, Langdon Farm Holiday Cottages, Langdon Farm, Launceston PL15 8NW
t (01566) 785389 **e** g.f.rawlinson@btinternet.com **w** langdonholidays.com

One- and two-bedroom, well-equipped cottages, four-poster beds, countryside setting, near pub, ten miles from sea. Easy drive to Eden Project. Short breaks available.

open All year
payment Credit/debit cards, cash/cheques

Pets 🐕 🐾 Unit 🛏 📺 ▨ ▣ ▤ 🗄 🔌 🖥 ❀
General 🛋 🏠 🅿 🅢 Leisure ∪ 🚲 ⛰ Shop 4 miles Pub 1 mile

LAUNCESTON, Cornwall Map ref 1C2 — SELF CATERING

★★★
SELF CATERING

Units **2**
Sleeps **2–8**

Low season per wk
£185.00–£350.00
High season per wk
£380.00–£620.00

Lower Dutson Farm, Launceston

contact Francis and Kathryn Broad, Lower Dutson Farm, Dutson, Launceston PL15 9SP
t (01566) 776456 **e** holidays@farm-cottage.co.uk **w** farm-cottage.co.uk

open All year
payment Cash/cheques

Meadow Cottage and Swallows (two bathrooms each) offer great accommodation in an ideal touring location on the Devon/Cornwall border. Ideal for visiting Launceston's Norman castle and steam railway, sandy beaches, moors, harbours, National Trust houses and gardens. Relax by the river or lake and maybe spot a kingfisher.

⊕ M5 jct 31, A30 to Launceston, then A388 towards Holsworthy. We are located 2 miles from Launceston on right.

♥ Free coarse fishing on lake and River Tamar (trout, salmon and grayling) for 2 people per cottage.

Pets 🐕 £🐾 🐾 Unit 🛏 📺 ▨ ▣ 🗄 🔌 🖥 🔲 ❀
General 🛋 🏠 🅿 🅢 Leisure ● ∪ ⛰ Shop 1 mile Pub 1 mile

LITTLEDEAN, Gloucestershire Map ref 2B1 — SELF CATERING

★★★
SELF CATERING

Units **1**
Sleeps **3**

Low season per wk
£160.00–£260.00
High season per wk
£260.00–£360.00

Brambles, Littledean, Cinderford

contact Mrs Norman, Brambles, Sutton Baynham Farm, Sutton Road, Cinderford GL14 2TU
t (01594) 827311 **f** (01594) 827345 **e** lynda@searanckes.com

open All year
payment Cash/cheques, euros

We welcome you to our 30-acre farm in wooded Soudley Valley. Brambles provides tranquillity next to our farmhouse. Foray into the woods or picnic in our fields. Stone steps lead to accommodation with wooden balcony and view over valley. Sleeps two adults and two children. One mile to Dean Heritage Centre.

⊕ From A48 Elton Corner take A4151 to Littledean. In village, turn left for Soudley, then take lane on right-hand side after 0.7 miles.

Pets 🐕 £🐾 🐾 Unit 🛏 📺 ▣ ▨ ▣ 🗄 🔌 🖥 ❀
General 🛋 🏠 🅿 🅢 Leisure ∪ 🚲 ⛰ Shop 1 mile Pub 1 mile

Town, country or coast

The entertainment, shopping and innovative attractions of the big cities, the magnificent vistas of the countryside or the relaxing and refreshing coast – this guide will help you find what you're looking for.

LOOE, Cornwall Map ref 1C2 — HOTEL

★★★
HOTEL

B&B per room per night
s £48.00–£78.00
d £88.00–£140.00
HB per person per night
£50.00–£86.00

Hannafore Point Hotel

Marine Drive, Looe PL13 2DG t (01503) 263273 f (01503) 263272
e stay@hannaforepointhotel.com w hannaforepointhotel.com

open All year
bedrooms 33 double, 4 single
bathrooms All en suite
payment Credit/debit cards, cash/cheques

A warm welcome awaits you. Set in picturesque Cornish village with spectacular, panoramic sea views. Indulge in superb home-cooked food. Varied dining options featuring quality local produce and fresh fish. The terrace is a popular rendezvous for cream teas or cocktails alike. Extensive leisure facilities. Traditional hospitality and excellent service.

⊕ *A38 from Plymouth, then A387 to Looe. Cross over stone bridge, turn 1st left (sign 'Hannafore') and uphill until overlooking bay.*

♥ *Special-event packages. Extensive range of conference and business facilities. Weddings and special occasions. Christmas and New Year celebrations.*

Pets Room General Leisure

LOOE, Cornwall Map ref 1C2 — SELF CATERING

Rating Applied For
SELF CATERING

Units 8
Sleeps 2–6

Low season per wk
£275.00–£775.00
High season per wk
£855.00–£1,375.00

Barclay House Luxury Cottages, Looe

contact Mr Graham Brooks, Barclay House Luxury Cottages, St Martins Road, East Looe, Looe PL13 1LP
t (01503) 262929 f (01503) 262632 e info@barclayhouse.co.uk w barclayhouse.co.uk

open All year
payment Credit/debit cards, cash/cheques

Luxury, award-winning holiday cottages. Breathtaking views over the Looe River valley. Heated pool nestled in a natural sun trap. Five minutes' walk to harbour, town and beach. Superb award-winning restaurant and bar/lounge on site. Come stay at Barclay House, you will be glad you did!

⊕ *From A387 signposted Looe. After 1 mile turn right and follow road for 8 miles. First hotel on left on entering Looe.*

♥ *Special short breaks available – please call for details.*

Pets Unit General Leisure Shop < 0.5 miles Pub < 0.5 miles

LOOE, Cornwall Map ref 1C2 — SELF CATERING

★★★★
SELF CATERING

Units 6
Sleeps 2–5

Low season per wk
£150.00–£350.00
High season per wk
£350.00–£615.00

Summercourt Coastal Cottages, Looe

contact Mr Hocking, Summercourt Coastal Cottages, Bodigga Cliff, St Martin PL13 1NZ
t (01503) 263149 e sccottages@freenet.co.uk w holidaycottagescornwall.tv

Stone barns converted to comfortable and well-equipped cottages in a rural Area of Outstanding Natural Beauty. Close to sea and beaches.

open All year
payment Credit/debit cards, cash/cheques

Pets Unit General Leisure Shop 2 miles Pub 2 miles

Using map references

Map references refer to the colour maps at the front of this guide.

LOOE, Cornwall Map ref 1C2 — SELF CATERING

★★★
SELF CATERING

Units **5**
Sleeps **2–5**

Low season per wk
£165.00–£450.00
High season per wk
£319.00–£665.00

Talehay, Looe

contact Neil & Theresa Dennett, Talehay, Tremaine, Looe PL13 2LT
t (01503) 220252   **e** infobooking@talehay.co.uk   **w** talehay.co.uk

open All year
payment Credit/debit cards, cash/cheques

Tastefully converted and very comfortable stone holiday cottages set around 17thC non-working farmstead. Set in unspoilt, peaceful countryside with breathtaking coastal walks and beaches nearby. Close to Eden Project, Lost Gardens of Heligan and many National Trust properties. An ideal base for exploring the many varied delights of Cornwall.

⊕ *Over Tamar bridge, A38 for 16 miles. Dobwalls traffic lights, A390 St Austell road (2.5 miles). B3359, left on Looe road. After 6 miles right at crossroads.*

♥ *Short breaks available Oct-Mar (excl Christmas and New Year), minimum 2 nights.*

Pets ♈ ⌂♈ ♈.   Unit ▥ ⊡ ⑮⊡⊟ ▣ ◌ ⌾ ⬚ ✻
General ⬤ ⊞ ♨ P ✄   Leisure ∪ ♵ ⌂   Shop 1 mile   Pub 1 mile

LOSTWITHIEL, Cornwall Map ref 1B2 — SELF CATERING

★★★–★★★★★
SELF CATERING

Units **8**
Sleeps **1–6**

Low season per wk
£210.00–£330.00
High season per wk
£330.00–£895.00

Lanwithan Cottages, Lostwithiel

contact Mr V B Edward-Collins, Lanwithan Cottages, Lanwithan Road, Lostwithiel PL22 0LA
t (01208) 872444   **f** (01208) 872444   **e** info@lanwithancottages.co.uk   **w** lanwithancottages.co.uk

open All year
payment Cash/cheques, euros

Charming selection of Georgian estate cottages nestling in the Fowey Valley with two delightful waterside properties. Cottages with leaded-light windows, crackling log fires, four-poster bed and glass-topped well. Parkland, river frontage and boat. Woodland and riverside walks from your garden gate. Come and relax and soak up the Cornish atmosphere.

⊕ *Liskeard – Lostwithiel A390, pass National garage on left. 1st left, Great Western units, 1st left again. 300yds sign - follow to house, not farm.*

♥ *Short breaks out of season. Reduced green fees. Pets accepted in some cottages. Canoe trips available with safety boat.*

Pets ♈ ⌂♈ ♈.   Unit ▥ ⊡ ⑮⊡⊟ ▣. ⊟⊟ ◌ ⌾ ⬚ ✻
General ⬤ ⊞ ♨ P ☐   Leisure ● ◌ ∪ ♵ ⌂   Shop 0.5 miles   Pub 0.5 miles

The great outdoors

Discover Britain's green heart with this easy-to-use guide. Featuring a selection of the most stunning gardens in the country, The Gardens Explorer is complete with a handy fold-out map and illustrated guide. You can purchase the Explorer series from good bookshops and online at visitbritaindirect.com.

LULWORTH COVE, Dorset Map ref 2B3 — HOTEL

★★
HOTEL

B&B per room per night
s £42.50–£60.00
d £66.00–£95.00
HB per person per night
£49.00–£69.00

Cromwell House Hotel

Lulworth Cove, West Lulworth, Wareham BH20 5RJ t (01929) 400253 f (01929) 400566
e cromwell@lulworthcove.co.uk w lulworthcove.co.uk

open All year except Christmas and New Year
bedrooms 7 double, 7 twin, 2 single, 3 family
bathrooms All en suite
payment Credit/debit cards, cash/cheques

Lulworth Cove 200yds, all en suite rooms, spectacular sea views, direct access Jurassic Coast, excellent walking and country pursuits. Good home cooking – local fish, including Lulworth Cove lobsters, a speciality. Bar and extensive wine list, beautiful gardens and sea-facing terrace, home-made cream teas, all-day refreshments, swimming pool (May to October). Groups welcome.

⊕ M3, M27, A31 to Bere Regis, B3071 to West Lulworth. Hotel situated on slip road, on left, 200yds beyond end of West Lulworth village heading for Lulworth Cove.

♥ Art and photography courses – apply for details. 3-day special breaks available.

Pets 🐕 £🐈 🐾 🐎 🐴 Room 🛏 📞 📺 🕹 🍵 ✍ General 🖥 ▥ ☂ P 🍽 🎱 ♟ ▣ ✿ Leisure ⚡ ♾ 🌊

LYME REGIS, Dorset Map ref 1D2 — SELF CATERING

★★★★
SELF CATERING

Units   2
Sleeps   2–4

Low season per wk
£295.00–£420.00
High season per wk
£465.00–£595.00

Sea Tree House, Lyme Regis

contact Mr David Parker, Sea Tree House, 18 Broad Street, Lyme Regis DT7 3QE
t (01297) 442244 f (01297) 442244 e seatree.house@ukonline.co.uk
w lymeregis.com/seatreehouse

open All year
payment Cash/cheques

Romantic, elegant apartments overlooking the sea, three minutes from the beach. Spacious living room with dining area overlooking the sea. Central position giving easy access to restaurants, pubs and walks in Area of Outstanding Natural Beauty. Wi-Fi Internet. Warm, friendly welcome from owners.

⊕ Approach Lyme Regis from either A35 or A3052. Sea Tree House is on Broad Street, the main street, just before you reach the sea.

♥ Short breaks available in the low season.

Pets 🐕 £🐈 Unit ▥ 📺 🍳 🖥 🔲 📀 🍴 📱 🔲 📵 ✿
General 🖥 ▥ ☂ P ▣ Ⓢ Leisure ♾ Shop 0.5 miles Pub 0.5 miles

LYME REGIS, Dorset Map ref 1D2 — SELF CATERING

★★★★
SELF CATERING

Units   1
Sleeps   5

Low season per wk
£350.00–£390.00
High season per wk
£450.00–£875.00

Sheepwash Green, Fishpond Bottom, Bridport

contact Mrs Ambra Edwards, Guppys Lodge, Fishpond, Bridport DT6 6NN
t (01297) 678598 e ambra@sheepwashgreen.co.uk w sheepwashgreen.co.uk

open All year
payment Cash/cheques

Imagine a secret valley untouched by time, with glorious views over rolling hills to Dorset's Jurassic Coast. Hidden in this Area of Outstanding Natural Beauty, stands Sheepwash Green, a cosy cob cottage with beams, log fires and large sunny garden. No traffic. No noise. No light pollution. Just perfect peace, with outstanding walking from the door. World Heritage coast and beach: four miles.

⊕ Fishpond Bottom is reached from the B3165 at Marshwood, or the A35 at Morcombelake. Please telephone the owner for directions.

♥ Midweek breaks: 4 nights for the price of 3. Bluebell breaks; Christmas escapes – see website for details.

Pets 🐕 Unit ▥ 📺 🍳 🖥 🔲 🍴 📱 🔲 📵 ✿
General 🖥 ▥ ☂ P ✂ Ⓢ Leisure 🌊 Shop 4 miles Pub 2 miles

LYME REGIS, Dorset Map ref 1D2

★★★
SELF CATERING

Units **4**
Sleeps **6–8**

Low season per wk
£180.00–£290.00
High season per wk
£295.00–£795.00

Westover Farm Cottages, Bridport

contact Jon Snook or Debby Snook, Westover Farm Cottages, Westover Farm, Wootton Fitzpaine, Bridport DT6 6NE
t (01297) 560451 & (01297) 561395 **e** wfcottages@aol.com **w** westoverfarmcottages.co.uk

open All year
payment Cash/cheques, euros

Lovely three-bedroomed cottages with wood-burning stoves, inglenook and open fires on edge of picturesque village. Additional three-bedroomed, stone-built cottages with adjoining games room overlooking gentle valley. Parking and large garden at all cottages. In an Area of Outstanding Natural Beauty, 1.5 miles from World Heritage Coastline.

⊕ *A35 from Dorchester. Right to Wootton Fitzpaine 0.75 miles beyond Charmouth roundabout. Westover Farm is 1st house on left. From Axminster turn left 0.75 miles before roundabout.*

♥ *Short-break bookings a speciality and very welcome.*

Pets 🐕 £🐕 🐕. Unit 🛏 📺 ▦ ▣ ■. ▦ 🔲 🔲 ✿
General ☌ ▥ 🅿 Ⓢ Leisure ● ∪ Shop 1.5 miles Pub 1.5 miles

LYNTON, Devon Map ref 1C1

★
HOTEL

B&B per room per night
s £34.00–£40.00
d £64.00–£76.00
HB per person per night
£52.00–£58.00

North Cliff Hotel

North Walk, Lynton EX35 6HJ **t** (01598) 752357 **e** holidays@northcliffhotel.co.uk
w northcliffhotel.co.uk

open All year
bedrooms 7 double, 2 twin, 1 single, 4 family
bathrooms All en suite
payment Credit/debit cards, cash/cheques, euros

Overlooking Lynmouth Bay and Watermeet Valley with magnificent coastal views. A minute's walk from village on coastal footpath. All bedrooms en suite with tea-/coffee-making facilities and colour TV. Private car parking. English home cooking. Children, groups and dogs welcome. Ideal for walking or touring Exmoor.

⊕ *M5 jct 27, follow A361 (Barnstaple). After 25 miles take A399 to Blackmoor Gate, then A39 to Lynton. Turn down by church.*

♥ *Check our website for special offers.*

Pets 🐕 £🐕 🖳 Room 📺 ✋ 🍽 General ☌ ▥ 🅿 ✂ 🍷 🍴 🏮 ✿ Leisure ∪

MARLBOROUGH, Wiltshire Map ref 2B2

★★★★
BED & BREAKFAST
SILVER AWARD

B&B per room per night
s £32.50–£37.50
d £65.00–£75.00
Evening meal per person
£15.00–£20.00

Crofton Lodge

Crofton, Marlborough SN8 3DW **t** (01672) 870328 **e** ali@croftonlodge.co.uk **w** croftonlodge.co.uk

open All year except Christmas and New Year
bedrooms 1 double, 1 twin, 1 single
bathrooms 1 en suite, 2 private
payment Cash/cheques, euros

Comfortable, welcoming home with large gardens in hamlet next to Kennet and Avon Canal, Crofton Beam Engines and Savernake Forest. Close to Great Bedwyn and good pubs. Easy reach Marlborough and Hungerford. Excellent base for walkers and cyclists. Home grown or local produce.

⊕ *From Great Bedwyn (2 miles south of A4 between Marlborough and Hungerford) follow Crofton Beam Engine signs. Crofton Lodge is 1.5 miles on right.*

♥ *Stay for 3 nights and enjoy a free dinner.*

Pets 🐕 🖳 🐕 🐕. Room 📺 ✋ 🍽 General ☌ 12 ✕ 🍴 🏮 🐾 ✿ Leisure 🎣 ⚲ 🏞

MELCOMBE BINGHAM, Dorset Map ref 2B3   **SELF CATERING**

★★★★
SELF CATERING

Units **1**
Sleeps **1–7**

Low season per wk
£400.00–£575.00
High season per wk
£625.00–£800.00

Greygles, Melcombe Bingham, Dorchester

contact Mr Paul Sommerfeld, 22 Tiverton Road, London NW10 3HL
t (020) 8969 4830   **f** (020) 8960 0069   **e** enquiry@greygles.co.uk   **w** greygles.co.uk

open All year
payment Cash/cheques, euros

Rural peace in spacious, well-equipped stone cottage with delightful views. Hardy Country, on edge of friendly village with well-known pub. Four bedrooms, one on ground floor. Log fire. Wendy house in garden. In an Area of Outstanding Natural Beauty, just off Wessex Ridgeway walkers' path. Coast, abbeys, castles, gardens, many attractions within 30 minutes' drive.

⊕ *From Winterbourne Whitechurch on A354 Blandford/Dorchester road, follow sign to Milton Abbas, then through Milton, Hilton and Ansty to Melcombe Bingham.*

♥ *Short breaks available outside summer peak, Christmas and Easter. Min 3-night stay. Linen, towels and heating included.*

Pets 🐕   Unit 🛏 📺 📠 ▦ ⊡ 🖃 📠 🍳 🔔 🧺 🎕
General 🌳 ⛩ ⓟ P ✂ ⊙   Leisure 🎣   Shop 0.5 miles   Pub 0.5 miles

MENHENIOT, Cornwall Map ref 1C2   **SELF CATERING**

★★★★
SELF CATERING

Units **6**
Sleeps **1–6**

Low season per wk
£198.00–£305.00
High season per wk
£260.00–£750.00

Hayloft Courtyard Cottages, Liskeard

contact Michele & Stephen Hore, Hayloft Courtyard Cottages, Lower Clicker Road, Menheniot, Liskeard PL14 3PU
t (01503) 240879   **e** courtyardcottage@btconnect.com   **w** hayloftcourtyardcottages.com

open All year
payment Credit/debit cards, cash/cheques

A warm welcome and Cornish cream tea await your arrival at our family-run cottages. Lovingly converted from original stone barns and equipped to a high standard with many home-from-home comforts. Recently refurbished bathrooms all with jacuzzi baths. Ideally situated for touring coast, moors and attractions. Children's play area. Restaurant on-site offering popular meal delivery service.

⊕ *Tamar Bridge, A38 for Liskeard. Three miles from 2nd roundabout, up hill on dual carriageway. Sign right for Menheniot. Cross dual carriageway. Hayloft opposite (2nd entrance for cottage).*

♥ *Short breaks – off-peak. Special offers spring/autumn.*

Pets 🐕 🐈 🐾   Unit 🛏 📺 ▦ 🖃 📠 🍳 🧺 🎕
General 🌳 ⛩ ⓟ P ⊙ Ⓢ   Leisure ∪ 🚲   Shop 1 mile   Pub < 0.5 miles

MOORSHOP, Devon Map ref 1C2   **SELF CATERING**

★★★
SELF CATERING

Units **2**
Sleeps **1–4**

Low season per wk
£150.00–£250.00
High season per wk
£220.00–£400.00

Higher Longford, Tavistock

Higher Longford, Tavistock PL19 9LQ
t (01822) 613360   **f** (01822) 618722   **e** stay@higherlongford.co.uk   **w** higherlongford.co.uk

Excellently presented, comfortable, stone-built cottages with all the comforts from home, set within the Dartmoor National Park. Ideal for touring Devon and Cornwall. Children/pets welcome.

open All year
payment Credit/debit cards, cash/cheques

Pets 🐕 🐈 🐾   Unit 🛏 📺 ⊡ ▦ 🖃 📠 🍳 🧺 🎕
General 🌳 ⛩ ⓟ P ✂ ⊙ Ⓢ   Leisure 🎣 ∪ 🚲   Shop < 0.5 miles   Pub 1 mile

Confirm your booking
It's always advisable to confirm your booking in writing.

MULLION, Cornwall Map ref 1B3 — HOTEL

★★★
HOTEL

B&B per room per night
s £53.00–£84.00
d £106.00–£168.00
HB per person per night
£63.00–£94.00

Polurrian Hotel

Polurrian Road, Mullion, Helston TR12 7EN t (01326) 240421 f (01326) 240083
e relax@polurrianhotel.com w polurrianhotel.com

open All year
bedrooms 14 double, 14 twin, 2 single, 8 family, 1 suite
bathrooms All en suite
payment Credit/debit cards, cash/cheques

Friendly, privately owned hotel set in 12 acres overlooking our sandy beach with stunning views across Mounts Bay. Sun terraces, secluded small walled gardens and leisure club. Two restaurants serve local seasonal produce. Facilities include indoor and outdoor pools, snooker room, beauty room, gym, squash, tennis, games room, climbing frames and creche.

⊕ A3083 from Helston towards The Lizard for about 6m. Then right on B3296 to Mullion. 0.5m past Mullion turn right at brown sign 'Polurrian Hotel'.

♥ Christmas packages. Reduced rates for 7 days and for children sharing with adults. Occasional themed weekends. Free Leisure Club membership.

Pets 🐕 £🏠 🐎 🐾 Room 🛁 📞 📺 🍴 🍳 General 🛋 🏛 🏄 P 🍽 🎱 🎯 🖥 ✿ Leisure 🎣 🏹 🎾 🏊 ⛳ 🚲

NETHER STOWEY, Somerset Map ref 1D1 — GUEST ACCOMMODATION

★★★★★
GUEST ACCOMMODATION
SILVER AWARD

B&B per room per night
s £42.00–£92.00
d £104.00–£142.00
Evening meal per person
£16.00–£24.00

Castle of Comfort Country House

Dodington, Nether Stowey, Bridgwater TA5 1LE t (01278) 741264 f (01278) 741144
e reception@castle-of-comfort.co.uk w castle-of-comfort.co.uk

16thC country house and restaurant nestling in the Quantock Hills with four acres of grounds. Luxurious accommodation of the highest standard.

open All year except Christmas and New Year
bedrooms 3 double, 1 twin, 1 single, 1 family
bathrooms All en suite
payment Credit/debit cards, cash/cheques

Pets 🐕 🐎 🐾 Room 🛁 📞 📺 🍴 🍳 General 🛋 🏛 🏄 P 🍽 🍽 ✕ 🎱 🎯 ✿ Leisure 🏹 🏊 ⛳ 🚣

OWLPEN, Gloucestershire Map ref 2B1 — SELF CATERING

★★★–★★★★★
SELF CATERING

Units **9**
Sleeps **2–8**

Low season per wk
£295.00–£855.00
High season per wk
£395.00–£1,495.00

Owlpen Manor, Uley

contact Mrs Jayne Simmons, Estate Office, Owlpen Manor, Owlpen, Uley, Nr Dursley GL11 5BZ
t (01453) 860261 f (01453) 860819 e sales@owlpen.com w owlpen.com

open All year
payment Credit/debit cards, cash/cheques

Romantic Cotswold hamlet, manor house and church in a hidden beech wood valley. Nine self-catering period and historic cottages spread around the 215-acre estate. Antiques, log fires and four-posters in some. 15thC restaurant. Midweek and weekend breaks available all year round. 'The most beautiful place in England' – Fodor's Guide 2000.

⊕ B4066 to Uley. In Uley, follow signs to Owlpen at the Green, by the Old Crown public house.

♥ Excellent value four-night midweek breaks available all year round (excl Xmas and New Year). Also three-night weekend breaks available.

Pets 🐕 £🏠 Unit 🛏 📺 🍴 🍳 🔲 🖥 📷 🔥 🍳 🍽 📻 ✿
General 🛋 🏛 🏄 P S Leisure 🏊 ⛳ Shop 1 mile Pub 1 mile

Mention our name
Please mention this guide when making your booking.

PADSTOW, Cornwall Map ref 1B2 — GUEST ACCOMMODATION

★★★★★
GUEST ACCOMMODATION SILVER AWARD

B&B per room per night
s £57.00–£65.00
d £90.00–£132.00

Woodlands Country House

Treator, Padstow PL28 8RU t (01841) 532426 f (01841) 533353 e info@woodlands-padstow.co.uk
w woodlands-padstow.co.uk

bedrooms 7 double, 1 twin, 1 family
bathrooms All en suite
payment Credit/debit cards, cash/cheques, euros

Woodlands Country House: an award-winning, family-run guesthouse, with wonderful views of the North Cornish countryside and coastline. Nine stylish rooms, all en suite, designed for comfort and relaxation. In the morning, our famous Cornish breakfasts. Bed and breakfast with a touch of splendour. Closed festive season and January.

⊕ On the B3276 0.5 miles from Padstow to St Merryn.
♥ Nov-Apr: 3 nights for the price of 2, weekday nights only. Excl Easter, Christmas and January.

Pets ... Room ... General ... Leisure ...

PADSTOW, Cornwall Map ref 1B2 — SELF CATERING

★★★
SELF CATERING

Units **2**
Sleeps **2–4**

Low season per wk
£220.00–£520.00
High season per wk
£240.00–£550.00

Sable Cottage & Chiff Chaff, Padstow

contact Mrs Denise Daw, Sable Cottage & Chiffchaff, 16 Harbury Road, Bristol BS9 4PL
t (0117) 907 9348 e denisedaw@blueyonder.co.uk w sablecottage.co.uk

Sable Cottage is a delightful, modern-style cottage; Chiffchaff is a superb detached bungalow. Each is well equipped with two bedrooms and garage. Located eight minutes' walk from the harbour.

open All year
payment Credit/debit cards

Pets ... Unit ...
General ... Leisure ... Shop < 0.5 miles Pub 0.5 miles

PAIGNTON, Devon Map ref 1D2 — HOTEL

★★
HOTEL

B&B per room per night
s £20.00–£40.00
d £40.00–£80.00
HB per person per night
£30.00–£50.00

Marine Hotel

Seafront, Paignton TQ4 6AP t (01803) 559778 f (01803) 553162 e stay@marinehotelpaignton.co.uk
w marinehotelpaignton.co.uk

open All year
bedrooms 12 double, 21 twin, 11 single, 8 family
bathrooms All en suite
payment Credit/debit cards, cash/cheques

A family-run hotel set in the middle of Paignton right on the seafront, commanding beautiful views across Torbay. Convenient level walk to all amenities. Here you will always find a smile and quality comfort and company within a lively, yet relaxed atmosphere. Simply, great value.

⊕ From A30 or M5 follow signs to Paignton and then seafront. Marine Hotel is a large blue building directly facing the crazy-golf course adjacent to the Apollo multiplex cinema.
♥ Great-value weekend breaks Oct-May.

Pets ... Room ... General ...

Check the maps

Colour maps at the front pinpoint all the places you will find accommodation entries in the regional sections. Pick your location and then refer to the place index at the back to find the page number.

PAIGNTON, Devon Map ref 1D2 — SELF CATERING

★★
SELF CATERING

Units **8**
Sleeps **2–6**
Low season per wk
£121.00–£204.00
High season per wk
£258.00–£465.00

Tregarth, Paignton

contact Mr & Mrs Haskins, Tregarth, 8 Adelphi Road, Paignton TQ4 6AW
t (01803) 558458 **e** tregarthpaignton@aol.com **w** tregarthpaignton.co.uk

These delightful holiday flats are located on the English Riviera, close to the sea and Paignton railway station. Modern, fully equipped rooms and on-site parking. An ideal base to explore the Devon coast.

open All year
payment Cash/cheques

Pets 🐾 Unit 📶 📺 💻 ▦
General ♨ 🍴 🅿 ◻ Shop < 0.5 miles Pub 0.5 miles

PENZANCE, Cornwall Map ref 1A3 — SELF CATERING

★★★
SELF CATERING

Units **2**
Sleeps **3–8**
Low season per wk
£200.00–£300.00
High season per wk
£350.00–£450.00

Rospannel Farm, Penzance

contact Mr Hocking, Rospannel Farm, Crows-An-Wra, Penzance TR19 6HS
t (01736) 810262 **e** gbernardh@btinternet.com **w** rospannel.com

Old-fashioned, very quiet and peaceful farm. Own pool and hide for bird-watchers. Moth light for insect enthusiasts. Badgers, foxes and lots of wildlife.

open All year
payment Cash/cheques

Pets 🐾 🐾 Unit 📶 📺 💻 🗄 ▦ ▦ ✿
General ♨ P

PIDDLETRENTHIDE, Dorset Map ref 2B3 — GUEST ACCOMMODATION

★★★★
INN

B&B per room per night
s £52.50–£70.00
d £74.00–£120.00
Evening meal per person
£12.00–£22.00

The Poachers Inn

Piddletrenthide, Dorchester DT2 7QX **t** (01300) 348358 **f** (01300) 348153
e thepoachersinn@piddletrenthide.fsbusiness.co.uk **w** thepoachersinn.co.uk

open All year
bedrooms 8 double, 8 twin, 3 family, 2 suites
bathrooms All en suite
payment Credit/debit cards, cash/cheques

Set in the heart of the beautiful Piddle Valley, the family-run Poachers Inn has an excellent choice of food in its 17thC restaurant and riverside garden. All bedrooms are en suite and tastefully furnished with the very-best-quality fixtures and fittings. Colour TV, tea- and coffee-making facilities, shaving point, hairdryer, radio and direct-dial telephones.

⊕ *From Dorchester head north on B3143 (Piddletrenthide and Sturminster Newton). The Poachers Inn is approx 7 miles from Dorchester on the north side of Piddletrenthide.*

Pets 🐾 £🐾 🐾 🐾 🐾 Room 🛏 ☎ 📺 ☕ 🗄 General ♨ 🍴 🅿 ⚑ ✕ 🍴 🎱 ✿ Leisure ⚘ ∪ 🏊

Take a break

Look out for special promotions and themed breaks. It's a golden opportunity to indulge an interest, find a new one, or just relax and enjoy exceptional value. Offers and promotions are highlighted in colour (and are subject to availability).

PLYMOUTH, Devon Map ref 1C2 **HOTEL**

★★★
HOTEL

B&B per room per night
s £75.00–£125.00
d £85.00–£145.00
HB per person per night
£85.00–£95.00

Kitley House Hotel and Restaurant

Kitley Estate, Yealmpton, Plymouth PL8 2NW **t** (01752) 881555 **f** (01752) 881667
e sales@kitleyhousehotel.com **w** kitleyhousehotel.com

open All year
bedrooms 8 double, 2 twin, 1 single, 1 family,
7 suites
bathrooms All en suite
payment Credit/debit cards, cash/cheques, euros

Unique country-house hotel, set in own valley and overlooking a trout lake. Luxury suites and standard bedrooms feature contemporary facilities with magnificent views. Restaurant is popular with local residents and is open for lunch and dinner. Grade I Listed building, originally a Tudor Revival house and remodelled by George Repton in the 1820s.

⊕ *M5, A38, A3121, A379 to Yealmpton.*

♥ *Christmas and New Year events. Midweek and weekend short breaks available all year. Murder Mystery events autumn-spring. Honeymoon destination.*

Pets 🐕 🐾 🦮 🐈. Room 🛏 📞 📺 ♿ 🍵 🔥. General 🚭 🏧 🅿 ⚡ 🍽 🎱 ✿ Leisure ∪

POLPERRO, Cornwall Map ref 1C3 **GUEST ACCOMMODATION**

★★★
INN

B&B per room per night
s £40.00–£45.00
d £60.00–£70.00
Evening meal per person
£6.00–£16.00

Crumplehorn Inn and Mill

Crumplehorn, Polperro, Looe PL13 2RJ **t** (01503) 272348 **f** (01503) 273148
e host@crumplehorn-inn.co.uk **w** crumplehorn-inn.co.uk

open All year
bedrooms 6 double, 3 twin, 2 family, 8 suites
bathrooms All en suite
payment Credit/debit cards, cash/cheques

14thC character Cornish inn and mill in quaint, historic fishing village. B&B and self-catering available. En suite, non-smoking rooms with TV, telephone, clock radio and tea and coffee. Local ales and scrumpy. Varied bar menu with daily specials featuring locally caught fish. Pets welcome. Car parking on site.

⊕ *Full directions (via car, train and taxi) available on our website.*

♥ *Winter-break scheme in operation.*

Pets 🐕 £🐕 🐾 🦮 Room 🛏 📞 📺 ♿ 🍵 General 🚭 🏧 🅿 ⚡ 🎱 ✿ Leisure ∪

POOLE, Dorset Map ref 2B3 **SELF CATERING**

★★★
SELF CATERING

Units **1**
Sleeps **4**

Low season per wk
£250.00–£440.00
High season per wk
£440.00–£655.00

Fripps Cottage, Wimborne

contact Mrs Helen Edbrooke, Stoneleigh House, 2 Rowlands Hill, Wimborne BH21 1AN
t (01202) 884908 **f** 0870 471 2861 **e** helen@stoneleighhouse.com
w stoneleighhouse.com/frippscottage

Two-bedroom detached bungalow set in five acres in beautiful country location, close to town and coast. Large, enclosed, well-maintained garden. All mod cons, and fully equipped for a very comfortable stay.

open All year
payment Cash/cheques

Pets 🐕 £🐕 🐾 Unit 🖼 📺 🔌 🍽 📺 🍴 🍵 ✿
General 🚭 🏧 🅿 ⚡ Leisure ∪ 🏊 Shop 1.5 miles Pub 1 mile

What's in an award?

Further information about awards can be found at the front of this guide.

POOLE, Dorset Map ref 2B3 — SELF CATERING

★★
SELF CATERING

Units **2**
Sleeps **6–8**

Low season per wk
£275.00–£495.00
High season per wk
£590.00–£760.00

Harbour Holidays, Poole

contact Mrs Beryl Saunders, Harbour Holidays, 1 Harbour Shallows, 15 Whitecliff Road, Poole BH14 8DU
t (01202) 741637

Bungalow with three bedrooms, wheelchair access, garden and summerhouse, and ample parking. Waterside townhouse with three bedrooms, balcony, harbour view, patio, barbecue and ample parking. Pets welcome in both properties.

open All year
payment Cash/cheques, euros

Pets 🐕 🐾 Unit ▦ TV ⊞ ⊟ ⊡ ⬛ ⬚ ▦ ❄
General ⬒ ▥ ⚎ P S Shop 0.5 miles Pub 0.5 miles

PORLOCK, Somerset Map ref 1D1 — GUEST ACCOMMODATION

★★★★
GUEST HOUSE
SILVER AWARD

B&B per room per night
s £30.00–£40.00
d £60.00–£70.00
Evening meal per person
£10.00–£20.00

Rose Bank Guest House

High Street, Porlock TA24 8PY **t** (01643) 862728 **f** (01643) 862728
e info@rosebankguesthouse.co.uk **w** rosebankguesthouse.co.uk

Restored Victorian house in the village high street. Private parking. All rooms en suite. TV, radio, CD and tea-making facilities. Internet access. Sea views. Dog friendly. Welcoming hosts.

open All year
bedrooms 2 double, 2 twin, 1 single, 1 family
bathrooms All en suite
payment Credit/debit cards, cash/cheques

Pets 🐕 £🐾 🐾 Room TV ⬛ ☕ General ⬒ ▥ ⚎ P ✕ ▦ ⚲ ❄ Leisure ∪ ⌂

PORTLAND, Dorset Map ref 2B3 — SELF CATERING

★★★★
SELF CATERING

Units **1**
Sleeps **2**

Low season per wk
£175.00–£325.00
High season per wk
£375.00–£450.00

Portland Hideaway, Portland

contact Mr H Marshall, 7 East Castle Avenue, Largs KA30 8JU
t 07957 138054 **e** howard@bestlimited.co.uk

Romantic, spacious, peaceful, sunny studio near Portland Bill with large, private, enclosed suntrap patio garden. Secure parking. Close to shops, village pub, bistros, spectacular coastal footpaths and varied outdoor activities.

open All year
payment Cash/cheques

Pets 🐕 £🐾 🐾 Unit ▦ ⬛ TV ⊡ ⊟ ⊡ ⬛ ⬚⬚ ⬚ ⬛ ⬛ 🖂 ❄
General P ✄ S Leisure ⚲ Shop < 0.5 miles Pub < 0.5 miles

PORTLAND, Dorset Map ref 2B3 — SELF CATERING

★★★★
SELF CATERING

Units **1**
Sleeps **7**

Low season per wk
£275.00–£425.00
High season per wk
£575.00–£650.00

Portland Retreat, Portland

contact Mr H Marshall, 7 East Castle Avenue, Largs KA30 8JU
t 07957 138054 **e** howard@bestlimited.co.uk

Uniquely spacious, peaceful detached house near Portland Bill with conservatory and large enclosed sunny garden. Secure parking. Close to shops, village pub, sailing, diving, para sports, climbing, walks and birdwatching.

open All year
payment Cash/cheques

Pets 🐕 £🐾 🐾 Unit ▦ ⬛ TV ⊡ ⊟ ⊡ ⬛ ⬚⬚ ⬚ ⬛ ⬛ 🖂 ❄
General ⬒ ▥ P ✄ S Leisure ∪ ⚲ Shop < 0.5 miles Pub < 0.5 miles

It's all in the detail

Please remember that all information in this guide has been supplied by the proprietors well in advance of publication. Since changes do sometimes occur it's a good idea to check details at the time of booking.

PORTWRINKLE, Cornwall Map ref 1C2 — **SELF CATERING**

★★★–★★★★
SELF CATERING

Whitsand Bay Self Catering, Torpoint

contact J Earle, Parade House, The Parade, Liskeard PL14 6AH
t (01579) 345688 **f** (01579) 343323 **e** enwbsc@hotmail.com **w** whitsandbayselfcatering.co.uk

Units **6**
Sleeps **4–10**
Low season per wk
£210.00–£800.00
High season per wk
£610.00–£2,500.00

open All year
payment Credit/debit cards, cash/cheques

Six beautiful cottages right by the sea with unrivalled sea views and close to golf course. Indoor pool available, and one house with private pool.

Pets 🐾 🐈 Unit 🏠 📺 ▦ 🖥 ▣ 📠 🔌 💢
General 🛏 📶 🔥 P ⊙ Leisure 🎣 🍺 Shop 0.5 miles Pub 0.5 miles

PRAA SANDS, Cornwall Map ref 1B3 — **SELF CATERING**

★★★
SELF CATERING

Sea Meads Holiday Homes, Penzance

contact Ms Pierpoint, Best Leisure, Old House Farm, Slough SL3 6HU
t (01753) 664336 **f** (01753) 663740 **e** enquiries@bestleisure.co.uk **w** bestleisure.co.uk

Units **5**
Sleeps **2–8**
Low season per wk
£330.00–£465.00
High season per wk
£745.00–£1,195.00

open All year
payment Cash/cheques

Well-equipped detached houses, each with private garden, situated in superb sub-tropical position on a private estate. Spacious lounge with large patio windows. Balcony to the first floor from which to enjoy the view of the glorious mile-long Praa Sands beach, only five minutes' walk away.

⊕ *From Helston take A394 to Penzance, halfway at Ashton Village turn left at Hendra Lane, follow road to the sea.*

Pets 🐾 Unit 🏠 📺 ▦ 🖥 ▣ 📠 🔌 🔲 💢
General 🛏 📶 🔥 P ✂ ⑤ Leisure 🍺 ∪ Shop 0.5 miles Pub 0.5 miles

RUAN HIGH LANES, Cornwall Map ref 1B3 — **GUEST ACCOMMODATION**

★★★
FARMHOUSE

Trenona Farm Holidays

Ruan High Lanes, Truro TR2 5JS **t** (01872) 501339 **f** (01872) 501253
e info@trenonafarmholidays.co.uk **w** trenonafarmholidays.co.uk

B&B per room per night
s £26.00–£38.00
d £52.00–£56.00

bedrooms 1 double, 3 family
bathrooms 3 en suite, 1 private
payment Credit/debit cards, cash/cheques

Enjoy a warm welcome in our Victorian farmhouse on a working farm on the beautiful Roseland Peninsula. Our guest bedrooms have en suite or private bathrooms, and we welcome children and pets. Public footpaths lead to Veryan and the south coast (three miles). Open between March and November.

⊕ *A390 to Truro. At Hewaswater take B3287 to Tregony then A3078 to St Mawes at Tregony Bridge. After 2 miles, pass Esso garage. 2nd farm on left-hand side.*

♥ *Discounts for stays of 4 or more nights for children and for family rooms.*

Pets 🐾 🐈 🐎 🐕 Room 📺 👤 🔌 General 🛏 📶 🔥 P ✂ 🅿 💢 Leisure ∪

Travel update

Get the latest travel information – just dial RAC on 1740 from your mobile phone.

ST IVES, Cornwall Map ref 1B3 — **HOTEL**

★★★
HOTEL
SILVER AWARD

B&B per room per night
s £65.00–£135.00
d £130.00–£210.00
HB per person per night
£84.00–£115.00

Garrack Hotel

Burthallan Lane, St Ives TR26 3AA t (01736) 796199 f (01736) 798955 e etc@garrack.com
w garrack.com

open All year except Christmas
bedrooms 11 double, 5 twin, 2 single
bathrooms All en suite
payment Credit/debit cards, cash/cheques

Small, family-run hotel and restaurant. Secluded position, set in two acres of gardens with 30 miles of coastal views. Overlooking Porthmeor beach and the Tate Gallery St Ives. Facilities include indoor pool, sauna, four-poster bed, sea-view rooms and car park. Award-winning restaurant with an emphasis on local seafood.

⊕ *Exit A30 for A3074, past garden centre, left at 1st roundabout, left at 2nd. Follow signs for St Ives B3311 and brown signs for Tate Gallery.*

♥ *Special winter rates available.*

Pets 🐾 £🐾 🐴 Room 🛏 ✆ 📺 🌙 🗝 🎞 General 🛎 🖤 🏃 P 🍽 🍴 🗟 ◉ ✳ Leisure 🏊 ⮡

ST IVES, Cornwall Map ref 1B3 — **SELF CATERING**

★★
SELF CATERING

Units **1**
Sleeps **7–9**
Low season per wk
£325.00–£485.00
High season per wk
£530.00–£715.00

The Studio, St Ives

contact Carol Holland, Little Parc Owles, Pannier Lane, Carbis Bay, St Ives TR26 2RQ
t (01736) 793015

Well-equipped five-bedroom cottage in the picturesque old fishermen's and artists' quarter of St Ives. This converted sail loft also has a spacious living room, kitchen, bath/wc and shower/wc.

open All year
payment Cash/cheques

Pets 🐾 £🐾 Unit 🏠 📺 📼 🖨 🗟 🗜 🖲 General 🛎 Shop < 0.5 miles Pub < 0.5 miles

ST MAWGAN, Cornwall Map ref 1B2 — **GUEST ACCOMMODATION**

★★★★
GUEST ACCOMMODATION

B&B per room per night
s £51.00–£54.00
d £72.00–£78.00
Evening meal per person
£18.00

Dalswinton House

St Mawgan-in-Pydar, Nr Padstow TR8 4EZ t (01637) 860385 e dalswintonhouse@tiscali.co.uk
w dalswinton.com

A former farmhouse standing in eight acres of grounds, specialising in holidays for dogs and their owners. Dog-friendly beach and coastal path 1.5 miles. Good food cooked with local ingredients. Open March to October inclusive.

bedrooms 5 double, 3 twin
bathrooms All en suite
payment Credit/debit cards, cash/cheques, euros

Pets 🐾 🗣 🐴 🐕 Room 🛏 📺 🌙 🗝 General P ⤢ 🍴 ✕ 🍽 🎞 ◉ ✳ Leisure ⮡ ∪ ⮡

SANDHURST, Gloucestershire Map ref 2B1 — **SELF CATERING**

★★★★
SELF CATERING

Units **3**
Sleeps **2–6**
Low season per wk
Min £250.00
High season per wk
Max £550.00

Great Coverden, Sandhurst, Gloucester

contact Mrs Deb Warren, Bengrove Farm, Base Lane, Sandhurst GL2 9NU
t (01452) 730231 f (01452) 730895 e Debs@bengrovefarm.fsnet.co.uk w greatcoverden.com

Located on a farm, these converted barns with oak beams offer a high standard of spacious, well-equipped accommodation. Large gardens with fantastic views, close to many places of interest.

open All year
payment Cash/cheques, euros

Pets 🐾 £🐾 🐴 Unit 🏠 📺 🗟 🖨 📼 🗄 🗜 🖲 🖲 ✳
General 🛎 🖤 🏃 P ⤢ [S] Leisure ∪ 🏊 Shop 3 miles Pub 3 miles

SHAFTESBURY, Dorset Map ref 2B3 — HOTEL

★★★
HOTEL

B&B per room per night
s £58.50–£130.00
d £67.00–£185.00
HB per person per night
£59.00–£89.00

Best Western Royal Chase Hotel

Royal Chase Roundabout, Shaftesbury SP7 8DB t (01747) 853355 f (01747) 851969
e royalchasehotel@btinternet.com w theroyalchasehotel.co.uk

open All year
bedrooms 14 double, 10 twin, 2 single, 6 family, 1 suite
bathrooms All en suite
payment Credit/debit cards, cash/cheques

Rural country-town hotel situated in two acres of grounds. Friendly welcome, indoor swimming pool, stylish dining and extensive bar food. Standard or added-quality bedrooms.

⊕ Off roundabout at junction of A30 to Salisbury/A350 to Blandford and Poole.

♥ See news and offers page on our website.

Pets 🐕 🐈 🐾 Room 🛏 📺 🕭 ♨ General ⏰ ♨ ♟ P ♟ ♨ ✿ Leisure ♨ ∪

SHERBORNE, Dorset Map ref 2B3 — SELF CATERING

★★★–★★★★★
SELF CATERING

Units   5
Sleeps   2–6

Low season per wk
£235.00–£405.00
High season per wk
£335.00–£670.00

White Horse Farm, Sherborne

contact Mr & Mrs Stuart & Audrey Winterbottom, White Horse Farm, Middlemarsh, Sherborne DT9 5QN
t (01963) 210222 e enquiries@whitehorsefarm.co.uk w whitehorsefarm.co.uk

open All year
payment Credit/debit cards, cash/cheques

Situated in rural Dorset and surrounded by miles of 'outstanding natural beauty' countryside. Four charming, featured, barn-conversion cottages and a luxurious three-bed farmhouse annex within two acres of gardens and paddock with a large duck pond. Local, well recommended, inn just next door. Many places of interest nearby.

⊕ We are located on the A352, 6.5 miles south of Sherborne and 12 miles north of Dorchester, immediately beside the Hunters Moon Inn.

♥ Short breaks available – low season.

Pets 🐕 🐾 Unit ⏚ 📺 ☑ 📺 ♨ 📺 ✿
General ⏰ P ◎ Leisure ⚘ ∪ 🚲 ⛱ Shop 2.5 miles Pub < 0.5 miles

SIDMOUTH, Devon Map ref 1D2 — GUEST ACCOMMODATION

★★★
GUEST HOUSE

B&B per room per night
s £25.00–£35.00
d £50.00–£70.00

Ryton Guest House

52-54 Winslade Road, Sidmouth EX10 9EX t (01395) 513981 f (01395) 519210
e info@ryton-guest-house.co.uk w ryton-guest-house.co.uk

Ryton is a friendly, established guesthouse, offering spacious, comfortable en suite rooms, private parking and hospitality second to none. River walks and coastal path close by.

open All year except Christmas and New Year
bedrooms 3 double, 1 twin, 3 single, 2 family
bathrooms 6 en suite, 3 private
payment Cash/cheques

Pets 🐕 🐈 🐾 Room 📺 🕭 General ⏰5 P ♨ ♨ ◨ ✿ Leisure ∪ 🚲 ⛱

Check the maps

Colour maps at the front pinpoint all the cities, towns and villages where you will find accommodation entries in the regional sections. Pick your location and then refer to the place index at the back to find the page number.

SIDMOUTH, Devon Map ref 1D2 — SELF CATERING

★★★★
SELF CATERING

Units **8**
Sleeps **4**

Low season per wk
£194.00–£329.00
High season per wk
£345.00–£648.00

Leigh Cottages, Sidmouth

contact Mr & Mrs Terry & Alison Clarke, Leigh Cottages, Leigh Farm, Weston, Sidmouth EX10 0PH
t (01395) 516065 **f** (01395) 512563 **e** alison@leigh-cottages.co.uk
w streets-ahead.com/leighcottages

open All year
payment Credit/debit cards, cash/cheques

Bungalows and cottages in delightful gardens and countryside. 150yds from a National Trust valley leading to the World Heritage Coastline and Weston Mouth beach. Lovely coastal path and cliff-top walks and level walks around nearby donkey sanctuary fields. Ideal base for exploring the coastal towns and villages in the area.

⊕ M5 jct 30, join A3052. At Sidford straight on then right at top of hill, signposted Weston. Follow signs to hamlet, 1st property on right.

Pets 🛏 ⏣ Unit 🛏 TV 🗔 🖃 🔲 🕈 🖫 🗔 ✿
General ⌂ 🏛 🅿 ✂ 🔲 Leisure ∪ ᪵ Shop 1.5 miles Pub 1.5 miles

STOKE GABRIEL, Devon Map ref 1D2 — SELF CATERING

★★★★★
SELF CATERING

Units **1**
Sleeps **1–6**

Low season per wk
£420.00–£595.00
High season per wk
£610.00–£895.00

Aish Cross Holiday Cottages, Totnes

contact Mrs Angela Pavey, Aish Cross House, Aish, Stoke Gabriel, Totnes TQ9 6PT
t (01803) 782022 **f** (01803) 211307 **e** info@aishcross.co.uk **w** aishcross.co.uk

open All year
payment Cash/cheques

Original coach house attached to lovely Regency home. Set in tranquil countryside and offering spacious, character, all-year accommodation in Area of Outstanding Natural Beauty close to River Dart and Totnes. Two king-size/twin-bedded rooms with en suite (third twin/double available), large lounge/conservatory, separate kitchen/dining area. See website for pictures etc.

⊕ Totnes: A385 to Paignton (1.5 miles). At Longcombe Cross turn right to Stoke Gabriel. Aish is 1 mile. Aish Cross House is on left, just after postbox.

Pets 🛏 ⏣ 🛏 Unit 🛏 TV 🗄 🖥 🗔 🖃 🖫 🗔 ✿
General ⌂ 🏛 🅿 🔲 🆂 Leisure ∪ ᪵ 🚣 Shop 1.5 miles Pub 1.5 miles

STOW-ON-THE-WOLD, Gloucestershire Map ref 2B1 — GUEST ACCOMMODATION

★★★★
INN

B&B per room per night
s Min £85.00
d £85.00–£110.00
Evening meal per person
£8.95–£35.00

Westcote Inn

Nether Westcote, Chipping Norton OX7 6SD **t** (01993) 830888 **f** (01993) 831657
e info@westcoteinn.co.uk **w** westcoteinn.co.uk

open All year
bedrooms 3 double, 1 family
bathrooms All en suite
payment Credit/debit cards, cash/cheques

Traditional Cotswold inn situated in glorious countryside with views as far as the eye can see, complete with all modern facilities. Westcote serves traditional British food from our fine dining restaurant, or if you are looking for something simpler the Tack Room menu serves fabulous pub grub in front of open fireplaces. Situated between Burford and Stow-on-the-Wold, and three miles from Kingham Station with direct trains from Paddington.

Pets 🛏 ⏣ 🐾 🛏 Room ☎ TV 🛁 🕈 General ⌂ 🏛 🅿 🍽 ✕ 🎱 🎿 🎧 🖥 ✿ Leisure ∪ ᪵ 🚣

Star ratings

Detailed information about star ratings can be found at the back of this guide.

STOW-ON-THE-WOLD, Gloucestershire Map ref 2B1 · SELF CATERING

★★★★
SELF CATERING

Units **1**
Sleeps **4**
Low season per wk
Min £290.00
High season per wk
Min £510.00

Bottom End Cottage, Stow-on-the-Wold

contact Ms Karen Hawkes, Cottage in the Country and Cottage Holidays, Tukes Cottage, 66 West Street, Chipping Norton OX7 5ER
t 0870 027 5930 **f** 0870 027 5934 **e** enquiries@cottageinthecountry.co.uk
w cottageinthecountry.co.uk

open All year
payment Credit/debit cards, cash/cheques

Delightful Victorian Cotswold-stone semi-detached cottage, in a quiet street just five minutes' walk from the Market Square. Recently renovated and comfortably furnished, but retaining many original features including stripped pine doors, flagstone floors and an original range in the breakfast kitchen. Conservatory at the rear overlooks pleasant enclosed garden.

⊕ *A429 south to Stow. Left at 3rd set of traffic lights. Into Sheep Street, which leads into Park Street. Opposite the Bell Pub, left into Union Street.*

Pets 🐾 ♿ Unit ▥ TV 📺 📱 🖥 ▣ 🗄 🍽 🍴 🔥
General ➰ P ✂ [S] Shop < 0.5 miles Pub < 0.5 miles

STUDLAND, Dorset Map ref 2B3 · HOTEL

★★
HOTEL
SILVER AWARD

HB per person per night
£98.00–£134.00

The Manor House Hotel

Manor Road, Studland BH19 3AU **t** (01929) 450288 **f** (01929) 452255
e themanorhousehotel@lineone.net **w** themanorhousehotel.com

open All year
bedrooms 8 double, 4 twin, 5 family, 4 suites
bathrooms All en suite
payment Credit/debit cards, cash/cheques

Romantic 18thC manor house in 20 acres of secluded grounds overlooking the sea. Residential and restaurant licence. All rooms en suite with central heating, TV, telephone, radio, hairdryer, tea/coffee-making facilities. Four-poster beds. Menus feature fresh local seafood. Oak-panelled bar and dining room with conservatory. Two hard tennis courts. Riding and golf nearby.

♥ *Good discounts on stays of 3 nights or more. Christmas 3-day package and New Year 2-day package available.*

Pets 🐾 ♿ Room 🛏 🕯 TV 👜 🍴 General ➰5 P 🍽 🛁 🔥 Leisure ⚲ ∪

SWANAGE, Dorset Map ref 2B3 · HOTEL

★★★
HOTEL

B&B per room per night
s **£61.00–£82.00**
d **£61.00–£176.00**
HB per person per night
£74.00–£90.00

The Pines Hotel

Burlington Road, Swanage BH19 1LT **t** (01929) 425211 **f** (01929) 422075
e reservations@pineshotel.co.uk **w** pineshotel.co.uk

open All year
bedrooms 17 double, 8 twin, 2 single, 8 family, 8 suites
bathrooms All en suite
payment Credit/debit cards, cash/cheques

Family-run hotel in the Purbeck countryside at the quiet end of Swanage Bay. Own access to the beach and walks encompassing marvellous coastal views. The Pines prides itself on the friendliness of its staff, the comfort of its sea-facing lounges and its reputation for cuisine served in our recently refurbished restaurant.

⊕ *A351 into Swanage. Left at seafront. 2nd right at the end of Burlington Road.*

♥ *Details of bargain breaks/autumn and winter specials/ Christmas and New Year available on request.*

Pets 🐾 🍴 Room 🛏 🕯 TV 👜 🍴 General ➰ ▥ 🍴 P 🍽 🛁 🔥 Leisure ∪ 🚲 🎣

SWANAGE, Dorset Map ref 2B3 — SELF CATERING

★★
SELF CATERING

Units **2**
Sleeps **1–8**

Low season per wk
£300.00–£500.00
High season per wk
£500.00–£700.00

The Pinnacles, Swanage

contact Mrs Alyson Greenfield, Dolserau Cottage, Abbotswell Road, Frogham, Fordingbridge SP6 2JD
t (01425) 654358 f (01425) 654358 e alyson.greenfield@btinternet.com

Centrally located flats, year-round stunning views over Swanage Bay. Adjacent to beach, directly on seafront. Parking at front door.

open All year
payment Cash/cheques

Pets 🐾 Unit ▥ TV ▢ ▣ ✿
General ⌚ P ✂ Ⓢ Shop < 0.5 miles Pub < 0.5 miles

SWIMBRIDGE, Devon Map ref 1C1 — SELF CATERING

★★★★
SELF CATERING

Units **4**
Sleeps **2–9**

Low season per wk
£190.00–£443.00
High season per wk
£355.00–£959.00

Lower Hearson Farm, Barnstaple

contact Mr & Mrs G Pelling, Swimbridge, Barnstaple EX32 0QH
t (01271) 830702 e info@hearsoncottagesdevon.co.uk w hearsoncottagesdevon.co.uk

open All year
payment Cash/cheques

Former dairy farm set in 13 acres of gardens, field and woodland. Tucked away in the heart of the North Devon countryside, it's perfect for a relaxing holiday. Our holiday cottages, games facilities and pool are surrounded by two acres of gardens, making this a safe place for children.

Pets 🐾 ⛺ 🐾. Unit ▥ TV ▢ ▣ ⊟⊟ ⊡ ▣ ✿
General ⌚ ▦ ♿ P ✂ Ⓢ Leisure ⟍ ◉ Shop 2 miles Pub 1.5 miles

TAUNTON, Somerset Map ref 1D1 — SELF CATERING

★★★
SELF CATERING

Units **1**
Sleeps **5**

Low season per wk
£225.00–£345.00
High season per wk
£275.00–£400.00

Higher House, Taunton

contact Mrs Kirsten Horton, Hillcommon, Taunton TA4 1DU
t (01823) 400570 e mail@higherhouse.co.uk w higherhouse.co.uk

open All year
payment Cash/cheques

A spacious, airy apartment on the second floor of a converted barn standing in five acres, featuring a lake, lovely gardens, as well as fields and woodland areas. Fully equipped, centrally heated and within walking distance of the pub serving tasty meals. Excellent touring base, with easy access to north and south coasts and Taunton.

⊕ A358 to Minehead. At Cross Keys pub, B3227 to Wiveliscombe for 4 miles, right at sign for Blagroves in Hillcommon. Higher House is 40yds up lane on right.

♥ Short breaks available throughout the year.

Pets 🐾 Unit ▥ TV ▢ ▣ ▣ ▣ ✿
General ⌚ ▦ ♿ Ⓢ Leisure ∪ 🚲 ⛰ Shop 1.5 miles Pub < 0.5 miles

TORQUAY, Devon Map ref 1D2 — HOTEL

★★
HOTEL

B&B per room per night
s £38.00–£48.00
d £56.00–£76.00
HB per person per night
£35.00–£53.00

Red House Hotel

Rousdown Road, Torquay TQ2 6PB t (01803) 607811 f (01803) 200592
e stay@redhouse-hotel.co.uk w redhouse-hotel.co.uk

Small, friendly hotel offering indoor/outdoor pools, spa, sauna, gym and beauty salon. Adjoining self-catering or serviced apartments. Convenient for seafront and other amenities.

open All year
bedrooms 5 double, 2 twin, 3 family
bathrooms 10 en suite
payment Credit/debit cards, cash/cheques

Pets 🐾 ⛺ 🐾 ⊟ Room ☎ TV 🖐 ✎ 𝄐 General ⌚ ▦ ♿ P ☂ 🍴 🃏 ⚌ ✿ Leisure ⟍ ⟍ ◉

TORQUAY, Devon Map ref 1D2 — GUEST ACCOMMODATION

★★★★
GUEST ACCOMMODATION

B&B per room per night
s £25.00–£30.00
d £50.00–£60.00
Evening meal per person
Min £10.00

Abingdon House

104 Avenue Road, Torquay TQ2 5LF t (01803) 201832 e abingdon-house@zen.co.uk
w abingdon-house.co.uk

Informal, friendly bed and breakfast. Comfortable lounge and cheerful breakfast room. Small patio. Parking. Short walk to sea and all attractions. Family rooms are for triple occupancy. Ground-floor room suitable for the mobility-impaired and wheelchair-users.

open All year except Christmas
bedrooms 2 double, 1 twin, 2 family
bathrooms 4 en suite, 1 private
payment Credit/debit cards, cash/cheques

Pets 🐕 ⛨ 🐾   Room ♿ 📺 ☕ ✎   General P ⚲ ✗ 🎱 🏛 ❄   Leisure 🚴

TORQUAY, Devon Map ref 1D2 — SELF CATERING

★★★
SELF CATERING

Units **24**
Sleeps **1–6**

Low season per wk
£200.00–£420.00
High season per wk
£330.00–£715.00

Maxton Lodge Holiday Apartments, Torquay

contact Mark Shephard and Alex Brook, Maxton Lodge Holiday Apartments, Rousdown Road, Torquay TQ2 6PB
t (01803) 607811 f (01803) 605357 e stay@redhouse-hotel.co.uk w redhouse-hotel.co.uk

Well-appointed, self-contained apartments providing superior accommodation. Close to shops and seafront and an ideal base for touring. Indoor/outdoor pools, spa, sauna, gymnasium. Beauty salon, solarium, games room, licensed bar, restaurant.

open All year
payment Credit/debit cards, cash/cheques

Pets 🐕 ⛨   Unit 🛏 📺 ☕ 🍳 🔌 🔥 🗑 ❄
General 🍽 🎱 ♿ P 🖨 Ⓢ   Leisure 🎣 ⚑ 🎿 ᑌ   Shop < 0.5 miles   Pub < 0.5 miles

TOTNES, Devon Map ref 1D2 — HOTEL

★★★
HOTEL

B&B per room per night
s £85.00–£115.00
d £109.00–£140.00

Royal Seven Stars Hotel

The Plains, Totnes TQ9 5DD t (01803) 862125 f (01803) 867925 e enquiry@royalsevenstars.co.uk
w royalsevenstars.co.uk

An ancient coaching inn at the heart of Totnes. Its stylish decor provides a unique blend of tradition with a contemporary twist.

open All year
bedrooms 14 double, 2 twin, 1 single, 1 family
bathrooms All en suite
payment Credit/debit cards, cash/cheques

Pets 🐕 ⛨ 🐾 🏇   Room 📞 📺 ☕ 🍳 ♿   General 🍽 🎱 ♿ P ☕ 🏛 🖨 ❄

TROWBRIDGE, Wiltshire Map ref 2B2 — GUEST ACCOMMODATION

★★★
GUEST HOUSE

B&B per room per night
s £40.00–£45.00
d £65.00–£70.00

Ring O' Bells

321 Marsh Road, Hilperton Marsh, Trowbridge BA14 7PL t (01225) 754404 f (01225) 340325
e ringobells@blueyonder.co.uk w ringobells.biz

open All year
bedrooms 1 double, 1 twin, 2 single, 2 family
bathrooms All en suite
payment Credit/debit cards, cash/cheques

Two miles north of Trowbridge. Formerly a pub, we now offer non-smoking, comfortable en suite rooms on the ground and first floors. Rooms have TV, tea/coffee facilities, radio/alarm, hairdryer and room safes. Private car park, disabled access, Wi-Fi internet via BT Openzone, friendly atmosphere. Child- and pet-friendly. CCTV operating.

⊕ *From the A361 follow B3105 into Hilperton, Staverton & Holt. Ring O' Bells is a mile down on your left. Car park in Horse Road.*

Pets 🐕 ⛨ 🐾   Room ♿ 📺 ☕ 🍳   General 🍽 🎱 ♿ P ⚲ 🏛 ❄   Leisure ᑌ 🚴 ⛵

Take a break

Look out for special promotions and themed breaks highlighted in colour.
(Offers subject to availability.)

TRURO, Cornwall Map ref 1B3 — SELF CATERING

★★★★★
SELF CATERING

Units **46**
Sleeps **1–7**

Low season per wk
£480.00–£850.00
High season per wk
£740.00–£1,545.00

The Valley Cottages, Carnon Downs, Carnon Downs, Truro

The Valley, Bissoe Road, Carnon Downs, Truro TR3 6LQ
t (01872) 862194 f (01872) 864343 e info@the-valley.co.uk w the-valley.co.uk

open All year
payment Credit/debit cards, cash/cheques, euros

A secluded hamlet of contemporary holiday cottages in the centre of Cornwall's beauty and life. Relax in architect-designed luxury with an ambience of contemporary living. Explore spectacular countryside, with indoor, outdoor and spa pools, gym, squash/tennis courts and the stylish Café Azur serving exquisite cuisine on your doorstep … Cornwall's chic country retreat.

⊕ A30 from Exeter to A39/A3076 (Truro). Bypass Truro to A39 (Falmouth). The Valley is signposted from A39 Falmouth road at Carnon Downs roundabout, about 3 miles outside Truro.

♥ Call for short-break special offers and out-of-season discounts at Cornwall's chic country retreat.

Pets 🐕 🐈 Unit 🛏 📺 ⬛ 💻 🍳 🔌 ♨ 🔲 💺 ✿
General 🛒 🏚 🚪 P Ⓢ Leisure 🏊 🔍 ⚲ 🚴 Shop 0.5 miles Pub 0.5 miles

VERYAN, Cornwall Map ref 1B3 — SELF CATERING

★★★★
SELF CATERING

Units **2**
Sleeps **6**

Low season per wk
£240.00–£470.00
High season per wk
£470.00–£760.00

Trenona Farm Holidays, Veryan

contact Mrs Pamela Carbis, Trenona Farm, Ruan High Lanes, Truro TR2 5JS
t (01872) 501339 f (01872) 501253 e pam@trenonafarmholidays.co.uk
w trenonafarmholidays.co.uk

open All year
payment Credit/debit cards, cash/cheques

The former farmhouse, and old stone workshop, have been tastefully converted to provide quality accommodation with modern furnishings and appliances for relaxing holidays on a mixed working farm on the beautiful Roseland Peninsula. Private gardens and patios. Many public gardens and attractions nearby. Children/pets welcome. Disabled access.

⊕ A30 past Bodmin, A391 to St Austell, A390 towards Truro. Just beyond Probus take A3078 to St Mawes. After 8 miles pass Esso garage, Trenona Farm 2nd on left.

♥ Short breaks available Oct–Mar.

Pets 🐕 🐈 Unit 🛏 📺 ⬛ 💻 🍳 🔌 ♨ 🔲 💺 ✿
General 🛒 🏚 🚪 P ✂ Leisure U Shop 1 mile Pub 2 miles

WAREHAM, Dorset Map ref 2B3 — SELF CATERING

★
SELF CATERING

Units **1**
Sleeps **5**

Low season per wk
Min £320.00
High season per wk
Max £450.00

Dormer Cottage, Woodlands, Hyde, Wareham

contact Mrs Madeleine Constantinides, Hyde, Wareham BH20 7NT
t (01929) 471239

Converted 400-year-old barn in the lovely Dorset countryside – perfect for relaxation and peace. Large wood and play areas. Children and pets welcome.

open All year
payment Cash/cheques

Pets 🐕 🐈 Unit 📺 ⬛ 💻 🔲 💺 ✿
General 🛒 🏚 🚪 P Leisure U 🚴 Shop 3.5 miles Pub 3.5 miles

Stay focused

Don't forget your camera. Take home shots of the greatest scenery, super seascapes and family fun.

WELCOME, Devon Map ref 1C2 — SELF CATERING

★★★–★★★★★
SELF CATERING

Units **5**
Sleeps **2–8**

Low season per wk
£205.00–£404.00
High season per wk
£562.00–£1,154.00

Mead Barn Cottages, Welcombe, Bideford

contact Mr & Mrs Rob & Lisa Ireton, Mead Barn Cottages, Welcombe, Bideford EX39 6HQ
t (01288) 331721 **e** holidays@meadbarns.com **w** meadbarns.com

open All year
payment Cash/cheques

Five comfortable, well-equipped stone barns, two/four bedrooms sleeping four/eight people. Located on coast in North Devon Area of Outstanding Natural Beauty, 0.5 miles from unique local cove, beach, rock pools, surfing, walking. Providing good additional facilities: trampoline, swings, barbecue area etc. Three miles from A39 and Cornwall/Devon border, we offer easy access for touring.

⊕ *Turn off A39 at Welcombe Cross (Devon/Cornwall border) signposted Welcombe. Follow lane for 3 miles. Gate 150yds after Mead Corner on right.*

♥ *Short breaks and discounts offered for couples, and two-week bookings, off-peak. Special Romantic Retreat with flowers, chocolates, wine and four-poster.*

Pets 🐾 Unit 🖩 📺 ▣ ▤ ▣ ▤▤ ▤ ▤ ▤ ✿
General ▤ 🛏 🅟 Ⓢ Leisure ● ⚲ ∪ Shop 2.5 miles Pub 0.5 miles

WEST BEXINGTON, Dorset Map ref 2A3 — SELF CATERING

★★★
SELF CATERING

Units **3**
Sleeps **2–4**

Low season per wk
£180.00–£450.00
High season per wk
£270.00–£560.00

Gorselands, Dorchester

contact Miss Brenda Parker, Gorselands Caravan Park, West Bexington Road, Dorchester DT2 9DJ
t (01308) 897232 **f** (01308) 897239 **w** gorselands.co.uk

open All year
payment Credit/debit cards, cash/cheques

House divided into three self-contained apartments. Set in its own grounds with lovely sea views. Ground-floor studio sleeps two, ground-floor one-bedroom sleeps four, first-floor two-bedroom sleeps four.

⊕ *Via B3157 to Swyre. Opposite The Bull Inn take turning to West Bexington. Gorselands is 100m along on right-hand side.*

Pets 🐾 £🐾 Unit 🖩 📺 ▣ ▣ ▤ ✿
General ▤ 🅟 Ⓢ Shop 3 miles Pub < 0.5 miles

WOOLACOMBE, Devon Map ref 1C1 — SELF CATERING

★★
SELF CATERING

Units **1**
Sleeps **5**

Low season per wk
£200.00–£250.00
High season per wk
£300.00–£525.00

Cove Cottage Flat, Woolacombe

contact Mrs Vivien Lawrence, Sharp Rock, Mortehoe, Woolacombe EX34 7EA
t (01271) 870403 **f** (01271) 870403 **e** vlawrence05@aol.com

Self-contained flat overlooking sandy beach (ten-minute walk). Washer/dryer, fridge/freezer, microwave, TV/video/DVD, garden. Pets welcome. Open all year. Central heating included early/late season. Parking.

open All year
payment Cash/cheques

Pets 🐾 £🐾 Unit 🖩 📺 ▣ ▤ ▣ ▤ ▤ ▤ ✿
General ▤ 🛏 🅟 Ⓢ Leisure ∪ Shop 0.5 miles Pub 0.5 miles

enjoyEngland.com

Big city buzz or peaceful panoramas? Take a fresh look at England and you may be surprised at what's right on your doorstep. Explore the diversity online at enjoyengland.com

Visitor Services Assistant,
Wakefield, Yorkshire.

Enjoy England more. Ask an Expert.

Planning a short break or escape in this country
An England expert will make it extra special.
You'll find one at your nearest Tourist Informatic
provider, and they'll be bursting with knowledg
and tips to help you get so much more from you
break. Go on, ask away - you'll find they have
the very latest information on every corner of
England; everything from booking your perfect
place to stay, travel advice to top ideas for great
days out. So wherever you've set your heart on
a memorable experience is here for the asking.

Visit our website for even more great ideas:

enjoyEngland.com

The official website for tourism in England.
Where to go. What to do. Where to stay.

enjoyEngland
OFFICIAL PARTNER

enjoyEngland ®

Further information

Enjoy England Quality Rose scheme

When you're looking for a place to stay, you need a rating system you can trust. Enjoy England ratings are your clear guide to what to expect, in an easy-to-understand form.

Enjoy England professional assessors pay unannounced visits to establishments that are new to the rating scheme and stay overnight where appropriate. Once in the scheme establishments receive an annual pre-arranged day visit, with an overnight stay generally every other year for hotel and bed and breakfast accommodation. On these occasions the assessors book in anonymously, and test all the facilities and services.

Based on internationally recognised star ratings, the system puts great emphasis on quality, and reflects exactly what consumers are looking for. Ratings are awarded from one to five stars – the more stars, the higher the quality and the greater the range of facilities and services provided – and are the sign of quality assurance, giving you the confidence to book the accommodation that meets your expectations.

Look out, too, for Enjoy England Gold and Silver Awards, which are awarded to hotels and bed and breakfast accommodation achieving the highest levels of quality within their star rating. While the overall rating is based on a combination of facilities and quality, the Gold and Silver Awards are based solely on quality.

Hotels

All hotels that are awarded a star rating will meet the minimum standards – so you can be confident that you will find the basic services that you would expect, such as:

- All bedrooms with an en suite or private bathroom
- A designated reception facility and staff members who will be available during the day and evening (24hrs in case of an emergency)
- A licence to serve alcohol (unless a temperance hotel)
- Access to the hotel at all times for registered guests

- Dinner available at least five days a week (with the exception of a Town House Hotel or Metro Hotel)
- All statutory obligations will be met.

Hotels have to provide certain additional facilities and services at the higher star levels, some of which may be important to you:

TWO-STAR hotels must provide:
- Dinner seven nights a week.

THREE-STAR hotels must provide:
- All en suite bedrooms (ie no private bathrooms)
- Direct dial phones in all rooms
- Room service during core hours
- A permanently staffed reception.

FOUR-STAR hotels must provide:
- 24-hour room service
- 50% of all en suites with bath **and** shower.

FIVE-STAR hotels must provide:
- Some permanent suites
- Enhanced services, such as concierge.

Sometimes a hotel with a lower star rating has exceptional bedrooms and bathrooms and offers its guests a very special welcome, but cannot achieve a higher rating because, for example, it does not offer dinner every evening (two star), room service (three star) or does not have the minimum 50% of bathrooms with bath and shower (four star).

Quality
The availability of additional services alone is not enough for an establishment to achieve a higher star rating. Hotels have to meet exacting standards for quality in critical areas. Consumer research has shown the critical areas to be: cleanliness, bedrooms, bathrooms, hospitality and service, and food.

Bed and breakfast accommodation

All bed and breakfast accommodation that is awarded a star rating will meet the minimum standards – so you can be confident that you will find the basic services that you would expect, such as:

- A clear explanation of booking charges, services offered and cancellation terms
- A full cooked breakfast or substantial continental breakfast
- At least one bathroom or shower room for every six guests
- For a stay of more than one night, rooms cleaned and beds made daily
- Printed advice on how to summon emergency assistance at night
- All statutory obligations will be met.

TWO-STAR accommodation provides all of the above but the rating reflects a higher quality of services and facilities than one-star accommodation.

Proprietors of bed and breakfast accommodation have to provide certain additional facilities and services at the higher star levels, some of which may be important to you:

THREE-STAR accommodation must provide:
- Private bathroom/shower room (cannot be shared with the owners)
- Bedrooms must have a washbasin if not en suite.

FOUR-STAR accommodation must provide:
- 50% of bedrooms en suite or with private bathroom.

FIVE-STAR accommodation must provide:
- All bedrooms with en suite or private bathroom.

Sometimes a bed and breakfast establishment has exceptional bedrooms and bathrooms and offers guests a very special welcome, but cannot achieve a higher star rating because, for example, there are no en suite bedrooms, or it is difficult to put washbasins in the bedrooms (three star). This is sometimes the case with period properties.

Quality
The availability of additional facilities alone is not enough for an establishment to achieve a higher star rating. Bed and breakfast accommodation has to meet exacting standards for quality in critical areas. Consumer research has shown the critical areas to be: cleanliness, bedrooms, bathrooms, hospitality and food.

Self-catering accommodation

All self-catering accommodation that is awarded a star rating will meet the minimum standards – so you can be confident that you will find the basic services that you would expect, such as:

- Clear information prior to booking on all aspects of the accommodation including location, facilities, prices, deposit, policies on smoking, children etc
- No shared facilities, with the exception of a laundry room in multi-unit sites
- All appliances and furnishings will meet product safety standards for self-catering accommodation, particularly regarding fire safety
- At least one smoke alarm in the unit and a fire blanket in the kitchen
- Clear information on emergency procedures, including who to contact
- Contact details for the local doctor, dentist etc
- All statutory obligations will be met including an annual gas check and public liability insurance.

Certain additional facilities and services are required at the higher star levels, some of which may be important to you:

TWO-STAR accommodation must provide:
- Single beds which are a minimum of 3ft wide and double beds a minimum of 4ft 6in.

THREE-STAR accommodation must provide:
- Bed linen (with or without additional charge).

FOUR-STAR accommodation must provide:
- All advertised sleeping space in bedrooms (unless a studio)
- Bed linen included in the hire charge and beds are made up for arrival.

FIVE-STAR accommodation must provide:
- Full-size beds, including those for children
- At least two of the following items: tumble-dryer, telephone, Hi-Fi, video, DVD.

Some self-catering establishments offer a choice of accommodation units that may have different star ratings. In this case, the entry shows the range available.

Quality
The availability of additional facilities, such as a dishwasher or DVD, is not enough to achieve a higher star rating. Self-catering accommodation with a lower star rating may offer some or all of the above, but to achieve the higher star ratings, the overall quality score has to be reached and exacting standards have to be met in critical areas. Consumer research has shown these to be: cleanliness, bedrooms, bathrooms, kitchens and public areas.

Help before you go

When it comes to your next English break, the first stage of your journey could be closer than you think.

You've probably got a Tourist Information Centre nearby which is there to serve the local community – as well as visitors. Knowledgeable staff will be happy to help you, wherever you're heading.

Many Tourist Information Centres can provide you with maps and guides, and it's often possible to book accommodation and travel tickets too.

You'll find the address of your nearest centre in your local phone book, or look at the beginning of each regional section in this guide for a list of Official Partner Tourist Information Centres.

Advice and information

Making a booking

When enquiring about accommodation, make sure you check prices, the quality rating and other important details. You will also need to state your requirements clearly and precisely, for example:

- Arrival and departure dates, with acceptable alternatives if appropriate
- The type of accommodation you need – for example, room with twin beds, en suite bathroom
- The terms you want – for example, room only, bed and breakfast
- The age of any children with you, whether you want them to share your room or be next door, and any other special requirements, such as a cot
- Any particular requirements you may have, such as a special diet, ground-floor room.

Confirmation

Misunderstandings can easily happen over the telephone, so do request a written confirmation, together with details of any terms and conditions.

Deposits

If you make a hotel or bed and breakfast reservation weeks or months in advance, you will probably be asked for a deposit, which will then be deducted from the final bill when you leave. The amount will vary from establishment to establishment and could be payment in full at peak times.

Proprietors of self-catering accommodation will normally ask you to pay a deposit immediately, and then to pay the full balance before your holiday date. This safeguards the proprietor in case you decide to cancel at a late stage or simply do not turn up. He or she may have turned down other bookings on the strength of yours and may find it hard to re-let if you cancel.

Payment on arrival

Some establishments, especially large hotels in big towns, ask you to pay for your room on arrival if you have not booked it in advance. This is especially likely to happen if you arrive late and have little or no luggage.

If you are asked to pay on arrival, it is a good idea to see your room first, to make sure it meets your requirements.

Cancellations

Legal contract

When you accept accommodation that is offered to you, by telephone or in writing, you enter a legally binding contract with the proprietor. This means that if you cancel your booking, fail to take up the accommodation or leave early, the proprietor may be entitled to compensation if he or she cannot re-let for all or a good part of the booked period. You will probably forfeit any deposit you have paid, and may well be asked for an additional payment.

At the time of booking you should be advised of what charges would be made in the event of cancelling the accommodation or leaving early. If this is not mentioned you should ask so that future disputes can be avoided. The proprietor cannot make a claim until after the booked period, and during that time he or she should make every effort to re-let the accommodation. If there is a dispute it is sensible for both sides to seek legal advice on the matter. If you do have to change your travel plans, it is in your own interests to let the proprietor know in writing as soon as possible, to give them a chance to re-let your accommodation.

And remember, if you book by telephone and are asked for your credit card number, you should check whether the proprietor intends charging your credit card account should you later cancel your reservation. A proprietor should not be able to charge your credit card account with a cancellation fee unless he or she has made this clear at the time of your booking and you have agreed. However, to avoid later disputes, we suggest you check whether this is the intention.

Insurance

A travel or holiday insurance policy will safeguard you if you have to cancel or change your holiday plans. You can arrange a policy quite cheaply through your insurance company or travel agent. Some hotels also offer their own insurance schemes and many self-catering agencies insist their customers take out a policy when they book their holidays.

Arrival time

If you know you will be arriving late in the evening, it is a good idea to say so when you book. If you are delayed on your way, a telephone call to say that you will be late would be appreciated.

It is particularly important to liaise with the owner of self-catering accommodation about key collection as he or she will not necessarily be on site.

Service charges and tipping

These days many places levy service charges automatically. If they do, they must clearly say so in their offer of accommodation, at the time of booking. The service charge then becomes part of the legal contract when you accept the offer of accommodation.

If a service charge is levied automatically, there is no need to tip the staff, unless they provide some exceptional service. The usual tip for meals is 10% of the total bill.

Telephone charges

Establishments can set their own charges for telephone calls made through their switchboard or from direct-dial telephones in bedrooms. These charges are often much higher than telephone companies' standard charges (to defray the cost of providing the service).

Comparing costs

It is a condition of Enjoy England's Quality Rose assessment scheme that an establishment's unit charges are on display by the telephones or with the room information. It is not always easy to compare these charges with standard rates, so before using a telephone for long-distance calls, you may decide to ask how the charges compare.

Security of valuables

You can deposit your valuables with the proprietor or manager during your stay, and we recommend you do this as a sensible precaution. Make sure you obtain a receipt for them. Some places do not accept articles for safe custody, and in that case it is wisest to keep your valuables with you.

Disclaimer

Some proprietors put up a notice that disclaims liability for property brought on to their premises by a guest. In fact, they can only restrict their liability to a minimum laid down by law (The Hotel Proprietors Act 1956). Under that Act, a proprietor is liable for the value of the loss or damage to any property (except a car or its contents) of a guest who has engaged overnight accommodation, but if the proprietor has the notice on display as prescribed under that Act, liability is limited to £50 for one article and a total of £100 for any one guest. The notice must be prominently displayed in the reception area or main entrance. These limits do not apply to valuables you have deposited with the proprietor for safekeeping, or to property lost through the default, neglect or wilful act of the proprietor or his staff.

Bringing pets to England

Dogs, cats, ferrets and some other pet mammals can be brought into the UK from certain countries without having to undertake six months' quarantine on arrival provided they meet all the rules of the Pet Travel Scheme (PETS).

For full details, visit the PETS website at
w defra.gov.uk/animalh/quarantine/index.htm or contact the PETS Helpline
t +44 (0)870 241 1710
e pets.helpline@defra.gsi.gov.uk
Ask for fact sheets which cover dogs and cats, ferrets or domestic rabbits and rodents.

What to expect

The proprietor/management is required to undertake the following:

- To maintain standards of guest care, cleanliness and service appropriate to the type of establishment;
- To describe accurately in any advertisement, brochure or other printed or electronic media, the facilities and services provided;
- To make clear to visitors exactly what is included in all prices quoted for accommodation, including taxes, and any other surcharges. Details of charges for additional services/facilities should also be made clear;
- To give a clear statement of the policy on cancellations to guests at the time of booking ie by telephone, fax, email, as well as information given in a printed format;
- To adhere to and not to exceed prices quoted at the time of booking for accommodation and other services;
- To advise visitors at the time of booking, and

subsequently if any change, if the accommodation offered is in an unconnected annexe or similar and to indicate the location of such accommodation and any difference in comfort and/or amenities from accommodation in the establishment;

- To register all guests on arrival (except self-catering accommodation);

- To give each visitor on request details of payments due and a receipt, if required;

- To deal promptly and courteously with all enquiries, requests, bookings and correspondence from visitors;

- To ensure complaint handling procedures are in place and that complaints received are investigated promptly and courteously and that the outcome is communicated to the visitor;

- To give due consideration to the requirements of visitors with disabilities and visitors with special needs, and to make suitable provision where applicable;

- To provide public liability insurance or comparable arrangements and to comply with all applicable planning, safety and other statutory requirements;

- To allow an Enjoy England assessor reasonable access to the establishment on request, to confirm the VisitBritain Code of Conduct is being observed.

Comments and complaints

The law
Places that offer accommodation have legal and statutory responsibilities to their customers, such as providing information about prices, providing adequate fire precautions and safeguarding valuables. Like other businesses, they must also abide by the Trades Description Acts 1968 and 1972 when they describe their accommodation and facilities. All the places featured in this guide have declared that they do fulfil all applicable statutory obligations.

Information
The proprietors themselves supply the descriptions of their establishments and other information for the entries, (except Enjoy England ratings and awards). VisitBritain cannot guarantee the accuracy of information in this guide, and accepts no responsibility for any error or misrepresentation. All liability for loss, disappointment, negligence or other damage caused by reliance on the information contained in this guide, or in the event of bankruptcy or liquidation or cessation of trade of any company, individual or firm mentioned, is hereby excluded. We strongly recommend that you carefully check prices and other details when you book your accommodation.

Quality Rose signage
All establishments displaying a Quality Rose sign have to hold current membership of the Enjoy England Quality Rose assessment scheme. When an establishment is sold the new owner has to reapply and be reassessed.

Problems
Of course, we hope you will not have cause for complaint, but problems do occur from time to time. If you are dissatisfied with anything, make your complaint to the management immediately. Then the management can take action at once to investigate the matter and put things right. The longer you leave a complaint, the harder it is to deal with it effectively.

In certain circumstances, VisitBritain may look into complaints. However, VisitBritain has no statutory control over establishments or their methods of operating. VisitBritain cannot become involved in legal or contractual matters, nor can they get involved in seeking financial recompense.

If you do have problems that have not been resolved by the proprietor and which you would like to bring to our attention, please write to: Quality in Tourism, Farncombe House, Broadway, Worcestershire WR12 7LJ.

Log on to **enjoyengland.com** to find a break that matches your mood. **experience** scenes that inspire and traditions that baffle. **discover** the world's most inventive cultural entertainment and most stimulating attractions. **explore** vibrant cities and rugged peaks. **relax** in a country pub or on a sandy beach.

 enjoy**England**.com

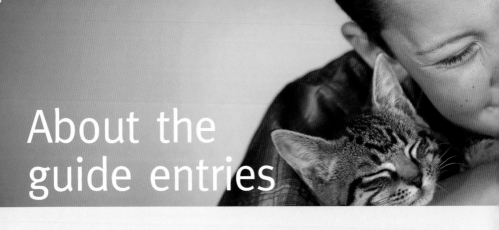

About the guide entries

Entries

All the accommodation featured in this guide has been assessed or has applied for assessment under Enjoy England Quality Rose assessment schemes.

Proprietors have paid to have their establishment featured in either a standard entry (includes description, facilities and prices) or enhanced entry (photograph and extended details).

Pets

Pets are welcome at all the establishments in this guide, however, you should always advise proprietors in advance that you plan to bring your pet with you. It is also wise to check the facilities on offer, such as food and water bowls, and any restrictions on where they can go. The acceptance of dogs is not always extended to cats and it is strongly advised that cat owners contact the establishment well in advance.

The quarantine laws have changed in England, and dogs, cats and ferrets are able to come into Britain from certain countries. For details of the Pet Travel Scheme (PETS) please turn to page 248.

Locations

Places to stay are generally listed under the town, city or village where they are located. If a place is in a small village, you may find it listed under a nearby town (providing it is within a seven-mile radius).

Place names are listed alphabetically within each regional section of the guide, along with the name of the ceremonial county they are in and their map reference.

Complete addresses for self-catering properties are not given and the town(s) listed may be a distance from the actual establishment. Please check the precise location at the time of booking.

Map references

These refer to the colour location maps at the front of the guide. The first figure shown is the map number, the following letter and figure indicate the grid reference on the map. Some entries were included just before the guide went to press, so they do not appear on the maps.

Addresses

County names, which appear in the place headings, are not repeated in the entries. When you are writing, you should of course make sure you use the full address and postcode.

Telephone numbers

Telephone numbers are listed below the accommodation address for each entry. Area codes are shown in brackets.

Prices

The prices shown are only a general guide; they were supplied to us by proprietors in summer 2007. Remember, changes may occur after the guide goes to press, so we strongly advise you to check prices when you book your accommodation.

Prices are shown in pounds sterling and include VAT where applicable. Some places also include a service charge in their standard tariff, so check this when you book.

Bed and breakfast: the prices shown are per room for overnight accommodation with breakfast. The double room price is for two people. (If a double room is occupied by one person there is sometimes a reduction in price.)

Half board: the prices shown are per person per night for room, evening meal and breakfast. These prices are usually based on two people sharing a room.

Evening meal: the prices shown are per person per night.

Some places only provide a continental breakfast in the set price, and you may have to pay extra if you want a full English breakfast.

According to the law, establishments with at least four bedrooms or eight beds must display their overnight accommodation charges in the reception area or entrance. In your own interests, do make sure you check prices and what they include.

Self catering: prices shown are per unit per week and include VAT.

Children's rates

You will find that many places charge a reduced rate for children, especially if they share a room with their parents. Some places charge the full rate, however, when a child occupies a room which might otherwise have been let to an adult. The upper age limit for reductions for children varies from one hotel to another, so check this when you book.

Seasonal packages and special promotions

Prices often vary through the year and may be significantly lower outside peak holiday weeks. Many places offer special package rates – fully inclusive weekend breaks, for example – in the autumn, winter and spring. A number of establishments taking an enhanced entry have included any special offers, themed breaks etc that are available.

You can get details of other bargain packages that may be available from the establishments themselves, regional tourism organisations or your local tourist information centre (TIC). Your local travel agent may also have information and can help you make reservations.

Bathrooms (hotels and bed and breakfast)

Each accommodation entry shows you the number of en suite and private bathrooms available. En suite bathroom means the bath or shower and wc are contained behind the main door of the bedroom. Private bathroom means a bath or shower and wc solely for the occupants of one bedroom, on the same floor, reasonably close and with a key provided. If the availability of a bath, rather than a shower, is important to you, remember to check when you book.

Meals (hotels and bed and breakfast)

It is advisable to check availability of meals and set times when making your reservation. Some smaller places may ask you at breakfast whether you want an evening meal. The prices shown in each entry are for bed and breakfast or half board, but many places also offer lunch.

Opening period

If an entry does not indicate an opening period, please check directly with the establishment.

Symbols

The at-a-glance symbols included at the end of each entry show many of the services and facilities available at each establishment. You will find the key

to these symbols on the back-cover flap – open it out and check the meanings as you go.

Smoking

In the UK, it is illegal to smoke in enclosed public spaces and places of work. This means that smoking is banned in the public and communal areas of hotels, guesthouses and B&Bs, and in restaurants, bars and pubs.

Some hotels, guesthouses and B&Bs may choose to provide designated smoking bedrooms, and B&Bs and guest houses may allow smoking in private areas that are not used by any staff. Smoking may also be allowed in self-contained short-term rental accommodation, such as holiday cottages, flats or caravans, if the owner chooses to allow it.

If you wish to smoke, it is advisable to check whether it is allowed when you book.

Alcoholic drinks

All hotels (except temperance hotels) hold an alcohol licence. Some bed and breakfast accommodation may also be licensed, however, the licence may be restricted – to diners only, for example. If a bar is available this is shown by the ☻ symbol.

Payment accepted

The types of payment accepted by an establishment are listed in the payment accepted section. If you plan to pay by card, check that the establishment will take your particular card before you book. Some proprietors will charge you a higher rate if you pay by credit card rather than cash or cheque. The difference is to cover the percentage paid by the proprietor to the credit card company. When you book by telephone, you may be asked for your credit card number as confirmation. But remember, the proprietor may then charge your credit card account if you cancel your booking. See under Cancellations on page 247.

Rating Applied For

At the time of going to press some establishments featured in this guide had not yet been assessed and so their new rating could not be included. Rating Applied For indicates this.

Diamond ratings

Establishments with a diamond rating were awaiting re-assessment under the star-rating scheme at the time of going to press (August 07).

Getting around England

England is a country of perfect proportions – big enough to find a new place to discover, yet small enough to guarantee it's within easy reach. Getting from A to B can be easier than you think...

Planning your journey

Make transportdirect.info your first portal of call! It's the ultimate journey-planning tool to help you find the best way from your home to your destination by car or public transport. Decide on the quickest way to travel by comparing end-to-end journey times and routes. You can even buy train and coach tickets and find out about flights from a selection of airports.

With so many low-cost domestic flights, flying really is an option. Just imagine, you could finish work in Bishop's Stortford and be in Newquay just three hours later for a fun-packed weekend!

You can island hop too, to the Isle of Wight or the Isles of Scilly for a relaxing break. No worries.

If you're travelling by car and want an idea of distances check out the mileage chart overleaf. Or let the train take the strain – the National Rail network is also shown overleaf.

Think green

If you'd rather leave your car behind and travel by 'green transport' when visiting some of the attractions highlighted in this guide you'll be helping to reduce congestion and pollution as well as supporting conservation charities in their commitment to green travel.

The National Trust encourages visits made by non-car travellers. It offers admission discounts or a voucher for the tea room at a selection of its properties if you arrive on foot, cycle or public transport. (You'll need to produce a valid bus or train ticket if travelling by public transport.)

More information about The National Trust's work to encourage car-free days out can be found at nationaltrust.org.uk. Refer to the section entitled Information for Visitors.

To help you on your way you'll find a list of useful contacts at the end of this section.

Counties and regions at-a-glance

If you know what county you wish to visit you'll find it in the regional section shown below.

County	Region	County	Region
Bedfordshire	East of England	Leicestershire	East Midlands
Berkshire	South East England	Lincolnshire	East Midlands
Bristol	South West England	Merseyside	England's Northwest
Buckinghamshire	South East England	Norfolk	East of England
Cambridgeshire	East of England	North Yorkshire	Yorkshire
Cheshire	England's Northwest	Northamptonshire	East Midlands
Cornwall	South West England	Northumberland	North East England
County Durham	North East England	Nottinghamshire	East Midlands
Cumbria	England's Northwest	Oxfordshire	South East England
Derbyshire	East Midlands	Rutland	East Midlands
Devon	South West England	Shropshire	Heart of England
Dorset	South West England	Somerset	South West England
East Riding of Yorkshire	Yorkshire	South Yorkshire	Yorkshire
East Sussex	South East England	Staffordshire	Heart of England
Essex	East of England	Suffolk	East of England
Gloucestershire	South West England	Surrey	South East England
Greater Manchester	England's Northwest	Tees Valley	North East England
Hampshire	South East England	Tyne and Wear	North East England
Herefordshire	Heart of England	Warwickshire	Heart of England
Hertfordshire	East of England	West Midlands	Heart of England
Isle of Wight	South East England	West Sussex	South East England
Isles of Scilly	South West England	West Yorkshire	Yorkshire
Kent	South East England	Wiltshire	South West England
Lancashire	England's Northwest	Worcestershire	Heart of England

To help readers we do not refer to unitary authorities in this guide.

By car and by train

Distance chart

The distances between towns on the chart below are given to the nearest mile, and are measured along routes based on the quickest travelling time, making maximum use of motorways or dual-carriageway roads. The chart is based upon information supplied by the Automobile Association.

To calculate the distance in kilometres multiply the mileage by 1.6

For example: Brighton to Dover
82 miles x 1.6 =131.2 kilometres

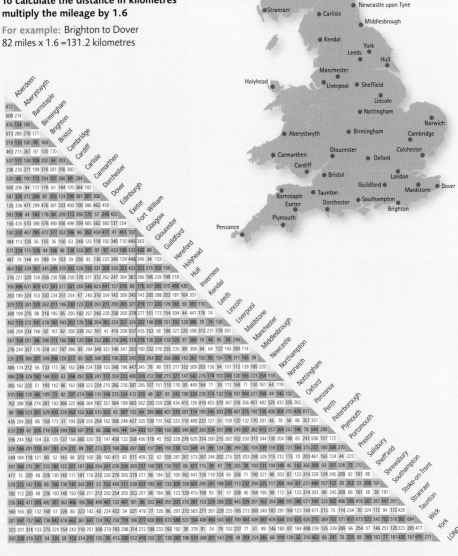

	Aberdeen	Aberystwyth	Barnstaple	Birmingham	Brighton	Bristol	Cambridge	Cardiff	Carlisle	Carmarthen	Dorchester	Dover	Edinburgh	Exeter	Fort William	Glasgow	Gloucester	Guildford	Hereford	Holyhead	Hull	Inverness	Kendal	Leeds	Lincoln	Liverpool	Maidstone	Manchester	Middlesbrough	Newcastle	Northampton	Norwich	Nottingham	Oxford	Penzance	Perth	Peterborough	Plymouth	Portsmouth	Preston	Salisbury	Sheffield	Shrewsbury	Southampton	Stoke-on-Trent	Stranraer	Taunton	Wick	York
Aberystwyth	472																																															
Barnstaple	608	214																																														
Birmingham	436	124	180																																												
Brighton	613	288	210	171																																										
Bristol	518	130	100	90	169																																								
Cambridge	463	215	267	97	120	170																																						
Cardiff	537	111	128	109	202	44	203																																				
Carlisle	236	236	371	199	376	281	256	300																																		
Carmarthen	520	48	190	172	264	107	266	68	284																																
Dorchester	600	206	94	172	119	62	184	120	364	182																														
Dover	587	326	272	208	82	205	124	239	381	301	200																												
Edinburgh	126	336	471	299	476	381	333	400	100	386	463	458																										
Exeter	593	198	44	165	178	84	259	113	356	175	57	248	455																									
Fort William	156	435	570	398	576	480	456	499	199	485	562	580	137	554																								
Glasgow	150	332	467	295	472	377	353	396	96	382	459	477	47	451	102																							
Gloucester	484	113	126	56	155	36	150	63	248	125	118	192	346	110	445	343																						
Guildford	571	224	175	128	44	106	96	139	335	201	97	97	433	150	532	430	99																					
Hereford	487	79	144	59	189	54	153	59	250	85	136	225	349	129	448	346	34	133																				
Holyhead	464	102	339	167	345	249	259	202	228	150	331	369	326	323	425	323	215	302	156																			
Hull	376	227	320	139	258	230	138	250	170	311	312	262	247	304	367	266	196	239	198	218																		
Inverness	106	496	631	459	637	541	517	561	260	546	623	641	157	616	66	176	507	595	510	488	430																	
Kendal	283	189	324	153	330	234	251	254	47	240	316	354	145	309	245	143	200	288	203	181	164	307																
Leeds	329	173	301	120	262	211	146	230	123	224	293	271	200	285	321	219	177	220	179	165	59	383	110															
Lincoln	388	199	275	98	216	185	95	205	182	267	246	220	258	260	379	277	151	173	154	204	44	441	176	74														
Liverpool	362	110	272	101	278	182	193	202	126	158	264	302	224	257	324	222	148	236	151	102	128	386	79	74	139													
Maidstone	545	284	234	166	50	167	82	200	339	262	161	41	416	209	537	435	153	58	186	327	220	599	313	231	178	261												
Manchester	357	134	261	89	266	171	160	190	120	184	253	290	219	245	318	216	136	224	139	125	97	380	74	44	85	34	248											
Middlesbrough	276	244	357	176	318	267	197	286	95	294	349	322	146	341	283	190	232	276	235	235	89	308	84	64	122	145	280	114										
Newcastle	235	275	388	207	349	298	229	317	60	325	380	353	106	372	242	153	264	307	266	266	142	267	102	95	154	176	311	145	39									
Northampton	486	174	212	56	133	115	56	162	249	224	159	155	348	196	447	345	79	90	111	217	152	509	203	136	94	151	113	139	189	220								
Norwich	488	278	329	160	168	233	63	266	282	328	241	172	359	313	480	378	212	160	215	321	147	542	276	174	103	240	130	185	223	254	118							
Nottingham	395	162	232	51	193	142	86	161	189	223	224	210	266	216	387	285	107	151	110	178	93	449	164	77	39	112	168	71	130	161	64	119						
Oxford	510	160	170	68	109	73	82	107	274	169	115	146	373	154	472	370	48	67	81	242	190	534	228	174	132	176	107	164	227	258	44	146	102					
Penzance	702	308	108	274	287	193	368	222	466	284	167	357	564	109	663	562	220	259	238	434	415	726	419	403	370	367	318	356	451	482	326	433	326	265				
Perth	86	388	523	351	529	433	378	453	152	438	515	503	42	507	102	64	399	486	401	379	291	114	199	245	303	278	461	275	192	150	400	404	310	426	617			
Peterborough	435	204	263	86	158	173	37	193	229	255	204	162	306	248	427	325	139	115	142	225	110	489	223	121	51	159	120	132	170	201	45	78	58	86	357	351		
Plymouth	633	239	62	205	218	124	299	153	397	215	98	288	495	44	594	493	151	190	169	365	346	657	350	334	301	298	249	287	382	413	257	364	257	196	78	544	288	
Portsmouth	596	244	162	154	53	125	137	158	360	220	73	141	458	132	558	456	118	45	152	328	276	620	314	260	215	262	102	250	313	344	130	204	188	85	241	508	157	172											
Preston	326	146	281	110	287	191	209	211	89	197	273	311	188	266	287	185	157	245	160	138	122	349	43	69	134	36	269	35	103	139	159	235	121	184	375	237	180	306	270										
Salisbury	549	184	118	121	90	52	145	98	313	160	39	160	411	93	511	409	72	62	105	281	261	573	267	244	202	215	121	203	298	329	115	212	173	70	203	461	165	134	44	223									
Sheffield	397	166	272	91	233	182	122	201	161	263	264	247	236	256	359	257	148	191	150	157	66	421	115	38	47	79	205	39	100	131	104	148	45	142	366	309	93	297	228	73	212								
Shrewsbury	417	75	220	48	226	130	140	111	181	110	212	250	279	205	379	277	96	184	52	105	162	441	135	119	124	65	208	71	190	221	98	203	87	123	314	329	129	245	209	92	161	88							
Southampton	578	225	142	135	66	106	136	140	342	201	53	152	440	111	539	437	100	49	133	309	258	601	295	241	199	243	113	232	294	325	111	204	169	67	221	489	157	152	20	252	23	209	191						
Stoke-on-Trent	392	112	220	48	226	130	140	150	156	211	212	250	254	205	353	251	96	184	99	123	129	415	109	93	91	57	208	46	164	195	98	172	54	123	314	303	99	245	209	66	161	50	38	191					
Stranraer	235	342	477	305	482	387	363	406	106	392	469	487	132	461	181	86	352	440	355	333	276	261	153	229	288	232	445	229	201	163	354	388	295	380	571	149	333	502	466	195	418	267	287	447	261				
Taunton	560	165	50	132	160	51	226	80	323	142	45	224	422	34	521	419	77	126	96	291	272	583	277	261	228	225	185	213	309	340	183	291	184	123	144	471	215	75	114	234	70	224	172	94	172	429			
Wick	207	597	732	560	738	642	618	662	361	647	724	742	258	716	166	277	608	695	610	588	531	104	408	484	543	487	700	484	409	367	609	644	550	635	826	215	589	757	721	451	673	523	542	702	516	362	684		
York	323	201	314	133	275	224	154	243	116	251	306	279	193	298	314	212	189	233	192	192	38	376	91	24	79	102	237	71	51	89	146	180	87	184	408	239	125	339	269	96	254	57	146	251	120	223	265	477	
LONDON	550	239	216	121	54	120	59	153	314	215	125	78	413	200	512	410	102	31	136	282	186	574	268	201	143	216	39	204	254	285	68	118	129	56	310	462	86	241	75	225	85	169	163	77	161	420	167	675	211

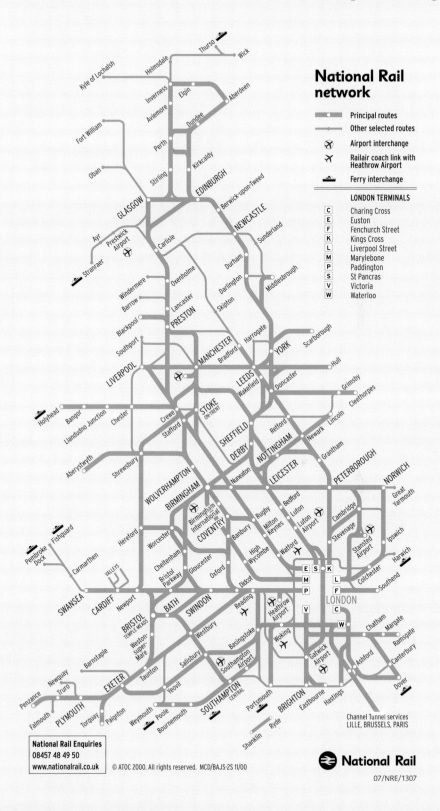

National Rail network

- 〰️ Principal routes
- ─── Other selected routes
- ✈ Airport interchange
- ✈ Railair coach link with Heathrow Airport
- ⛴ Ferry interchange

LONDON TERMINALS

C	Charing Cross
E	Euston
F	Fenchurch Street
K	Kings Cross
L	Liverpool Street
M	Marylebone
P	Paddington
S	St Pancras
V	Victoria
W	Waterloo

Channel Tunnel services
LILLE, BRUSSELS, PARIS

National Rail Enquiries
08457 48 49 50
www.nationalrail.co.uk

© ATOC 2000. All rights reserved. MCD/BAJS-2S 11/00

National Rail

07/NRE/1307

Travel information

General travel information

Streetmap	streetmap.co.uk	
Transport Direct	transportdirect.info	
Transport for London	tfl.gov.uk	(020) 7222 1234
Travel Services	departures-arrivals.com	
Traveline	traveline.org.uk	0870 200 2233

Bus & coach

Megabus	megabus.com	0901 331 0031
National Express	nationalexpress.com	0870 580 8080
WA Shearings	washearings.com	(01942) 824824

Car & car hire

AA	theaa.com	0870 600 0371
Green Flag	greenflag.co.uk	0845 246 1557
RAC	rac.co.uk	0870 572 2722
Alamo	alamo.co.uk	0870 400 4562*
Avis	avis.co.uk	0844 581 0147
Budget	budget.co.uk	0844 581 2231
Easycar	easycar.com	0906 333 3333
Enterprise	enterprise.com	0870 350 3000*
Hertz	hertz.co.uk	0870 844 8844*
Holiday Autos	holidayautos.co.uk	0870 400 4461
National	nationalcar.co.uk	0870 400 4581
Thrifty	thrifty.co.uk	(01494) 751500

Air

Airport information	a2btravel.com/airports	0870 888 1710
Air Southwest	airsouthwest.com	0870 043 4553
Blue Islands (Channel Islands)	blueislands.com	0845 620 2122
BMI	flybmi.com	0870 607 0555
BMI Baby	bmibaby.com	0871 224 0224
British Airways	ba.com	0870 850 9850
British International (Isles of Scilly to Penzance)	islesofscillyhelicopter.com	(01736) 363871*
Eastern Airways	easternairways.com	0870 366 9100*
Easyjet	easyjet.com	0871 244 2366
Flybe	flybe.com	0871 522 6100
Jet2.com	jet2.com	0871 226 1737*
Ryanair	ryanair.com	0871 246 0000
Skybus (Isles of Scilly)	islesofscilly-travel.com	0845 710 5555
VLM	flyvlm.com	0871 666 5050

Train

National Rail Enquiries	nationalrail.co.uk	0845 748 4950
The Trainline	trainline.co.uk	
UK train operating companies	rail.co.uk	
Arriva Trains	arriva.co.uk	0845 748 4950
c2c	c2c-online.co.uk	0845 601 4873
Chiltern Railways	chilternrailways.co.uk	0845 600 5165
CrossCountry	crosscountrytrains.co.uk	0845 748 4950
East Midlands Trains	eastmidlandstrains.co.uk	0845 748 4950
First Capital Connect	firstcapitalconnect.co.uk	0845 748 4950
First Great Western	firstgreatwestern.co.uk	0845 700 0125
Gatwick Express	gatwickexpress.co.uk	0845 850 1530
Heathrow Express	heathrowexpress.com	0845 600 1515
Hull Trains	hulltrains.co.uk	0845 071 0222
Island Line	island-line.co.uk	0845 748 4950
London Midland	londonmidland.com	0845 748 4950
Merseyrail	merseyrail.org	0845 748 4950
Northern Rail	northernrail.org	0845 748 4950
One Railway	onerailway.com	0845 600 7245
South Eastern Trains	southeasternrailway.co.uk	0845 000 2222
South West Trains	southwesttrains.co.uk	0845 600 0650
Southern	southernrailway.com	0845 127 2920
Stansted Express	stanstedexpress.com	0845 600 7245
Transpennine Express	tpexpress.co.uk	0845 600 1671
Virgin Trains	virgintrains.co.uk	0845 722 2333*

Ferry

Ferry information	sailanddrive.com	
Condor Ferries (Channel Islands)	condorferries.co.uk	0870 243 5140*
Steam Packet Company (Isle of Man)	steam-packet.com	0871 222 1333
Isles of Scilly Travel	islesofscilly-travel.co.uk	0845 710 5555
Red Funnel (Isle of Wight)	redfunnel.co.uk	0870 444 8898
Wight Link (Isle of Wight)	wightlink.co.uk	0870 582 0202

Phone numbers listed are for general enquiries unless otherwise stated.

* Booking line only

National cycle network

Sections of the National Cycle Network are shown on the maps in this guide.
The numbers on the maps will appear on the signs along your route ▣ .
Here are some tips about finding and using a route.

- **Research and plan your route online**
  Log on to **sustrans.org.uk** and click on 'Get cycling' to find information about routes in this guide or other routes you want to use.

- **Order a route map**
  Useful, easy-to-use maps of many of the most popular routes of the National Cycle Network are available from Sustrans, the charity behind the Network. These can be purchased online or by mail order – visit **sustransshop.co.uk** or call **0845 113 0065.**

- **Order Cycling in the UK**
  The official guide to the National Cycle Network gives details of rides all over the UK, detailing 148 routes and profiles of 43 days rides on traffic-free paths and quiet roads.

ROUTE NUMBER	ROUTE/MAP NAME	START/END OF ROUTE
South West		
3	The West Country Way	Padstow – Bristol/Bath
3 & 32	The Cornish Way	Land's End – Bude
27	The Devon Coast to Coast	Ilfracombe – Plymouth
South East		
4 & 5	Thames Valley	London – Oxford via Reading
4	Kennet & Avon	Reading – Bristol
2, 20 & 21	Downs & Weald	London – Brighton – Hastings
East of England		
1	East of England	Hull – Fakenham – Harwich
Heart of England		
5 & 54	West Midlands	Oxford – Derby via Birmingham
6 & 51	South Midlands	Oxford – Derby via Leicester
North East England		
1	Coast & Castles	Newcastle upon Tyne – Berwick-upon-Tweed – Edinburgh
68	Pennine Cycleway North	Appleby-in-Westmorland/Penrith – Berwick-upon-Tweed
7, 14 & 71	Sea to Sea (C2C)	Whitehaven/Workington – Sunderland/Newcastle upon Tyne
72	Hadrian's Cycleway	Ravenglass – South Shields
Yorkshire and North West England		
68	Pennine Cycleway (South Pennines & the Dales)	Holmfirth – Appleby-in-Westmorland/Kendal
1, 14 & 65	Yorkshire Moors & Coast	Barnard Castle - Whitby & Middlesborough – Thirsk
62 & 65	Trans Pennine Trail East	Yorkshire – North Sea
62	Trans Pennine Trail West	Irish Sea – Yorkshire
Regional 20	Walney to Wear (W2W)	Barrow-in-Furness – Sunderland

Index by property name

Accommodation with a detailed entry in this guide is listed below.

Establishments listed here have a detailed entry in this guide.

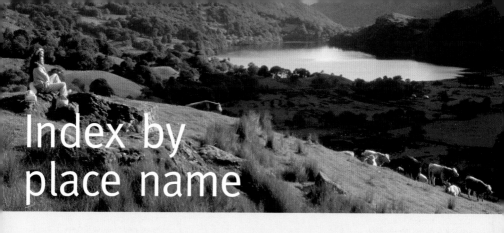

Index by place name

The following places all have detailed accommodation entries in this guide. If the place where you wish to stay is not shown, the location maps (starting on page 28) will help you to find somewhere to stay in the area.

Index by place name

Turn to the pages indicated for detailed accommodation entries in these places.

Published by: VisitBritain, Thames Tower, Blacks Road, London W6 9EL
in partnership with England's tourism industry
enjoyEngland.com
Publishing Manager: Tess Lugos
Production Manager: Iris Buckley
Compilation, design, copywriting, production and advertisement sales:
Jackson Lowe Marketing, 3 St Andrews Place, Southover Road, Lewes,
East Sussex BN7 1UP
t (01273) 487487 jacksonlowe.com
Typesetting: Marlinzo Services, Somerset and Jackson Lowe Marketing
Accommodation maps: Based on digital map data © ESR Cartography, 2007
Touring maps: © VisitBritain 2005. National Parks, Areas of Outstanding
Natural Beauty, National Trails and Heritage Coast based on information
supplied by Natural England Licence No. 1000 46223. Cycle Networks
provided by Sustrans
Printing and binding: Emirates Printing Press, Dubai, United Arab Emirates

Back cover (top): Headlam Hall Hotel, Spa and Golf Course, Darlington;
britainonview/ McCormick-McAdam; Yorke Lodge, Canterbury

Photography credits: britainonview/ANPA/Daniel Bosworth/Martin
Brent /brightononview/Coventry Cathedral/East Midlands Tourism/East
of England Tourism/Jakob Ebrey/Rod Edwards/Damir
Fabijanic/FCO/Adrian Houston/Kent Tourism Alliance/Simon
Kreitem/Leicester Shire Pr/Pawel Libera/James McCormick/McCormick-
McAdam/ NWDA/Tony Pleavin/Grant Pritchard/Ingrid Rasmussen /Ian
Shaw/Jon Spaull/Visit Chester & Cheshire/Visit London/Jenny
Woodcock; Matt Cardy; The Deep; East Midlands Development Agency;
Four Seasons Teesside White Water Centre; Johnny Haddock;
Herefordshire Council; Imperial War Museum North; Michael Jackson;
Marketing Birmingham; One NorthEast Tourism; Joan Russell; Trentham
Leisure; Visit London; visitlondonimages/britainonview

Important note: The information contained in this guide has been
published in good faith on the basis of information submitted to
VisitBritain by the proprietors of the premises listed, who have paid for
their entries to appear. VisitBritain cannot guarantee the accuracy of the
information in this guide and accepts no responsibility for any error or
misrepresentation. All liability for loss, disappointment, negligence or
other damage caused by reliance on the information contained in this
guide, or in the event of bankruptcy, or liquidation, or cessation of trade
of any company, individual or firm mentioned, is hereby excluded to the
fullest extent permitted by law. Please check carefully all prices, ratings
and other details before confirming a reservation.

© British Tourist Authority (trading as VisitBritain) 2008
ISBN 978-0-7095-8437-7

A VisitBritain Publishing guide

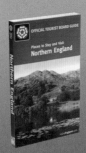